M S A Monograph Series

Optical Crystallography

F. Donald Bloss

Department of Geological Sciences
Virginia Tech
Blacksburg, Virginia 24060

Front Cover: Multiple-exposure photomicrograph of an asbestos fiber [variety: *grunerite,* often called 'amosite'] immersed in a high-dispersion liquid (n_D = 1.680) made as the stage of an E-W polarizing microscope was rotated at 10° intervals. The central-stop dispersion-staining (CSDS) deep blue color, observed when the fiber is E-W, indicates that $n_\parallel$, the fiber's refractive index for sodium light vibrating parallel to its length, exceeds 1.680. The orange-yellow color seen when the fiber is N-S indicates that $n_\perp$, the fiber's index for sodium light vibrating perpendicular to its length, is less than 1.680.   *Photo courtesy of Walter McCrone of the McCrone Research Institute.*

Back Cover: [Top] Interference figures of a uniaxial and a biaxial crystal ($2V$ = 46°).
[Bottom] Same, with "gypsum" plate inserted so as to determine optic sign.
Photos courtesy of Jan Hinsch of Leica Inc.

MINERALOGICAL SOCIETY of AMERICA
WASHINGTON, D.C.

. . . for Louise

OPTICAL CRYSTALLOGRAPHY
by *F. Donald Bloss*

ISBN 0-939950-49-9

MSA's MONOGRAPH SERIES, PUBLICATION #5

THE MINERALOGICAL SOCIETY OF AMERICA
1015 EIGHTEENTH STREET, NW, SUITE 601
WASHINGTON, DC 20036 U.S.A.

TABLE OF CONTENTS

PREFACE   vii

LIGHT REFLECTIONS   x

1 LIGHT AND RELATED PHENOMENA

   OVERVIEW   1
   NOMENCLATURE   1
   POLARIZED LIGHT   3
   RELATIONSHIPS   4
   REFRACTIVE INDEX   5
   ISOTROPIC AND ANISOTROPIC MEDIA   5
   QUESTIONS AND PROBLEMS   6

2 LIGHT IN ISOTROPIC MEDIA

   OVERVIEW   7
   REFLECTION AND REFRACTION OF RAYS   8
   DISPERSION   10
   LIGHT ABSORPTION AND COLOR TRANSMISSION   13
   EFFECT OF ABSORPTION ON DISPERSION   15
   QUESTIONS AND PROBLEMS   16

3 LENSES AND THE COMPOUND MICROSCOPE

   OVERVIEW   17
   NOMENCLATURE AND TYPES OF LENSES   17
   THIN-LENS FORMULA AND GRAPHIC SOLUTIONS   18
   THE COMPOUND MICROSCOPE   21
   QUESTIONS AND PROBLEMS   23

4 THE POLARIZING LIGHT MICROSCOPE

   OVERVIEW   25
   INTRODUCTION   25
   ELEMENTS AND THEIR FUNCTION   26
   ADJUSTMENTS OF THE MICROSCOPE   33
   STUDENT MODEL PLMS   35

5 OPTICAL EXAMINATION OF ISOTROPIC SUBSTANCES

   OVERVIEW   39
   INTRODUCTION   40
   REFRACTIVE INDEX MEASUREMENT IN LIQUIDS   40
   REFRACTIVE INDEX MEASUREMENT IN SOLIDS   41

DETERMINATION OF $n_{D,g}$ BY BECKE LINES
 OR OBLIQUE ILLUMINATION   49
DETERMINATION OF $n_{D,g}$ BY DISPERSION STAINING   51
COMPARISON OF METHODS   59
PRACTICAL PROCEDURES   60
RECOMMENDED READINGS   62

6   OPTICAL INDICATRICES AND ELLIPSES

OVERVIEW   63
REVIEW OF TERMINOLOGY   64
GENERAL CONCEPT OF THE INDICATRIX   65
THE ISOTROPIC INDICATRIX   65
THE UNIAXIAL INDICATRIX   67
SUMMARY   80

7   THE INTERFERENCE OF LIGHT

OVERVIEW   83
WAVES POLARIZED IN THE SAME PLANE   84
WAVES POLARIZED IN PERPENDICULAR PLANES   86
TRANSMISSION BY THE ANALYZER   90
INTERFERENCE COLORS   91
ORTHOSCOPIC AND CONOSCOPIC OBSERVATION
 OF INTERFERENCE EFFECTS   95
ORTHOSCOPIC EXAMINATION OF CRYSTALS   96
CONOSCOPIC EXAMINATION (INTERFERENCE FIGURES)   96
TYPES OF UNIAXIAL INTERFERENCE FIGURES   100

8   OPTICAL EXAMINATION OF UNIAXIAL CRYSTALS

OVERVIEW   107
PREPARATION OF THE SAMPLE   108
ESTABLISHMENT OF UNIAXIALITY   108
COMPENSATORS AND COMPENSATION   109
DETERMINATION OF OPTIC SIGN   111
MEASUREMENT OF REFRACTIVE INDICES   114
DETERMINATION OF RETARDATION AND BIREFRINGENCE   117
EXTINCTION ANGLES: SIGN OF ELONGATION   120
ABSORPTION AND PLEOCHROISM   122
ABNORMAL INTERFERENCE COLORS   123
MINERAL IDENTIFICATION   124
REVIEW QUESTIONS   124

9 INTRODUCING THE SPINDLE STAGE

OVERVIEW   125
INTRODUCTION   125
THE DETENT SPINDLE STAGE   125
PRE-ADJUSTMENTS OF THE MICROSCOPE   126
CARTESIAN COORDINATE SYSTEM FOR MICROSCOPES   127
AXES OF ROTATION   127
DETERMINING OPTIC SIGN, ε, AND ω 128
WEB SITE SPINDLE STAGES   132

10 BIAXIAL CRYSTALS

OVERVIEW   135
INTRODUCTION   136
BIAXIAL INDICATRIX   137
GEOMETRIC RELATIONSHIPS BETWEEN WAVE NORMALS,
    VIBRATION DIRECTIONS, AND RAY PATHS   143
BIAXIAL INTERFERENCE FIGURES   149
RECOGNITION OF INTERFERENCE FIGURES   153
DISPERSION AND CRYSTALLOGRAPHIC
    ORIENTATION OF X, Y, AND Z 161

11 OPTICAL EXAMINATION OF BIAXIAL CRYSTALS

OVERVIEW   169
INTRODUCTION   170
DETERMINATION OF BIAXIALITY   170
DETERMINATION OF OPTIC SIGN   171
MEASUREMENT OF INDICES   173
MEASUREMENT OF $2V$ 176
MEASUREMENT AND SIGNIFICANCE OF EXTINCTION ANGLES   178
ABSORPTION AND PLEOCHROISM   182
RECORDING DATA   183
REVIEW QUESTIONS   184

12 SPINDLE STAGE STUDY OF BIAXIAL CRYSTALS

OVERVIEW   185
THE CONOSCOPIC METHOD   186
SOLUTION OF ORTHOSCOPIC DATA: EXCALIBR   188
MEASURING α_D, β_D, AND γ_D 195
COMPUTER-ASSISTED MINERAL IDENTIFICATION   195
POSSIBILITIES   195
APPLICATIONS   201

13 **RAPID OPTICAL DETERMINATION OF ASBESTOS FIBERS**
BY DISPERSION STAINING

OVERVIEW   203
STANDARD OPERATING PROCEDURES
    FOR ASBESTOS IDENTIFICATION   203
MEASURING A FIBER'S REFRACTIVE INDICES   203
PRECAUTIONS   213
RECOMMENDED READINGS   216

THE ISOGYRE   217
APPENDIX I : DATA FOR CARGILLE LIQUIDS   219
APPENDIX II : PROPERTIES OF ELLIPSES   225
APPENDIX III : RECORDING DATA   227
REFERENCES CITED   229
INDEX   233

PREFACE

The polarizing light microscope (PLM) remains the premier tool for rapidly identifying the minerals and mineral reactions that occur in petrographic thin sections of rocks. This present text, like its predecessor (*An Introduction to the Methods of Optical Crystallography*, 1961, Holt, Rinehart and Winston), is intended to supply a firm foundation for such petrographic studies. Thus it includes much of the material from the 1961 text, particularly the marvelous illustrations, drawn by Mark Klopp, that students found so helpful. An innovation is the brief overview that precedes each chapter. These may be sufficient to allow the reader to skip to the next chapter.

The PLM has also been quintessential for determination of the properties of single crystals or fragments thereof. In recent years, however, the precision and ease of such determinations has undergone a quantum leap, thanks to (1) the increased availability, speed, and power of personal computers and (2) an inexpensive device called a spindle stage, which permits remarkably precise optical measurements to be made on single crystals, particularly biaxial ones (see *The Microscope*, 1992, vol. 40, no. 1). Even the simplest spindle stage, if mounted on the stage of a PLM, allows a crystal to be rotated about two axes: The M-axis, the vertical axis of rotation routinely supplied by a PLM's rotatable stage, and the S-axis, the horizontal axis of rotation that a spindle stage supplies. These two rotational capabilities permit the principal refractive indices of any anisotropic, transparent crystal to be determined by the immersion method *without appreciable error from misorientation*. The procedures are so simple that beginning students, once they've learned the immersion method of determining refractive indices, can employ them almost immediately. The basic procedure involves rotating the crystal about axis S to each of the set positions — $S = 0°$, $S = 10°$... $S = 180°$ — and, at each such position, rotating the microscope stage to the position — M_0, M_{10} ... M_{180} — that causes crystal extinction. The resultant crystal extinction data, entered into a personal computer and solved by the computer program EXCALIBR (Bartelmehs, et al., 1992), will yield $2V$, the optic axial angle. It also computes S_X, M_X; S_Y, M_Y; and S_Z, M_Z —the settings of the spindle axis (S) and of the microscope stage (M) that respectively orient the crystal so that its principal indices (α, β, γ) can be measured as easily as if the crystal were isotropic.

EXCALIBR locates the five significant biaxial vectors—namely, the two optic axes plus X, Y, and Z—with unprecedented precision and calculates $2V$ to within a fraction of a degree. If crystal extinctions for up to five different wavelengths are submitted, EXCALIBR calculates the angular shifts in position (with wavelength) for each of the five significant vectors. It then estimates statistically whether these shifts can be ascribed to dispersion or to chance.

The ease and precision with which $2V$ can be determined at several different wavelengths for biaxial crystals suggests many practical uses for spindle stage data. For example, during the manufacture of biaxial pharmaceuticals, the angle $2V$, which is highly sensitive to compositional change and to changes in the crystal's atomic structure, could well prove to be a sensitive monitor for quality control. And in forensic studies, the finding that $2V$ for feldspar, amphibole, or pyroxene crystals occurring in soil or sand at the crime site agree to within one degree with similar crystals from soil or sand samples associated with the suspect should be compelling evidence.

It is a pleasure to acknowledge my debt to the many people who have been so helpful. I'll start with Ray E. Wilcox, now retired from the U. S. Geological Survey. I learned a lot under your gentle tutelage, Ray. And then there are the students that taught me. From 1951 to 1957 at the University of Tennessee, I learned from Louis S. Walter,

Robert Milici, and G.V. Gibbs, the latter also my colleague for over 30 years. At Southern Illinois University (1957-1967) I learned from Paul Robinson, Ray Kerns, and from my colleague there, Jen-Ho Fang. At Virginia Tech (1957-1991) I have had the pleasure of collaborating with many students, from undergraduates to postdoctorals. For example, Ed Wolfe helped me to get the ball rolling relative to precise optical studies of crystals at elevated temperatures and at wavelengths beyond the visible. As did the late John Louisnathan who went from my lab to Corning's and in 1996-97 won their Stookey Award for his development of a new technique to determine the core geometry in optical fibers with unprecedented precision. And during his master's study, Kevin Selkregg used combined X-ray and spindle stage studies of cordierites to explode the myth that the distortion index was a measure of structural state. Around 1979, a postdoctoral student from Germany, Thomas Armbruster, carried out many brilliant experiments on the optics and crystal structure of cordierite. Thomas successfully demonstrated why cordierite was sometimes optically positive instead of negative (CO_2 was occupying its channels). This also explained why, in one locality, all the cordierites on one side of a fault were (+) and on the other (–). Another student, Mickey Gunter, now at the University of Idaho, practically became a colleague while doing a master's and Ph.D. with me. During his X-ray/spindle stage study of the solid solution series between andalusite and kanonaite, Mickey found that the plots of principal refractive indices versus manganese content actually crossed so that, at one particular composition, an isotropic andalusite existed. In 1981 its existence was observed in a thin section by the late Jeff Grambling of the University of New Mexico. Also in 1981, Shu-Chun Su began a doctoral study (with Paul Ribbe and me) that showed how the optical properties of the K-feldspars *did* vary with structural state. The resultant paper, in which David Stewart of the U.S. Geological Survey joined us, showed that the optic axial angle $2V$, so easily and precisely determined by spindle stage methods, offered a ready measure of K-feldspar's structural state. Around this time, Laura Davis (now DeLoach) showed how the principal refractive indices of mica flakes could be precisely measured using an Abbé refractometer. Soon thereafter, Daniel Greiner showed that $2V$, as measured for members of the amblygonite-montebrasite series, allowed their fluorine contents to be estimated to within 2 mole per cent.

Looking beyond the scope of my own university, I thank Dr. Walter McCrone for his many kindnesses to me and my students. He has, with enthusiasm, taught the world about the practical use of optics in asbestos identification, in checking the authenticity of oil paintings, and in forensic studies.

Prof. Ann G. Wylie of the University of Maryland contributed to the initial draft of the section on dispersion staining (Chapter 5). Subsequently, Dr. Shu-Chun Su of the Research Center of Hercules Incorporated added greatly to this section. Moreover, Chapter 13 (Rapid Determination of Asbestos...) is largely based on *Rapidly and Accurately Determining Refractive Indices of Asbestos Fibers by Using Dispersion Staining*. This latter is the standard operating procedure for identifying asbestos fibers by polarized light microscopy which Dr. Su wrote in his capacity as a technical expert for NVLAP (the National Voluntary Laboratory Accreditation Program) currently administered by the National Institute of Standards and Technology (NIST). I thank Dr. Olaf Medenbach of the Institute for Mineralogy at Bochum for providing the illustration (see Fig. 12-8) of his outstandingly versatile spindle stage. I also thank Bob Sacher of R. P. Cargille Laboratories for supplying the refractive index data for the Cargille refractive index liquids.

Jan Hinsch of Leica, a friend for 30 years and always a source of bubbling enthusiasm relative to microscopy, kindly read (and improved) Chapter 4. He was also so kind as to advise me relative to Köhler illumination. I also thank Dr. Walter J. Patzelt of Leica Microsystems for allowing use of Leica's Michel-Levy charts and for assisting in the modifications which increase the chart's usefulness for identifying minerals in petrographic thin sections.

Jodi Rosso performed, in a remarkably short time, the task of optical scanning of the 1961 text and getting it on disk so that large portions of it could be integrated into this present text. Margie Sentelle added to it the bulk of the new material I wrote. Amy Braford Peterson did yeoman's work in putting finishing touches on the manuscript. My grandson, Andrew Kensler, used his considerable expertise in computer graphics to generate some remarkable new illustrations for this book.

I thank my colleague of over 30 years, Paul H. Ribbe, for editing this text and reading it critically. Other critical readers to whom I am grateful include Edward F. Lener, Dr. Mickey E. Gunter, Dr. Shu-Chun Su, and Dr. J. Alexander Speer.

Last but by no means least, I thank my wife Louise, to whom this book is dedicated, for giving the right answer to the question I asked her 55 years ago.

F. D. Bloss
Blacksburg, VA
April 1999

LIGHT REFLECTIONS

~~~~~~~~~~

Oh, Light! that poets oft do sing,
And wise men write about,
Thou art the darkest thing I've met,
I cannot make thee out.

Thou art of luminosity
Astonishingly chary,
Thou hast no ordinary ray,
Thou'rt all extraordinary.

Enough thou art to worry saints,
When thou art once refracted;
E'en then thy vibratory pranks,
Do drive me clean distracted.

But when thou splittest thyself up
Unto refraction double,
Oh, then, thy waves do me o'erwhelm
In roaring seas of trouble.

Thou and the mad polariscope,
In evil league combined,
Do play the most unhallowed tricks
Upon my simple mind.

Thy interference figures do
With my sleep interfere;
My appetite it faileth quite,
Thou dost behave so queer.

Broad smutty bars of darkness sweep
In dreams across my sight;
And pleochroic demons hold
Mad carnivals at night.

Bisectrices and axes pierce
My brain in all directions,
And oft I dream the class must be
Divided into sections!

And Oh, Inclined Dispersion is
Of all thy tricks the worst!
My wits when toward it they incline,
Are hopelessly dispersed.

Oh, much applauded light! when first
On Chaos thou didst shine,
Did not the Chaos nature get
Mixed up a bit with thine?

Oh, Light! Light! Light!
What mockery is here!
The blackest depths of darkest night,
More luminous appear.

Depart then to the Polar lands,
Be polarized forever!
We darkness choose; and let thy beams,
Disturb our slumbers never.

Henrietta L. Graves

In 1920 Dr. Norman L. Bowen discovered this poem in the effects of William Nicol of Queens University, Kingston, Ontario. No information is available about the author.

1 LIGHT AND RELATED PHENOMENA

OVERVIEW

In a vacuum, light travels with a velocity (c) of 3×10^{17} nanometers (nm) per second—where 1 nm = 10 Å = 10^{-9} m. In more dense transparent materials, it travels with a lesser velocity (c_m). A transparent material's refractive index n, by definition, equals c/c_m, a number always greater than 1.0.

Light travels (Fig. 1-3) as an electromagnetic wave by means of vibrations (oscillations) that are transverse (at high angles) to its direction of travel. For **unpolarized light** these vibrations occur along numerous random directions perpendicular to the light's direction of travel. Passage through a **polarizer** constrains the light to vibrate parallel to a single direction called the **privileged direction** (or vibration direction) of the polarizer. The resultant light (Fig. 1-3) is called **plane polarized** because its vibration directions and direction of travel lie in (and define) a plane. The wavelength (λ) for a given light equals the distance between the two closest points on its path that, *at all times*, vibrate in the same direction and amount. Such points, for example, the vibrations in planes 11 and 19 (Fig. 1-3), are **in phase**. The maximum displacement of vibrations from the rest position (*cf.* planes 11, 15 and 19) is called the **amplitude** of the wave. The intensity (brightness) of the light is proportional to the square of the amplitude.

White light consists of a range of wavelengths, ~390 nm to ~770 nm. Narrower bands of wavelengths, if isolated from white light, are perceived by the human eye as violet (390-446 nm), indigo (446-464), blue (464-500), green (500-578), yellow (578-592), orange (592-620), and red (620-770 nm)—these ranges and boundaries being somewhat arbitrary. Light consisting of a highly restricted range of wavelengths—for example, between 595 and 599 nm—is called **monochromatic**. The narrower the band, the more nearly monochromatic it will be.

Materials through which monochromatic light travels with the same velocity— *regardless of direction of vibration*—are said to be **isotropic**. Those for which it travels with different velocities for different directions of vibration are said to be **anisotropic**. In general, isotropic materials include glass, crystals of the isometric system, a vacuum, all gases and most liquids. Anisotropic materials include tetragonal, hexagonal, orthorhombic, monoclinic, and triclinic crystals.

Within isotropic materials, the angle between the ray's path and its vibration direction always equals 90°. For anisotropic crystals this is not necessarily true.

NOMENCLATURE

Gamma rays, x-rays, ultraviolet rays, visible light, infrared, and radio waves are all portions of the electromagnetic spectrum (Fig. 1-1). Each of these wave types travels, in a vacuum, at the common velocity (c) of 3×10^{17} nm[*] per second, the speed of light; each has a slightly different wavelength (λ) and frequency (f) from its nearest neighbor. Classified on the basis of wavelength in air, each part of the electromagnetic spectrum embraces a continuous range of wavelengths. Occasional overlaps in nomenclature exist;

---

[*] One nanometer (symbol: nm) equals one billionth (10^{-9}) of a meter (m) or 10^{-6} mm.

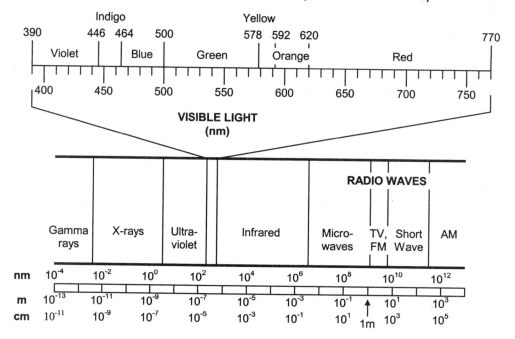

Figure 1-1. The relation of visible light to the electromagnetic spectrum. The expanded scale illustrates the range in wavelengths assigned by Hardy and Perrin (1932) to Newton's seven principal colors.

for example, rays ranging from 1.0 nm to 0.1 nm in wavelength are called gamma rays by some workers but x-rays by others.

Visible light represents a relatively limited band of wavelengths within the electromagnetic spectrum, ranging from 390 to 770 nm. By photochemical processes not yet understood, light of a particular wavelength within this range, if incident upon a normal human retina, produces a message that is interpreted within the brain as a particular color. The expanded scale of Figure 1-1 denotes the wavelength limits set by Hardy and Perrin (1932) for the seven distinctive "colors of the rainbow" recognized by Sir Isaac Newton. P.J. Bouma (1947), however, eliminates Newton's indigo and places the wavelength limits of the color responses as follows:

λ (nm)	380–436	436–495	495–566	566–589	589–627	627–780
Color sensation	violet	blue	green	yellow	orange	red

Bouma's longer limits for the visible range, 380 to 780 nm (as compared with the often-cited 390 to 770 nm), are probably inspired by the facts that (1) some human eyes can detect light of longer or shorter wavelengths than normal and (2) highly intense light sources may emit light at the extremities of the range of sufficient energy to stimulate a response in even a normal eye.

Each color of the visible spectrum, as may be noted in a rainbow, grades imperceptibly into its neighbor. Understandably, therefore, the preceding wavelength values delimiting the distinctive colors are somewhat arbitrary. One would have much difficulty, for example, in deciding whether light of 625 nm wavelength was orange or red. As a matter of fact, Bouma's limits differ from the Hardy-Perrin limits (Fig. 1-1) with respect to this region.

If light of all wavelengths (from 390 to 770 nm) simultaneously strikes the human retina, the light is interpreted by the brain as "white light." Monochromatic light, on the other hand, refers to light with a much narrower range of wavelengths; the narrower the range, the more highly monochromatic it is. A sodium vapor lamp, for example, is a source of highly monochromatic light since it chiefly emits light of wavelengths 589.0 and 589.6 nm. A tungsten-filament incandescent lamp, daylight from a north window, or direct sunlight, however, are polychromatic; that is, light energy is emitted at many different wavelengths (Fig. 1-2). Optical measurements of great accuracy require highly monochromatic light sources, and the sodium vapor lamp is commonly used. In routine work, however, either daylight from a north window or, more frequently, a tungsten lamp equipped with a blue "daylight" filter is used.

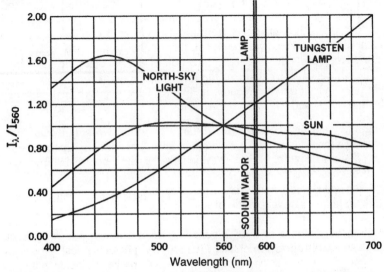

Figure 1-2. The light energy emitted at various wavelengths, symbolized $I\lambda$, as compared to that emitted at wavelength 560 nm—that is, I_{560}—for three polychromatic light sources: (1) the sun, (2) a typical gas-filled tungsten lamp (internal temperature 2600°C), and (3) north-sky light. If $I\lambda$ were plotted instead of $I_\lambda + I_{560}$, the sun's curve would be far above the other two. The energy emitted by a suitably filtered sodium vapor lamp, chiefly light of wavelengths 589 and 589.6 nm, is indicated by two vertical lines. Technically, the heights of these two lines are infinite, not because I_{589} or $I_{589.6}$ is so large, but rather because I_{560} equals zero for this monochromatic source. (In part after W.D. Wright, 1958.)

POLARIZED LIGHT

Light energy is generally considered to travel by means of a transverse wave motion in which the vibration of the particles is usually perpendicular to the direction of travel of the energy. As schematically shown on the left half of Figure 1-3, ordinary (unpolarized) sodium light is considered to vibrate in numerous directions, all of which are at right angles to its ray path. As the ray of light energy travels from plane 1 to plane 11, its vibration directions may be imagined to trace out a three-dimensional figure resembling a series of canoes, end to end, with alternate canoes upside down. As shown, the ray's vibration directions within any plane perpendicular to its path may be represented by a semi-circle of radius equal to the vibration of the wave within that plane. Planes 1, 5, and 9 are exceptions since they are located at points on the ray path for which, at that instant in time, the vibration is nil.

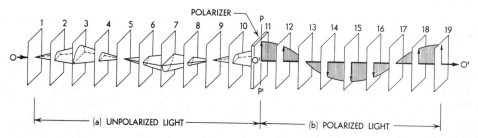

Figure 1-3. Instantaneous "photo" of unpolarized light traveling through imaginary planes 1 to 10 before and after it is polarized by a polarizer located at 11. After passing through the polarizer, the light exclusively vibrates parallel to PP', the privileged direction of the polarizer.

Light whose electric vibrations are restricted to a single direction in space, for example, the ray between O' and O'' in Figure 1-3, is said to be **plane polarized**. Those materials or devices that convert ordinary light to plane-polarized light are generally called polarizers (or "polars"). Light emergent from a polarizer has been made to vibrate parallel to one particular direction, which will be called, for simplicity, the "privileged direction" of the polarizer.[*] PP' represents the privileged direction of the polarizer located at plane 11 in Figure 1-3. The **plane of vibration** of the light may be defined as the plane parallel to both the ray's path and vibration direction; in Figure 1-3, therefore, it is the ruled plane parallel to the lines $O'O''$ and PP'.

Wavelength (λ) may be defined as the distance between two neighboring points at all times experiencing vibrations of the same amount and direction, such points being said to be "in phase." Thus in Figure 1-3 the wavelength for the unpolarized light equals the distance between construction planes 1 and 9 (or between planes 2 and 10); for the polarized light, the wavelength equals the distance between planes 11 and 19, the points at 11 and 19 being in phase. The amplitude of a wave is defined as the maximum vibrational displacement observed. The amplitudes are, for the unpolarized wave, the radii of the semicircles shown in planes 3 or 7 of Figure 1-3; for the polarized wave, amplitude is represented by the vectors shown in planes 11, 15, or 19.

Although its amplitude appears larger than that of the unpolarized wave in Figure 1-3, the polarized wave actually contains only one half of the total light energy of the unpolarized wave. Polarization of an ordinary light beam always produces a decrease in intensity. The reader will understand this more readily after study of future sections.

RELATIONSHIPS

The standard relationship between frequency (f), wavelength (λ), and velocity (c) for wave motion is

$$c = f\lambda \qquad \text{(Eqn. 1-1)}$$

Hence, if two of the three quantities are known, the third can be calculated. For example, consider a wave of orange light whose wavelength in a vacuum equals precisely 600 nm. Its speed in a vacuum, as for all light, is 3×10^{17} nm per second. Its frequency of vibration

---

[*] Following several British physicists—for example, R.W. Ditchburn (1952) and R.S. Longhurst (1957)—the term "privileged direction" has been substituted for the more conventional term "vibration direction." Privileged direction refers to the vibration direction that light must observe while passing through a polarizer (or through an anisotropic crystal as defined on p. 5). A privileged direction exists for a polarizer even when it is not transmitting light whereas a vibration direction technically exists only during transmission. Substitution of the phrase "privileged direction of the polarizer" for "vibration direction of the polarizer" also prevents the student from visualizing the polarizer as being in motion.

can thus be calculated as 5×10^{14} times per second. Similarly, the reader can easily calculate the frequency of sodium light (wavelength 589.3 nm).

The frequency of a given beam of monochromatic light never changes, even if the light enters an entirely different material (its pulse rate, so to speak, remains constant). The wavelength and velocity of this same light, on the other hand, *do change* upon entrance into a different medium. Let the velocity, frequency, and wavelength of this light—before and after it passes from medium *A* into medium *B*—be indicated as c_A, f_A, and λ_A and as c_B, f_B, and λ_B, respectively. Because of the immutability of its frequency, f_A equals f_B. Coupling this fact and Equation 1-1, it then follows that

$$\frac{c_A}{c_B} = \frac{\lambda_A}{\lambda_B}$$

(Eqn. 1-2)

that is, the wavelength of light entering a new medium changes in the same proportion as does its velocity. By way of example, if orange light of wavelength 600 nm in a vacuum enters a medium in which its velocity is 1.5×10^{17} nm per second, its wavelength becomes 300 nm.*

REFRACTIVE INDEX

The index of refraction (*n*) of a particular material may be defined as

$$n = \frac{c}{c_m}$$

(Eqn. 1-3)

where c and c_m symbolize the velocity of light in a vacuum and in the material, respectively. For transparent materials, c_m is less than c; consequently, their refractive indices (R.I.) will be greater than 1.0 in value. Air, through which light travels almost as fast as in a vacuum, has an index of refraction that may be assumed equal to 1.0 in most cases; actually, its index is approximately 1.0003. In general, but not inevitably, the higher the density of a transparent substance, the less rapidly light travels through it. High specific gravity and high refractive index therefore tend to be related physical properties.

The wavelength of light entering a new medium changes inversely proportionally to its refractive index in the new medium. Thus

$$\frac{\lambda_A}{\lambda_B} = \frac{n_B}{n_A}$$

(Eqn. 1-4)

where n_A and n_B refer to the refractive indices of the two media involved. The derivation of Equation 1-4 from Equations 1-2 and 1-3 is left to the reader.

ISOTROPIC AND ANISOTROPIC MEDIA

Those materials through which monochromatic light travels with the same speed, *regardless of its direction of vibration*, are called **isotropic** media. In addition to glass and crystals of the isometric system, a vacuum, all gases, and most liquids are isotropic with respect to light. Other materials, mainly the crystals of any nonisometric system, are **anisotropic** with respect to light; through them a light ray may travel with considerably different speeds for different directions of vibration within the crystal. Within isotropic

---

* An analogy may vivify Equation 1-2. Assume that a pendulum, swinging at a constant rate, is placed within an elevator. As the elevator rises at a constant velocity, the pendulum bob approximately traces out a sine curve because its to and fro motion is coupled with the upward motion of the elevator. If the velocity of the elevator is doubled, the wavelength of the sine curve will also be doubled.

media, the vibration direction of a light ray is always perpendicular to the ray path; within anisotropic media, the angle between vibration directions and ray path may be other than 90°.

QUESTIONS AND PROBLEMS

1. Light travels with a velocity of 2.25×10^{10} cm per second in water. What is the index of refraction of water? *Answer*: 1.333.

2. Calculate the frequency of light whose wavelength is 486.1 nm in a vacuum. *Answer*: 6.1716×10^{14} cycles per second.

3. Assume the index of refraction of the clear, colorless jelly (vitreous humor) within the human eye to be 1.336. What is the wavelength of orange light (wavelength 600 nm in a vacuum) while in this jelly? *Answer*: 449.1 nm.

1. What is the velocity of light while traveling in a glass whose index of refraction is (a) 1.5? (b) 1.9? *Answer*: (a) 2×10^{17} nm per second; (b) 1.579×10^{17} nm per second.

2   LIGHT IN ISOTROPIC MEDIA

OVERVIEW

When an incident ray (*IO*, Fig. 2-1) strikes the contact plane between two isotropic materials (R.I.: n_i and n_r, respectively), its energy divides into a reflected ray *OL* and a refracted ray *OR*. All three rays lie in the **plane of incidence**, the plane that contains both *IO* and *NOM*, the normal (= perpendicular) to the contact plane. Their angles, measured relative to *NOM*, are *i* (the angle of incidence), *l* (the angle of reflection), and *r* (the angle of refraction). Invariably, *l* = *i* (the **law of reflection**). However, angles *i* and *r* are related by **Snell's law** (Eqn. 2-2) which, rewritten, reads:

$$\sin r = \left(\frac{n_i}{n_r}\right)\sin i \qquad\qquad \text{(Eqn. 2-7)}$$

If $n_i < n_r$, Snell's law yields solutions for *r* for any value of *i* from 0° to 90°. Complexities arise, however, if $n_i > n_r$—that is, *IO* (Fig. 2-1) travels from a higher index (n_i) into a lower one (n_r). Now, values of *i* whereby $\sin i > n_r/n_i$ yield impossible solutions (i.e., $\sin r > 1.0$). In such case *all* the incident ray's energy is imparted to the reflected ray (= **total reflection**), and there is no refracted ray. The smallest angle *i* for which total reflection occurs is called the **critical angle** and has a sine that precisely equals n_r/n_i (see Fig. 2-2). Total reflection (and a critical angle) can occur only if a ray passes from a high-index material to a lower-index material.

Light traveling in air ($n = 1.0$) and entering a glass body ($n = 1.5$) will emerge parallel to its original direction after crossing two mutually parallel glass-air interfaces (Fig. 2-3A). If the two interfaces are non-parallel, as for a glass prism (Fig. 2-3B), it will be deflected *toward* the prism's thicker edge. However, if this prism is immersed in an oil whose index exceeds the glass's, the light ray will be deflected toward the prism's thinner edge (Fig. 2-3C). Should the oil's index precisely equal the glass's for the monochromatic light in use, the light will pass through the prism unchanged in direction (Fig. 2-3D).

Fraunhofer designated certain wavelengths which are absent from sunlight (they are absorbed by gases in the Sun's corona) as: A, 759.4 nm; B, 687.0; C, 656.3; D, 589.3; E, 526.9; F, 486.1; and G, 430.8 nm. A material's refractive index differs for the wavelengths composing white light, a phenomenon called **dispersion**. Conveniently, the Fraunhofer letters serve to designate a material's refractive index for the Fraunhofer wavelengths. Thus, n_C, n_D, n_F are examples. For ordinary dispersion, the material's refractive index decreases with wavelength.

Passage of sunlight through the glass prism of a spectroscope (Fig. 2-4A) disperses the light into its component wavelengths (and may disclose the black Fraunhofer lines).

A material's **coefficient of dispersion** is defined as $n_F - n_C$ and its **dispersive power** as $(n_F - n_C)/(n_D - 1)$.

Equations that relate a material's refractive index (*n*) to wavelength (λ) include: (1) Cauchy's equation (Eqn. 2-8); (2) Sellmeier's equation in either ordinary (Eqn. 2-11) or linearized form (Eqn. 2-12); and (3) Hartmann's equation, which will be discussed later.

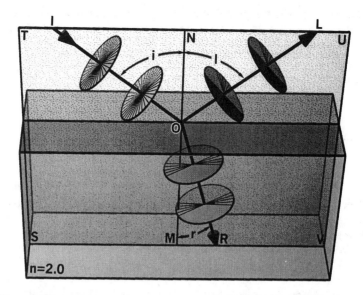

Figure 2-1. *IO*, an unpolarized ray that is incident in air upon the upper surface of a glass block of index 2.0, forms a reflected ray *OL* and a refracted ray *OR*. All ray paths—and thus the angles of incidence (*i*), reflection (*l*), and refraction (*r*)—lie within the plane of incidence *STUV*. Note that significant polarization has developed perpendicular to *STUV* for reflected ray *OL* (but within *STUV* for refracted ray *OR*). Polaroid sunglasses have a vertical privileged direction. Why?

REFLECTION AND REFRACTION OF RAYS

A ray of light incident upon an interface between two isotropic media will generally give rise to a reflected ray (which never crosses the interface) and a refracted ray (which does). Figure 2-1 illustrates a ray in air, *IO*, incident upon a glass block of refractive index 2.0. The plane of incidence (*STUV*) is defined as the plane that contains the incident ray (*IO*) and the line normal to the interface (that is, *NOM*). It also contains the reflected ray (*OL*) and the refracted ray (*OR*) in every case. The angles of incidence (*i*), of reflection (*l*), and of refraction (*r*) are defined as the angles between the normal (*NOM*) and the incident, the reflected, and the refracted ray paths, respectively. In all cases the reflected ray path can be determined from the incident ray path since

$$i = l \qquad \text{(Eqn. 2-1)}$$

Snell's Law

The relationship between the paths of the incident ray and of the refracted ray was determined by Snell in 1621 to be

$$n_i \sin i = n_r \sin r \qquad \text{(Eqn. 2-2)}$$

where n_i and n_r customarily refer to the refractive indices of the media in which the incident ray and the refracted rays travel, respectively. This relationship, known as Snell's law, permits calculation of the fourth value, given any three of them. In Figure 2-1, for example, if $n_i = 1.0$, $n_r = 2.0$, and $i = 50°$ one can calculate that $r = 22.5°$.

Polarization by Reflection and Refraction

As illustrated in Figure 2-1, the unpolarized ray *IO* gives rise to two partially polarized rays: (1) the reflected ray *OL* whose vibrations are chiefly perpendicular to the plane of incidence and (2) the refracted ray *OR* whose vibrations are principally within the plane of incidence. Brewster in 1812 reported these two rays attained a maximum degree of polarization when the angles of incidence and refraction were complementary—that is, when

$$\sin r = \cos i \qquad \text{(Eqn. 2-3)}$$

Rewriting Equation 2-2 to read

$$\frac{n_r}{n_i} = \frac{\sin i}{\sin r} \qquad \text{(Eqn. 2-4)}$$

and then substituting cos *i* for sin *r* in Equation 2-4, we obtain

$$\frac{n_r}{n_i} = \tan i \qquad \text{(Eqn. 2-5)}$$

Equation 2-5 is known as Brewster's law. Thus, maximum polarization of the reflected and refracted rays may be produced by adjusting the angle of incidence until its tangent equals n_r/n_i. Complete polarization, however, is not attainable in this manner. If air is the medium containing the incident light ray, then Brewster's law becomes

$$n_r = \tan i \qquad \text{(Eqn. 2-6)}$$

Critical Angle and Total Reflection

Snell's law (Eqn. 2-2) may be rewritten

$$\sin r = \frac{n_i}{n_r} \sin i \qquad \text{(Eqn. 2-7)}$$

Consequently, if the incident medium has a lesser index than the refracting medium, the fraction n_i/n_r must always be less than 1.0 in value. As a result, angle *r* must always be a smaller angle than angle *i*. For this case, therefore, true solutions of Snell's law exist for all possible values of angle *i*.

Whenever the medium of incidence has a larger index than the refracting medium, the fraction n_i/n_r will exceed 1.0 in value. In such case, as is apparent (from Eqn. 2-7), the angle *r* must exceed angle *i*. However, by its nature, angle *r* cannot exceed 90° (because its sine cannot exceed 1.0). Consequently, for values of *i* wherein the quantity

$$\left(\frac{n_i}{n_r} \sin i \right)$$

exceeds 1.0 in value, there are no true solutions of Snell's law. Such anomalous results merely indicate that there was no refracted ray, the incident ray being entirely reflected (= total reflection). The value of angle *i* that makes the quantity

$$\left(\frac{n_i}{n_r} \sin i \right)$$

exactly equal to 1.0 is called the critical angle. For values of *i* less than the critical angle, total reflection of the incident ray does not occur.

The physical significance of the critical angle is illustrated in Figure 2-2. The energy in each of the incident rays, *OA*, *OB*, and *OC*, is partitioned between a refracted ray (*AA'*, *BB'*, and *CC'*, respectively) and a reflected ray (*AO*, *BB"*, and *CC"*, respectively). The relative intensities of the reflected and the refracted ray, roughly shown in Figure 2-2 by different weights of lines, vary considerably according to the angle of incidence.

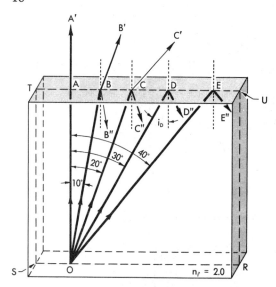

Figure 2-2. A source of light at point O within a glass block gives rise to rays OA, OB, OC, OD, and OE (among others). The relative intensities of the associated incident, reflected, and refracted rays are approximately indicated by the use of lines of different weight. The vibrations are omitted. Ray OD is incident at the critical angle since for it, i_D = 30° = arcsin n_r/n_i.. ["arcsin n_r/n_i" should be read "the angle whose sine equals n_r/n_i.."]

For normal incidence—for example ray OA—the intensity of reflected ray AO is at a minimum[1]. As the angle of incidence increases, however, the reflected ray becomes increasingly more intense whereas the refracted ray becomes less so. Ultimately, when the angle of incidence reaches its critical value, the reflected ray possesses the full 100 percent of the incident ray's intensity. Thus light rays incident at angles equal to or greater than the critical angle, for example, rays OD and OE in Figure 2-2, undergo total reflection, that is, none of the incident light energy is *refracted across the interface*.

Refraction of Light across Planar Surfaces

A light ray successively incident upon two parallel surfaces of a transparent body will always emerge parallel to the direction along which it entered. In Figure 2-3A, for example, the equality between i_1 and r_2 is readily proven by successive application of Snell's law at the bottom and top interfaces.

A light ray successively incident upon two nonparallel planar faces of a transparent body, for example, an optical prism, will generally not emerge from the second plane along its original direction. For example, in Figure 2-3B, where the glass prism is surrounded by a medium of lower refractive index, the exit ray is deflected toward the thick end (shaded) of the prism. However, in an oil of higher refractive index than the glass of the prism (Fig. 2-3C), the ray is deflected away from the thick end of the prism. If the solid and the surrounding medium have the same refractive index, light rays pass through the solid without deflection (Fig. 2-3D).

DISPERSION

Cauchy's Equation

The separation of a ray or beam of white light into its component colors after the beam enters a second medium is known as dispersion. Such occurs in media wherein the velocity, and therefore the index of refraction varies for different wavelengths of light. An approximate relationship between the value of the wavelength (λ) and the material's

---

[1] For normal incidence only, the relation between I_o and I_t, the intensities of the incident and reflected rays,

$$I_t = I_o \frac{(n_r - n_i)^2}{(n_r + n_i)^2}$$

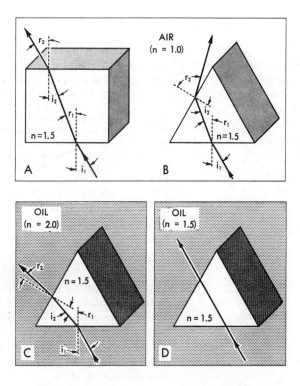

Figure 2-3. Successive refraction of a light ray by two parallel interfaces (A) and by two nonparallel interfaces (B), (C), or (D). The front half of each glass solid has been removed to expose the plane of incidence. In (C) the glass prism is immersed in an oil of larger index than the glass; in (D) the glass and oil have identical indices.

refractive index for that wavelength (n_λ) is, according to Cauchy,

$$n_\lambda = c_1 + \frac{c_2}{\lambda^2} + \frac{c_3}{\lambda^4} \dots \qquad \text{(Eqn. 2-8)}$$

Thus, if the corresponding indices of refraction ($n_{\lambda 1}$, $n_{\lambda 2}$, and $n_{\lambda 3}$) of a medium are known for at least three, preferably widely different, wavelengths of light (λ_1, λ_2, and λ_3), then each pair of values (for example, λ_1 and $n_{\lambda 1}$) may be successively substituted into Equation 2-8 to yield three linear equations (whose only unknowns are the Cauchy constants c_1, c_2, and c_3). The actual values of c_1, c_2, and c_3 can therefore be determined for the medium by simultaneous solution of these equations.

Dispersion of Sunlight

Assume that a glass prism has indices of refraction of 1.600 and 1.500 for light of wavelengths 390 nm and 770 nm, respectively. If, as in Figure 2-4A, this prism is arranged with its vertical edge parallel to the slit, SS', only a very narrow beam of sunlight would impinge upon the prism. The same angle of incidence, i, would pertain for SO, $S'O'$, and all the other rays of white light in this beam. However, the angles of refraction after the entry of each of these rays into the prism would be different for each wavelength of light. Thus, for solar ray SO (Fig. 2-4B), r_{770} and r_{390}, which are the angles of refraction within the prism for light of wavelengths 770 nm and 390 nm, respectively, may be calculated from Snell's law (Eqn. 2-2) to be

$$\sin r_{770} = \frac{\sin i}{1.500} \quad \text{and} \quad \sin r_{390} = \frac{\sin i}{1.600}$$

Consequently, the angle r_{770} exceeds angle r_{390}, as is generally the case for most substances. The angles of refraction for all the intermediate wavelengths represented in the white light of the parent ray, SO, would be somewhere between r_{770} and r_{390} in value, depending on the particular wavelength. As a result, SO, upon entry into the prism, forms a fan of rays of colored light, each ray being composed of light whose wavelength differs slightly from that of its neighbor. $S'O'$, and all the parallel rays between it and ray SO, would be similarly dispersed into fans of colored rays as illustrated in Figure 2-4B.

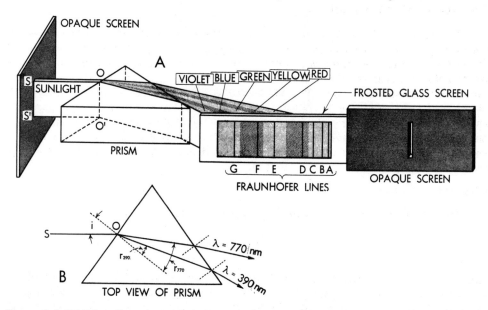

Figure 2-4. (A) Prism dispersing sunlight from slit SS'. Dark lines A to G in the resulting spectrum are the Fraunhofer lines. Note that if the opaque screen is slid toward the left, its slit would isolate monochromatic light of a relatively narrow range in wavelength. (B) Top view of prism. Note that two different angles of refraction, r_{390} and r_{770}, result from the same angle of incidence, i.

Fraunhofer Symbolism

The rainbow-colored wedge of light leaving the prism in Figure 2-4 is called a spectrum. It can be regarded as consisting of a series of contiguous vertical lines, each of a particular wavelength of light, these component colors being referred to as "spectral colors." Wollaston in 1802 and Fraunhofer in 1814 observed the presence of numerous dark vertical lines (shown on the glass screen in Fig. 2-4A) in the solar spectrum, an indication that certain wavelengths are absent from sunlight. Fraunhofer denoted the more important of these dark lines by the letters A to G. The wavelengths corresponding to these Fraunhofer lines (Table 2-1) are of

Table 2-1. Wavelengths of Fraunhofer lines

Symbol of line		Wavelength (nm)	
A		759.4	
B		687.0	
C		656.3	
D_1	} D	589.6	} 589.3
D_2		589.0	
E		526.9	
F		486.1	
G		430.8	

general interest with respect to the elements present in the Sun's atmosphere. The letter symbols are often used to refer to light of these particular wavelengths: the index of refraction of a substance for light of wavelength 589.3 nm, for example, can be symbolized as n_D rather than $n_{589.3}$. For refined optical work, the indices of refraction of a substance are generally determined for monochromatic light corresponding in wavelength to the C, D, and F values in Table 2-1. Precise measurements on crystals of NaCl indicate $n_C = 1.5407$, $n_D = 1.5443$, and $n_F = 1.5534$. If only one index is reported it is generally n_D. This is probably because, for many years, a filtered sodium vapor lamp represented the most intense, highly monochromatic source of light readily available to microscopists.

Coefficient of Dispersion

As already noted, the separation of a ray or beam of white light into its component colors is known as dispersion. As became apparent in Figure 2-4, the amount of dispersion—that is, the degree of angular separation—between light rays of two different wavelengths depends on the difference between the two indices of refraction of the substance for these wavelengths. The difference in a substance's refractive indices for the F (486.1 nm) and C (656.3 nm) Fraunhofer lines—that is, the value $n_F - n_C$—is generally known as the **coefficient of dispersion**; it is commonly cited in crystallographic literature and sometimes serves as a criterion for identification of an unknown. The mineral mullite, for example, is optically distinguishable from sillimanite only by its higher coefficient of dispersion.

Dispersive Power

The **dispersive power** of a material is commonly stated as

$$\frac{n_F - n_C}{n_D - 1}$$

This value, although somewhat superior to the coefficient of dispersion as a measure of the ability of a substance to disperse white light, is less frequently cited in crystallographic literature. Occasionally, particularly for liquids, the dispersive power is stated as the reciprocal of the foregoing value:

$$\frac{n_D - 1}{n_F - n_C}$$

LIGHT ABSORPTION AND COLOR TRANSMISSION

General and Specific Absorption

The intensity of a light beam decreases with passage through a material medium, because some light energy is converted to heat while in transit. This effect, called light absorption, is more pronounced in some media than in others. Many substances exhibit a "general absorption" of all the wavelengths of visible light (Fig. 2-5, glass C); others show a "specific or selective absorption" wherein particular wavelengths are more markedly absorbed (Fig. 2-5, glass B). Sunlit, stained-glass windows are examples of the color effects produced by selective absorption. The blue glass in the window, for example, preferentially absorbs the red wavelengths of the incident sunlight whereas the blue light of the Sun's spectrum is transmitted, relatively unabsorbed, to the room interior. The red glass, on the other hand, preferentially absorbs the blue wavelengths to transmit red light (see Fig. 2-5, glass B).

Selective absorption is responsible for the transmission colors of certain minerals and

text
text

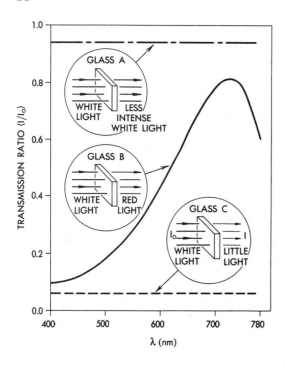

Figure 2-5. Light transmission curves for plates of transparent colorless glass (A), red glass (B), and dark gray, almost opaque glass (C). I_0 and I respectively signify the intensity of the light before entry and after passage through the glass.

crystals; thus the color transmitted is often a diagnostic property. In crystals the color is said to be **idiochromatic** if it is produced through selective absorption by the mineral itself, and **allochromatic** if it is the result of selective absorption (or scattering) of light by minute impurities dispersed through the mineral.

Relation to Thickness; Absorption Coefficients

The degree of absorption of light by a crystal is strongly dependent on its thickness. The relationship is expressed in Lambert's law,

$$\frac{I}{I_0} = e^{-kt} \tag{Eqn. 2-9}$$

where I_0 and I respectively signify the intensity of a beam of monochromatic light before and after passage through a thickness, t. The symbol e is the base of the natural logarithms and k is the **absorption coefficient** of the material in which the beam is traveling. Equation 2-9 may also be expressed

$$ln\frac{I}{I_0} = -kt \tag{Eqn. 2-10}$$

where ln signifies a natural logarithm.

The value of the absorption coefficient may vary for light of different wavelengths within the same material. For example, if one were to plot for glass B in Figure 2-5 the value of k, the resultant curve would slope downward to the right. In other words, for glass B the absorption coefficient would steadily decrease for the longer wavelengths of light. The advantage of plotting the absorption coefficient k instead of the transmission ratio is that the former is independent of thickness.

The thickness of the crystal may even affect the eye's interpretation of the transmitted color. For example, if glass B were 10,000 times thicker than the plate whose transmission curve is shown in Figure 2-5, its transmission curve would be a nearly horizontal line even below the curve for glass C; in this thickness, glass B would .transmit little light for any wavelength This illustrates why some crystals appear black and opaque for certain thicknesses but at their thin edges may transmit a particular color. On the other hand, for a plate of glass B which is only 10^{-4} times the thickness of the plate whose transmission curve is shown in Figure 2-5, the transmission curve would be similar to that for colorless glass A. Thus some minerals that are lightly colored in large masses may appear to be essentially colorless in small grains or thicknesses.

EFFECT OF ABSORPTION ON DISPERSION

Sellmeier's Equation

Cauchy's equation adequately fits the variation of n versus λ (solid line, Fig. 2-6A) within the visible range (segment NO) provided no selective absorption bands—as at λ_0 and λ_1—occur near or in the visible. As such bands are approached, it deviates (dashed line, Fig. 2-6A). As proximity to such absorption bands increases, Sellmeier's formula

$$n^2 = 1 + \frac{A\lambda^2}{\lambda^2 - \lambda_0^2}$$
(Eqn. 2-11)

where A is a constant and λ_0 represents the wavelength of maximum absorption, better fits the n, λ curve. However, it, **too, deviates (dotted line) in very** close proximity to λ_0.

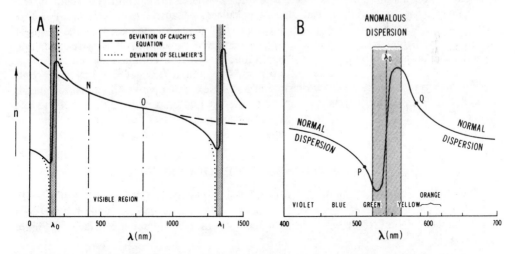

Figure 2-6. (A) Dispersion curve (solid line) for a crystal showing "normal dispersion" in the visible region. (B) Dispersion curve for a crystal showing "anomalous" dispersion in the visible region.

Since dispersion curves were first compiled for materials that were transparent throughout the visible spectrum, any absorption bands possessed by these materials were located, in general, well beyond the visible region. As a consequence, the concept of **normal dispersion** arose—namely, that the refractive index decreased for the longer wavelengths throughout the visible range (Fig. 2-6A). Later work was extended to materials possessing absorption bands within or near the visible range. Their dispersion curves within the visible region were considered abnormal since refractive index sometimes increased for the longer wavelengths (as shown from P to Q in Fig. 2-6B). Such materials were said to exhibit **anomalous dispersion.**

The Linearized Sellmeier Equation

Equation 2-11, can be linearized to become

$$y = a_0 + a_1 x \qquad \text{(Eqn. 2-12)}$$

by setting: $y = (n^2 - 1)^{-1}$; $a_0 = A^{-1}$; $a_1 = -\lambda_0^2/A$; and $x = \lambda^{-2}$. Consequently, after a material's refractive index has been measured at several different wavelengths, the resultant data pairs (λ_i, n_i) may be transformed by simple calculations into the equivalent pairs (x_i, y_i). This permits Equation 2-12 to be fitted to the transformed data by a simple linear regression. When this was done for refractive index values (n_i) measured at wavelengths (λ_i)—namely, 435.8, 486.1, 546.1, 589.3 and 656.3 nm—that the Cargille Company kindly supplied for 222 immersion oils, the squared coefficients of linear correlation (r^2) exceeded 0.999 for 217 oils and exceeded 0.997 for the remaining five. Wolfe's (1976) measurements of the principle indices α, β, and γ at various wavelengths for 35 low plagioclases of compositions from albite to anorthite similarly yielded r^2 values that averaged 0.99 for the 105 linear regressions performed. The Sellmeier equation in either form (Eqn. 2-11 or 2-12) thus fits the data exceeding well.

Each such linear regression yields values for a_0 and a_1 in Equation 2-12. With the constants a_0 and a_1 thus evaluated for a material, Equation 2-12 permits the corresponding refractive index to be calculated—or, speaking more precisely, to be estimated—for any desired wavelength within the visible or even, by extrapolation, beyond the visible. Moreover, the effect of random errors will be suppressed in the indices thus calculated because of the smoothing process inherent to a least-squares fit. Once the constants a_0 and a_1 are known for a material, λ_0 can also be calculated because it equals $(-a_1/a_0)^{1/2}$. This value for λ_0, according to Strens and Freer (1978), gives an indication of the optically significant transition energies and of their dependence on composition, structure, and volume. According to these authors, "for compounds of the common closed-shell ions (O^{2-}, F^-, Na^+, Mg^{2+}, Al^{3+}, Si^{4+}), $\lambda_0 \leq 125$ nm and the value $\lambda^2/(\lambda^2 - \lambda_0^2)$ is small, accounting for their transparency and low dispersion and index. For open-shell (transition metal) ions, $\lambda_0 > 125$ nm and [thus] their compounds are often colored, with high dispersion and index. The optical properties of materials containing both closed- and open-shell ions are often determined by the latter, as a comparison of (say) jadeite with acmite, or clino-zoisite with epidote will show."

QUESTIONS AND PROBLEMS

1. For the glass prism of Figure 2-3B (interfacial angles of its sides are 60°), if $i_1 = 0°$, what is the value of r_2? *Answer*: No correct value exists; the ray within the crystal undergoes total reflection when incident upon interface 2 (the upper left face) in Figure 2-3B.

2. Assume that the glass prism of Figure 2-3B is hollow, each side (interfacial angles again 60°) consisting of a thin plate of glass. The prism is filled with an unknown liquid, and sodium light is observed to enter the prism at interface 1 and leave from interface 2 at the angles $i_1 = 30°$ and $r_2 = 61.96°$. What is the refractive index of the liquid? *Answer*: 1.400.

3. Calculate the values of constants c_1 and c_2 (neglect c_3), in Cauchy's equation for the mineral halite ($n_C = 1.5407$, $n_D = 1.5443$, and $n_F = 1.5534$). *Answer*: $c_1 = 1.5253 \pm 0.0005$; $c_2 = 6.45$ to 6.73×10^3 nm^2.

4. Same question as 3, for fluorite ($n_C = 1.4325$, $n_D = 1.4338$, and $n_F = 1.4370$). *Answer*: $c_1 = 1.4270$; $c_2 = 2.35$ to 2.37×10^3 nm^2.

3 LENSES AND THE COMPOUND MICROSCOPE

OVERVIEW

A lens is a body of transparent isotropic material, usually glass, bounded by at least one curved surface. If the boundary surfaces are spherical, the lens' shape depends upon their radii and the relative location of their centers of curvature (Fig. 3-1). The **axis of a lens** is the line connecting its physical center to its center(s) of curvature.

Rays traveling parallel to the axis of a lens will be caused to intersect at O, the **principal focus**, if the lens is thin-edged (Fig. 3-3A). Or they will be diverged so they *appear* to have emanated from this principal focus (O', Fig. 3-3B) if the lens is thick-edged. The distance from a lens' center to its principal focus represents the lens' focal length f.

A thin lens ($\neq$ thin-edged lens) is one whose thickness is small relative to its radii of curvature. For an object at a distance p from the center of a thin lens, the lens will produce an image at a distance q such that

$$\frac{1}{f} = \frac{1}{p} + \frac{1}{q} \qquad \text{(Eqn. 3-1, thin-lens formula)}$$

A thin-edged thin lens captures rays emanating from all points on a neon arrow PR, although, in Figure 3-5, this is shown only for its tip, P. If the arrow's distance equals p, where $p > f$, the lens will focus these rays to form, at q, a **real inverted image** $P'R'$ (Fig. 3-5A), shimmering in space. However, if $p < f$ (Fig. 3-5B), the lens will diverge rays from points on the arrow, e.g., P. Consequently, arrow PR viewed through the lens will only *appear* to be at $P'R'$ (and at a distance q). The image $P'R'$ constitutes an **upright virtual image** of PR.

The ratio q/p represents the **magnification** of the image relative to the object.

A simple compound microscope (Fig. 3-6) consists of an objective lens that forms a real inverted image of PR (at $P'R'$). This real image is then, viewed by a second lens, the eyepiece. The distance P' (of $P'R'$ from the eyepiece) is less than f for the eyepiece. As a result one sees through the eyepiece a virtual image $P''R''$ of the real image $P'R'$. The object PR has thus been magnified twice—first by the objective lens and then by the eyepiece.

NOMENCLATURE AND TYPES OF LENSES

A lens may be defined as a body of glass (or other transparent isotropic substance) that is bounded by no less than one curved surface. The shape of lenses bounded by spherical surfaces (the simpler types) is dependent upon the radii of curvature of these surfaces as well as upon the relative locations of their centers of curvature (Fig. 3-1). The **axis of a lens** is the line connecting its physical center with its centers of curvature. By definition a **thin lens** (not to be confused with the term "thin-edged lenses" discussed in a following paragraph) is one whose thickness is small as compared to its radii of curvature.

The six basic shapes of lenses resulting from different combinations of radii of curvature and relative locations of centers of curvature (Fig. 3-2) may be grouped into two

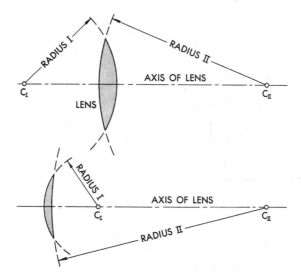

Figure 3-1. Two examples of the relationship between the cross-sectional shape of a lens (front view circular in all cases) to: (1) the radii of curvature of its spherical surfaces and (2) the relative locations of C_I and C_{II}, their centers of curvature. The line passing through the centers of curvature and the center of the lens is called the axis of the lens.

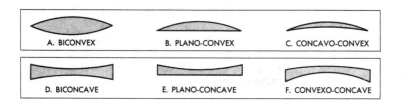

Figure 3-2. Cross sections through different types of lenses (top views would be circles): Top (A, B, C), thin-edged (converging) lenses; bottom (D, E, F), thick-edged (diverging) lenses.

types: (1) those that are thinner at the edges than at the center and (2) those that are not. The planar surfaces on lenses are considered to have an infinitely long radius of curvature.

Thin-edged lenses, the most important lens elements of polarizing microscopes, converge all monochromatic light rays traveling parallel to the lens axis so that they intersect at a point called the **principal focus** (point O in Fig. 3-3A); thick-edged lenses, less important for our purposes, diverge such rays so that they appear to have emanated from a point, again called the principal focus (Fig. 3-3B). In each case the distance of the principal focus from the center of the lens is called the **focal length** of the lens. Note that in Figure 3-3A a **real** point source of light is created at O; that is, the rays truly cross at and therefore secondarily emanate from point O. However in Figure 3-3B, O' is a **virtual** point source; that is, it appears to the eye that the rays emanate from O', but actually they do not.

THIN-LENS FORMULA AND GRAPHIC SOLUTIONS

A thin-edged lens intercepting the light rays emitted from a point, P, on its axis will cause these rays to converge to a point (Fig. 3-4A), become parallel (Fig. 3-4B), or become less divergent (Fig. 3-4C); the effect depends upon whether the point source is located beyond, at, or within the focal length of the lens, respectively. Using p and q to symbolize the distance from the center of the lens to the point source and its refracted

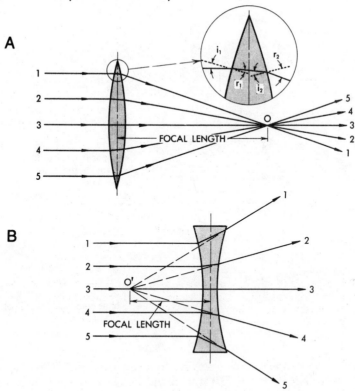

Figure 3-3. (A) Focusing of light rays parallel to the lens axis by a thin-edged lens (in cross section). The detailed view shows how the refraction at the lens surfaces is in accordance with Snell's law. (B) Focusing of rays by a thick-edged lens.

image, respectively, their relation to f, the focal length of the lens, is expressed for thin lenses as

$$\frac{1}{f} = \frac{1}{p} + \frac{1}{q}$$

(Eqn. 3-1)

The values f and p are always positive in sign but q may occasionally be negative. A negative value of q indicates that the image of the point is a virtual one and is located on the same side of the lens as the original point (Fig. 3-4C). The distances p and q are called conjugate distances; similarly points P and P' (Fig. 3-4A, C) are termed conjugate foci.

The location of the lens-formed image of a point located slightly off the lens' axis—for example, the arrow tip in Figure 3-5—can be determined graphically as a check on a solution of Equation 3-1. Thus, of the infinite number of light rays emanating from the arrow tip, the paths of three of them are known even after they pass through the lens. Their intersection (real or apparent) will thus establish P', the point where *all* of the light rays from the arrow tip P either intersect (Fig. 3-5A) or appear to intersect (Fig. 3-5B). Specifically, the paths of these three rays (Fig. 3-5) are as follows: Ray 1 travels parallel to the lens axis before entry into the lens, then through O_F, the principal focus, after its refraction by the lens; ray 2 travels through the optical center of the lens and therefore emerges undeviated (planes tangent to the lens at this ray's points of entry and exit are parallel; thus this case is like that shown in Fig. 2-3A); ray 3 either passes through O_B, the back focus (Fig. 3-5A), or has a direction as if it had come from O_B (Fig. 3-5B) and thus

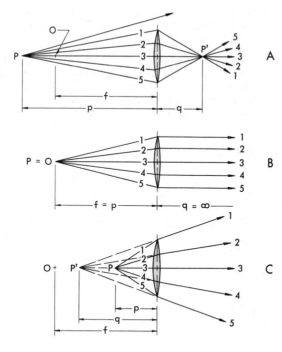

Figure 3-4. Relationship between *p* (the distance of *P*, a point source of light, from the lens center), *f* (the focal length of the lens), and *q* (the distance from the lens center of *P'*, the refracted image of the point source).

(A) *p* > *f*: *P* and its image, *P'*, lie on opposite sides of the lens. After passage through the "crossroads" at *P'*, ray 1 becomes the lowermost of the rays rather than the uppermost.

(B) *p* = *f*: No image *P'* is formed. The rays are parallel after passage through the lens.

(C) *p* < *f*: *P'* now lies on the same side of the lens as *P*. Rays 1 to 5, viewed after passage through the lens, appear to have emanated from a point at *P'*.

travels parallel to the lens axis after emerging from the lens. *R'P'* (Fig. 3-5A) is a **real image** of *PR* whereas *P'R'* (Fig. 3-5B) is a **virtual image**, only *seeming* to emit rays.

In Figure 3-5A and B, *SPR* and *SP'R'* are similar triangles. Consequently

$$\frac{R'S}{RS} = \frac{P'R'}{PR} \qquad \text{(Eqn. 3-2)}$$

However, *R'S* and *RS* are, by definition, *q* and *p*, respectively. The ratio *P'R'/PR* represents the ratio of image size to object size, that is, the **magnification**. Consequently, Equation 3-2 can be rewritten

$$\frac{q}{p} = magnification \qquad \text{(Eqn. 3-3)}$$

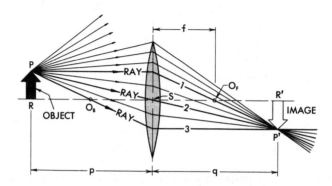

Figure 3-5A. The use of special rays 1, 2, and 3 to construct graphically the image *P'R'* that a lens produces of an object *PR* if it is located *beyond* the lens's focal length, *O_BS*.

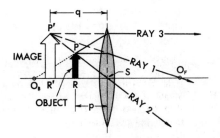

Figure 3-5B. The use of special rays 1, 2, and 3 to construct graphically the image $P'R'$ that a lens produces of an object PR if it is located *within* the lens's focal length, O_BS. All rays being emitted from P, except for the three construction rays, have been omitted. In graphical constructions, rays are assumed to change direction at the central plane of the lens (vertical line at S) rather than, as actually occurs, at lens surfaces. Note that the image in **(A)** is a real image and in **(B)** a virtual image.

THE COMPOUND MICROSCOPE

The compound microscope combines two converging lenses or systems of lenses, each mounted in fixed positions in the opposite ends of a metal tube of length L (Fig. 3-6). The lens system closest to the object being viewed is called the **objective lens**—or, simply, the objective. That closest to the viewer's eye is called the **eyepiece** (or **ocular**).

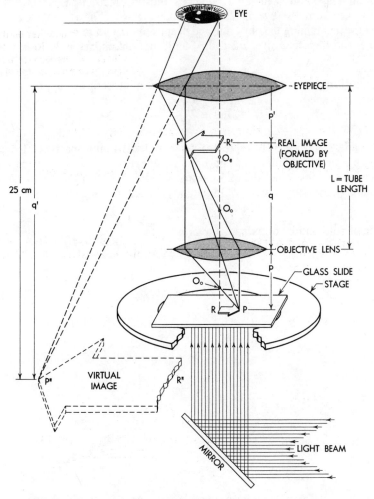

Figure 3-6. The elements of a compound microscope as shown by a combined perspective view (stage, object RP, images $P'R'$ and $P''R''$) and cross-sectional view (rays, mirror, and lenses). The optical tube length, L, has been disproportionately shortened for illustrative purposes only.

Basically, the objective lens forms an enlarged real image (of the object being examined) at a point closer to the eyepiece than the eyepiece's focal length. Consequently, the already enlarged real image is seen through the eyepiece as a further enlarged virtual image.

The object to be viewed—*RP* in Figure 3-6 is mounted on a glass slide and placed on the stage where it is illuminated by either daylight or lamplight (reflected upward by an adjustable mirror). When so illuminated, every point on the transparent arrow *RP* acts as a point source of light emitting an upward-directed hemispherical fan of rays in all directions. Considering one such point *P* and selecting from the hemispherical fan only the three special ray directions previously discussed, one notes that a real, inverted image of the object is formed at *P'R'* by the objective lens. Since it is a real image, every point on *P'R'* is again a point source of light emitting an upward-directed hemispherical fan of rays. The real image *P'R'*, however, is formed closer to the eye lens than O_e, the principal focus of the eye lens; consequently, *P'R'*, when viewed through the eyepiece, appears to be an enlarged virtual image, *P″R″*, located at a distance *q'* from the eyepiece.

The virtual image *P″R″* will generally appear most distinct, that is, in best focus, if its apparent distance from the eye is 25 cm.[*] If the image *P'R'* is not clearly seen, the microscope tube (containing the objective and eyepiece) may be racked up or down to alter the value of *p* and therefore of *q*, *p'*, and *q'* until the virtual image is 25 cm away from the eye.

The **magnifying power, *M.P.*,** of a compound microscope is approximately

$$M.P. = \frac{25cm \times L}{f_0 \times f_e} \qquad \text{(Eqn. 3-4)}$$

where *L*, f_0, and f_e respectively represent the tube length, and the focal lengths of the objective and eyepiece in centimeters. Since for some eyes, 25 cm may not be the distance of distinct vision, a value other than 25 cm may need to be substituted into Equation 3-4. Thus the same microscope may yield slightly different magnifications for different observers.

The line of collimation, or **axis**, of a microscope is the line coinciding with the axes of all its lenses. In Figure 3-6, it is the line containing points *R*, O_0, O_e, and *R'*.

---

[*] The normal human eye is unable to see clearly any objects closer than 25 cm, the so-called distance of distinct vision. This distance usually increases with age.

QUESTIONS AND PROBLEMS

1. A point of light is located along the axis of a biconvex lens at 8.1 cm distance from its center. If the focal length of the lens is 6.1 cm, determine the type of image and its distance from the lens' center. *Answer*: Real image, 24.4 cm from center.

2. A neon arrow is located on the axis of a biconvex lens ($f = 15$ cm) at a point 35 cm from the lens center. What is the magnification and type of image formed? *Answer*: Real image, 0.75×.

3. Same question as 2, but the distance of arrow is only 10 cm. *Answer*: Virtual image, 3×.

4. Two lenses are mounted in a vertical tube so that their axes coincide and their center-to-center distance is 16 cm. An object on this common axis is viewed through this double lens combination at a distance of 5 cm from the center of the lens nearest the object—that is, the objective lens. The focal length of this objective lens is 3 cm. The focal length of the lens nearer the eye—that is, the ocular—is 12 cm. What magnification is produced when the object is so viewed? *Answer*: 5.15×.

4 THE POLARIZING LIGHT MICROSCOPE

OVERVIEW

A polarizing light microscope (PLM) is a compound microscope equipped with a rotatable stage and two polarizers. One, located below the stage, is simply called the **polarizer** (Fig. 4-1). The second, located above the stage, is called the **analyzer**.

By custom, an observer using a polarizing microscope is assumed to face north. Under this assumption, the polarizer's privileged (or vibration) direction ordinarily constrains the light to vibrate within an E-W plane. By contrast, the analyzer's privileged direction is N-S; hence, it only transmits light vibrating within a N-S plane.

The analyzer can be withdrawn from the light path. In such case, an object on the stage is said to be observed in plane-polarized light. With the analyzer inserted, the object is said to be observed between **crossed polarizers** because the polarizer's privileged direction (E-W) is at 90° (= crossed) relative to the analyzer's. Frequently, the polarizer of a polarizing microscope can be rotated from its 0° position. If it is rotated 90° so that its privileged direction becomes N-S and thus parallel to the analyzer's, the object is now viewed between **parallel polarizers**.

Modern microscopes are usually equipped with turrets so that a high-, medium-, or low-power objective may be rotated into position for use (Fig. 4-8). The angular aperture (A.A.) of an objective represents the widest angle of light that will enter the objective when it is correctly focused on a grain. An objective's numerical aperture (N.A.) is actually the sine of one-half of the angular aperture. The depth of focus on an objective decreases as an objective's magnifying power increases (see Fig. 4-4).

Figure 4-9 describes a student-model microscope and the adjustments necessary to use it to best advantage.

INTRODUCTION

The polarizing light microscope (PLM) is little more than a compound microscope into which two polarizers have been integrated and the stage made rotatable (Fig. 4-1). The one below the stage is called the lower polarizer, or simply the polarizer. The one above the stage is called the analyzer. In most modern microscopes the polarizer transmits plane-polarized light vibrating in an east-west direction.[1] By contrast, the analyzer only transmits light (or that component thereof) that vibrates in a north-south direction. In some models of microscopes, the privileged directions of polarizer and analyzer may be reversed, that is, N-S and E-W, respectively.

If an object on the stage is viewed with the analyzer inserted, it is said to be viewed between **crossed polarizers**. If the analyzer's privileged direction is made parallel to the polarizer's, the object is viewed with **parallel polarizers**. If the analyzer is not inserted, the object is said to be observed with **plane light**; that is illuminated by plane-polarized light from the polarizer.

---

[1] The convention of referring to microscope directions as points of the compass perhaps arises from the youthful days of microscopy when an unobstructed north-facing window was considered to be a good light source. Today, consequently, an observer looking into a microscope is by custom assumed to face north, regardless of his or her actual orientation.

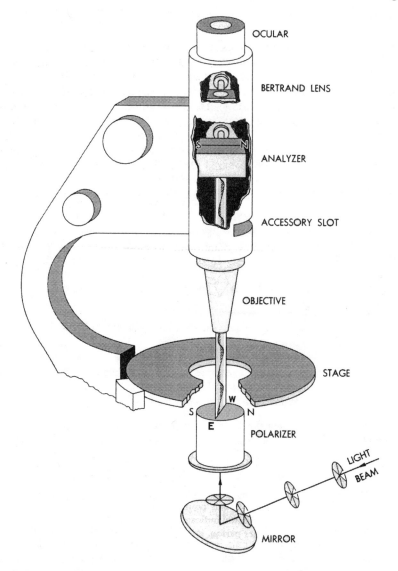

OCULAR

BERTRAND LENS

ANALYZER

ACCESSORY SLOT

OBJECTIVE

STAGE

POLARIZER

LIGHT
BEAM

MIRROR

Figure 4-1. Schematic diagram of the disposition of the more important parts of a polarizing microscope, mechanical details omitted.

ELEMENTS AND THEIR FUNCTION

The Illumination System

Early microscopes used a mirror, located below the stage, to direct light from an external source upwards along the microscope's axis. Present models frequently have a halogen light-source built into the microscope's base. A system of lenses and mirrors then directs the light upwards. And a rheostat may be present to control light intensity. A filter holder may be located above the light's exit port to allow insertion of filters (to isolate desired portions of the spectrum) or of a blue "daylight" filter to cause the light to approximate sunlight.

The Diaphragms

As necessary to a microscope as its lenses are the diaphragms used to control the diameters of the light beams passing through it. The central opening in these diaphragms may be fixed (= pinhole diaphragm) or variable (= iris diaphragm). The effect of constricting a diaphragm depends on its location in the optical path of the light. At certain sites, a diaphragm functions as an **aperture diaphragm**. So located, its constriction decreases the brightness of the image, increases the depth of field, decreases resolution and increases contrast, but leaves the size of the field of view unchanged. If located at certain other sites, an iris diaphragm functions as a **field diaphragm**, so called because its constriction limits the field of view. Any field diaphragm located below the microscope stage should routinely be constricted until it almost encroaches on the field of view. This reduces glare, which is haziness of image from stray light scattered by features of the object outside the field of view.

Under ordinary circumstances, a microscope is best used in a fairly well-lit room. This causes the eye's iris, itself an aperture diaphragm, to close down until its pupil is only about 3 mm in diameter, a condition which promotes sharp vision.

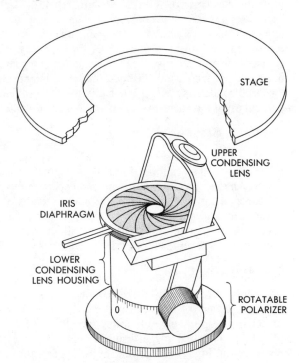

Figure 4-2. Schematic diagram of the substage assembly of a representative polarizing microscope, mechanical details omitted. Frequently this assembly includes two iris diaphragms, one an aperture diaphragm and the other a field diaphragm.

The Substage Assembly

The substage assembly (schematically shown in Fig. 4-2) generally consists of a polarizer, a pair of condensing lenses, and an iris diaphragm that functions as an aperture diaphragm. The entire assembly may be raised or lowered to control its distance below the microscope stage and thus the illumination of the object (see also the discussion of Köhler illumination near the end of this chapter).

Polarizer. As previously discussed, the polarizer in its normal position usually has an E-W privileged direction. In many models, however, the polarizer may be rotated on a vertical axis out of this position. If rotated back to normal operating position, it will make a slight "click" when the normal position is attained. In this position the index denoting the amount of rotation of the polarizer should indicate zero (see Fig. 4-2). If a microscope is being shared with another person, it is wise to make sure that the polarizer is in its zero position.

Lower (Fixed) Condensing Lens. This lens, located directly above the polarizer, cannot easily be removed from the path of the light. Its numerical aperture (discussed later) should preferably be about equal to that of the microscope's medium-power objective—that is, about 0.25.

Aperture Diaphragm. This iris diaphragm is located above (or below) the lower condensing lens. As previously noted, its setting should optimize the contrast, resolution, and depth of field for the image seen through the microscope. *It should not be used to regulate the image's brightness.* The illuminator's brightness adjustment should be used for this purpose.

Auxiliary Condensing Lens. The uppermost element of the substage assembly is a powerful converging lens that in most microscopes can be swung into or out of the path of the light as desired. With this lens inserted, the light illuminating the object on the stage becomes more strongly convergent than if only the lower condensing lens is used. The numerical aperture when both condensing lenses are inserted should approximately equal (or exceed) the numerical aperture of the high-power objective with which it will normally be used. In some microscopes this condensing lens does not swing out but instead is raised or lowered to increase or decrease the effective numerical aperture. For these microscopes the fixed condensing lens is itself designed to provide a strongly convergent cone of light, particularly if the aperture diaphragm is opened wide.

Rotatable Stage

The microscope's stage, onto which the microscope slides will be placed, should rotate freely and be calibrated so that its degrees of rotation can be determined on a vernier index. Angular measurements on microscopic preparations, which are very important in optical crystallography, can then be read to tenths of a degree. When a simple but elegant device called a spindle stage is used to study single crystals, such accuracy becomes necessary. A pair of stage clips to hold the microscope slide firmly on the stage will decrease the possibilities for error in these measurements.

The Objectives

Most PLM objectives are mounted on a rotatable nosepiece so that objectives with different powers of magnification can be rotated into position for use. Three achromatic objectives, respectively able to produce low (2.5× to 5×), medium (10× to 20×), or high (40× to 63×) initial magnifications (e.g., the magnification $P'R'/PR$ produced by the objective in Fig. 3-6) of an object, generally suffice for student work in optical crystallography and petrography. The low-power objective provides a good overall view of a rock thin section whereas the medium and high powers show the section in more detail.

The characteristic properties of some objectives are listed in Table 4-1. As illustrated in Figure 4-3, the angular aperture (A.A.) represents the angle between the most divergent rays that can enter the objective from a point on an object upon which the objective is focused. The angle equal to one half of the angular aperture is called u:

$$u = \frac{A.A.}{2}$$

Table 4-1. Properties of some commonly used
dry* objectives

Initial magnification	Angular aperture (A.A.)	Numerical aperture (N.A.)	Free working distance (F.W.D.) in mm	Depth of (clear) focus in mm
3.2×	14°	0.12	34.5	0.5
4×	11.5°	0.10		
10×	29°	0.25	5.8	0.04
40×	81°	0.65		
45×	116°	0.85	0.6	0.01

* Ordinary objectives, separated by an air space from the object being viewed, are called "dry" objectives. This is in contrast to the more powerfully magnifying "oil-immersion" objectives in which an immersion oil fills the gap between objective and object being viewed.

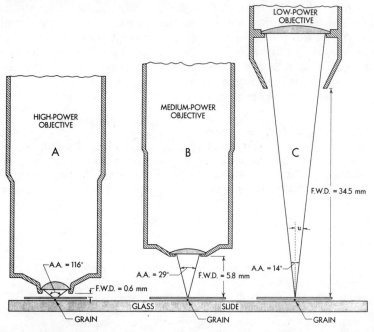

Figure 4-3. Comparison of the free working distances (F.W.D.) angular apertures (A.A.), and one-half angular aperture (u) for three of the objectives described in Table 4-1 above.

For dry objectives, the numerical aperture (N.A.) equals sin u:

$$N.A. = \sin u \qquad \text{(Eqn. 4-1)}$$

More broadly stated to apply to oil immersion lenses as well,

$$N.A. = n \sin u \qquad \text{(Eqn. 4-2)}$$

where n equals the lowest index of refraction of any medium filling the space between the objective and the object being viewed. As may be noted in Table 4-1, the higher power objectives, as a general rule, possess larger angular and numerical apertures.

The resolving power of a lens or combination of lenses may be defined in terms of h, the smallest distance between two points on the object which will yield separate images. For a microscope the resolving power depends solely upon the objective's N.A. and the wavelength of light being used. The working rule, substantiated by theory, is $h = \lambda/2N.A.$ In other words resolution increases (h decreases) to the extent λ is small or N.A. large.

Of prime importance to the student is the concept of free working distance (F.W.D.), that is, the distance between the lowest part of the objective (in many cases a protective metal ring) and the top of the cover glass overlying the object in focus. As illustrated in Figure 4-3, the free working distance is ordinarily very small for high-power objectives; therefore, rather than look through the eyepiece, the student should observe (with eye at the level of the stage) the air space between objective and coverglass as objective is lowered. When this air space is slightly less than the free working distance, he can look through the eyepiece and raise the objective slowly upward until a sharp focus is secured. Considerable damage to the sample or objective may result if caution is not used during this operation.

For some preparations the cover-glass thickness so far exceeds 0.16 to 0.18 mm, the preferred thickness, that the free working distance is less than zero for a high-powered objective and consequently the section cannot be brought into clear focus. Generally, however, when such difficulties arise for a petrographic thin section, the beginning student discovers that the thin section was placed upside down—that is, with cover glass down—on the stage of the microscope. If the cover glass is truly too thick, the student must switch to a lower-power objective.

Engraved on each objective (Fig. 4-4) will be: (1) its magnification, (2) its numerical aperture, (3) the tube length (in mm) of the microscope for which it is designed, and (4) the thickness (in mm) of cover glasses that can be used with it.

An objective, inserted into a microscope, may produce fairly sharp images of points lying both above and below the particular point upon which it is precisely focused.

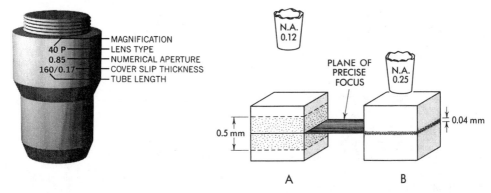

Figure 4-4 (left). Typical engravings on a polarizing microscope's objective. The P indicates a strain-free objective suitable for polarized light microscopy. Objectives less than 16× in power can be used with or without a cover slip.

Figure 4-5 (right). Comparison of the depths of focus for (A) a low-power objective with N.A. 0.12 and (B) a medium-power objective with N.A. 0.25. The stippling represents the dust particles in a glass cube that are in fair focus if the objective is precisely focused upon the level of the ruled plane.

Depth of focus, the distance between the upper and lower limit (Fig. 4-5), is an inverse function of numerical aperture, objectives with large numerical apertures generally having small depths of focus and vice versa.

The importance of this feature in microscopy will become apparent if one focuses on the center of a glass cube throughout which dust-like inclusions are distributed, the microscope (10× eyepiece) being successively equipped with two of the objectives described in Table 4-1. Using the 0.12 N.A. objective, all inclusions approximately 0.25 mm above or below the cube's center (Fig. 4-5A) would be in fairly sharp focus whereas with the 0.25 N.A. objective only the inclusions approximately 0.02 mm above or below this central point would be clearly visible (Fig. 4-5B). The high-power (0.85 N.A.) objective practically confines visibility to a plane through the point on which it is focused. Consequently, in studying crystals greater than 0.01 mm in thickness with a high-power objective, it is necessary to focus up or down to explore the crystal vertically for features that otherwise might be missed.

Accessory Slot

A slot, generally located in the lower end of the microscope tube (see Fig. 4-1), permits insertion of one of the three commonly used accessories (quartz wedge, full-wave plate, or quarter-wave plate) into the path of the light. The theory and utility of these three accessories will be discussed in a later section.

Analyzer

As already discussed, the polarizing element located above the accessory slot (Fig. 4-1) is called the analyzer and, as such, is readily withdrawable from the path of the light. In some models of microscopes, the privileged direction of the analyzer can be rotated as much as 90°. For most operations, however, the privileged direction of the analyzer must be at precisely 90° to that of the polarizer.

Bertrand Lens

This lens, located above the analyzer (Fig. 4-1), may also be withdrawn from or inserted into the light path as desired. If it is inserted, the object in focus on the stage cannot be viewed; instead, under proper conditions, its interference figure (to be discussed later) will appear in the field of view. Microscopes whose Bertrand lenses are equipped with an iris diaphragm permit observation of interference figures in smaller grains than is otherwise possible.[2]

Oculars (Eyepieces)

A 10× Huygenian-type ocular or eyepiece usually suffices for routine microscopy. Generally speaking, oculars higher than 12.5× in power, unless used in conjunction with objectives of the very highest quality, do not yield very satisfactory images. In general. if the ocular's power multiplied by the objective's power exceeds 1000 times the objective's numerical aperture, **empty magnification** results. In other words, the enlarged images lose crispness and reveal no additional details. Thus a 20× ocular should not be used with a 45×/0.65 objective because the resultant magnification (~900×) exceeds 650 (= 1000 × 0.65).

For photomicrography, a 10× Ramsden-type ocular may also be desirable. During microscopy, the observer's eye must be located at the ocular's "exit pupil" (Fig. 4-6A).

---

[2] The Universal Eyepiece designed by F.E. Wright is particularly useful for observing interference figures in small grains but is generally not used in student work.

This may not be possible while the observer is wearing eye glasses unless the ocular is a "high point" ocular, namely one whose exit pupil is high enough to permit use of spectacles.

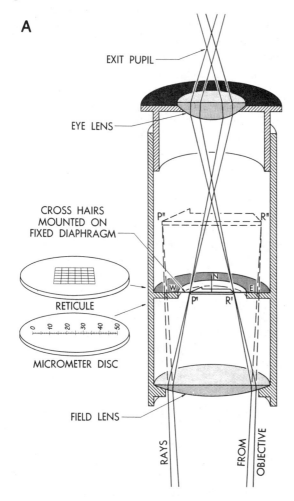

A

EXIT PUPIL

EYE LENS

CROSS HAIRS MOUNTED ON FIXED DIAPHRAGM

RETICULE

MICROMETER DISC

FIELD LENS

RAYS FROM OBJECTIVE

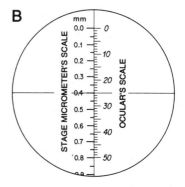

B

Figure 4-6. (A) The components and ray paths within a Huygenian ocular. The dashed lines indicate the ray paths and real image location if the field lens were removed. (B) Calibration of the scale of a micrometer ocular (right side of N-S cross hair) by focusing on the scale of a stage micrometer (left side). The divisions indicating 0.01 mm have been omitted for the stage micrometer scale.

A Huygenian ocular (Fig. 4-6A) consists of two lenses. The lower lens (field lens) increases the convergency of the light rays from the objective so that the real image is formed at $P'R'$ rather than at the normal $P''R''$. A fixed diaphragm, which limits the field of view, is located precisely at the plane containing the real image $P'R'$. A pair of mutually perpendicular cross hairs (actually single dark threads, in some cases from a spider web) may be mounted on the fixed diaphragm so as to appear in the field of view as two mutually perpendicular black lines. Instead of these spider threads, a thin glass disc, upon whose lower surface is etched a pair of fine, mutually perpendicular lines, may be mounted on the fixed diaphragm to provide cross hairs. For quantitative linear measurements of the mineral grains being viewed, either a reticule or a micrometer disc (Fig. 4-6A) may be mounted in place of the cross hairs. Such oculars, called micrometer oculars or micrometer eyepieces, are available commercially. This fixed-scale type of micrometer ocular is adequate for most, if not all, optical or petrographic work. If greater accuracy is desired, a micrometer ocular with a moving scale should be obtained; its cost, however, is considerably greater. Either type of micrometer ocular must be calibrated for each objective with which it is to be used. This is done by focusing on a stage micrometer, which is simply a glass slide whose central portion is engraved with a 2-mm-long line marked at intervals of 0.01 mm. When the scale of the stage micrometer is brought into focus (Fig. 4-6B, left scale), its divisions may be used to calibrate the divisions of the ocular (Fig. 4-6B, right scale). In Figure 4-6B, for example, 50 ocular divisions embrace 0.8 mm of the stage micrometer scale. Thus each ocular division equals 0.016 mm for the objective-ocular combination whose field of view appears in Figure 4-6B.

The upper part of the ocular (which houses the eye lens) slips sleevelike into the metal tube containing its field lens (Fig. 4-6A). This sleevelike motion permits the distance of the eye lens above the cross hairs to be adjusted so as to bring the cross hairs into sharpest focus for each observer. In turn, the entire assembly pictured in Figure 4-6A fits into the microscope tube. During this insertion *under very gentle pressure*, the ocular assembly should be rotated until it slips into one or the other of the two slotted positions. Having slipped into one, it must be raised slightly before being rotated into the second position. For one of these positions the cross hairs will be observed to be in the standard NS-EW positions. For the second, they will be at 45° thereto.

Coarse and Fine Adjustments

The height of the objective above an object on the microscope stage must occasionally be varied in order to obtain a sharply focused image. This is generally done by two knurled knobs. One of these, known as the "coarse adjustment," moves the objective vertically upward or downward at a very noticeable rate; the second, known as the "fine adjustment," does so at a very slow rate. The vertical movement produced by this fine-adjustment knob may generally be determined by counting the number of complete turns (or fractions thereof) of the knob by means of its attached calibrated drum. In some older models the same knob may control both the coarse and fine motions, the fine-adjustment motion being obtained by reversing the direction of knob rotation; with this system, unfortunately, an inexperienced student is more likely to damage a thin section or, worse yet, the objective.

ADJUSTMENTS OF THE MICROSCOPE

Centering the Objective

An objective is "centered" when its lens axis (*bo* in Fig. 4-7A) coincides with the vertical axis about which the microscope stage rotates (*sa*). Fortunately the intersections of both axes with the microscope field of view are readily determinable. The outcrop of axis *bo* always coincides with the cross-hair intersection; the outcrop of *sa* can be located by viewing a dust-speckled glass slide while rotating the microscope stage. One speck, at the point about which all the others revolve (like stars about the polar star), marks the outcrop of *sa* (point *a* in Fig. 4-7B). The cross-hair intersection can be brought to coincide with this point by turning the centering screws on the objective, by means of the two small centering wrenches provided. If the objective is now correctly centered, a speck seen at the cross-hair intersection will remain there during a 360° rotation of the stage. Each objective used with the microscope may require centering from time to time.

Verification of Perpendicularity of Polarizers

Adjust the substage mirror and open the iris diaphragm until maximum brightness of the field of view is obtained. If the analyzer is now inserted, the field of view should be completely dark; if it is not dark, the polarizers are not mutually perpendicular. In that event, one should check as to whether the polarizer has been "clicked" into its normal operating position and, in the case of microscopes with rotatable analyzers, whether the

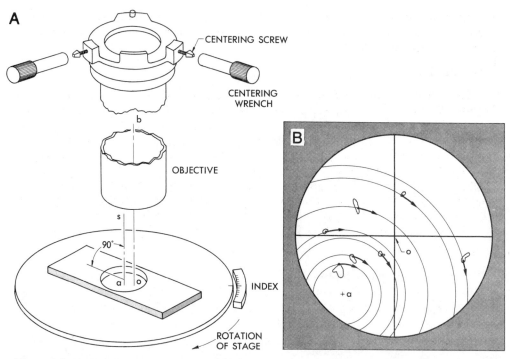

Figure 4-7. (A) Uncentered objective. All parts of the microscope have been removed except for the stage and objective. The axis of the lens, *bo*, and the vertical axis about which the stage rotates, *sa*, do not coincide; therefore the objective is uncentered. (B) Field of view showing movement of particles on glass slide in Figure 4-6A as the stage is rotated. The particles "orbit" around a point, *a*, which marks the outcrop of axis *sa* in the field.

analyzer is in its zero position. With both polarizers in their zero positions, true perpendicularity between their privileged directions should exist, a situation commonly described as "crossed polarizers."

Alignment of Cross Hairs to Polarizers

During routine measurements, the cross hairs in the ocular should be parallel to the privileged directions of the polarizers. This parallelism may be tested by observing, between crossed polarizers, an oil mount containing $PbCl_2$, $HgCl_2$, NH_4SO_4 or natrolite needles. If the desired parallelism exists, the needles will appear darkest when aligned

Figure 4-8. Rotation of a needle of $PbCl_2$, $HgCl_2$, or natrolite successively into positions 1 to 6 between crossed polarizers. The microscope used here has a correct cross-hair-polarizer alignment since the needle is parallel to a cross hair when at maximum darkness (positions 1 and 6).

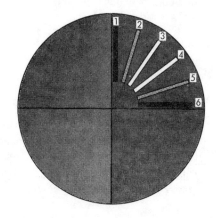

parallel to one of the cross hairs (Fig. 4-8). If parallelism does not exist, it is probably because (1) one of the polarizers is not in its zero position or (2) the ocular is not fitted into its proper slotted position.

Cleaning Lenses

Clear images will be formed only if the glass surfaces of the microscope are free of fingerprints and of the film that sometimes collects on glass. To clean a lens, first brush it with a soft camel's hair brush to remove any abrasive dust particles, then wipe it with a lens tissue slightly moistened with a water-based lens cleaner (available from any optician or camera shop). Next gently polish the lens with a dry lens tissue. Since the ocular and objective lenses are handled relatively frequently, they are most likely to be smudged with fingerprints and should be checked for such if the microscope images are blurred. The glass of the slide on which the material being examined is mounted should also be free of oil droplets, smudges, and fingerprints. For cleaning slides, less expensive tissue may be used instead of lens tissue. For lenses, however, use only the abrasive-free lens tissue.

Köhler Illumination

Optimally, the microscope's field of view should be (1) brightly and uniformly illuminated, and (2) the illumination should not extend beyond the field of view (thus reducing glare, that is, the haziness of the image from stray light scattered by features of the microscope outside the field of view). Even though the light source—for example, a coiled filament—is not itself uniformly bright, requirements (1) and (2) may be achieved by use of Köhler illumination. This is inherent to most modern microscopes with built-in illuminators. For microscopes lacking built-in illuminators, consult McCrone *et al.* (1978, p. 32)[3] for detailed instructions for achieving Köhler illumination.

STUDENT MODEL PLMs

The polarizing light microscope is one of the more powerful tools at the disposition of the geologist, mineralogist, forensic scientist, or chemist. The student should become familiar with the name, function, and routine adjustment of each of the important working parts of his or her microscope. Figure 4-9, on the following page, summarizes this for the Leica DMLSP polarizing microscope.

---

[3] Walter McCrone, Lucy B. McCrone, and John G. Delly (1978) *Polarized Light Microscopy*, Ann Arbor Science Publishers, P.O. Box 1425, Ann Arbor, Michigan).

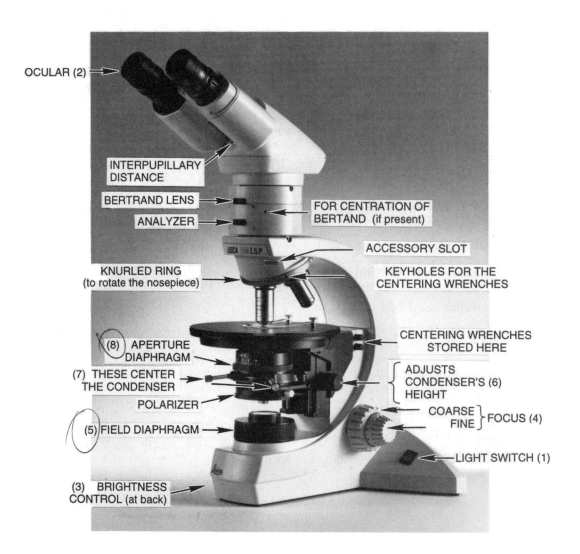

OCULAR (2)

INTERPUPILLARY DISTANCE

BERTRAND LENS

ANALYZER

FOR CENTRATION OF BERTAND (if present)

ACCESSORY SLOT

KNURLED RING (to rotate the nosepiece)

KEYHOLES FOR THE CENTERING WRENCHES

CENTERING WRENCHES STORED HERE

(8) APERTURE DIAPHRAGM

(7) THESE CENTER THE CONDENSER

ADJUSTS CONDENSER'S (6) HEIGHT

POLARIZER

COARSE FINE } FOCUS (4)

(5) FIELD DIAPHRAGM

LIGHT SWITCH (1)

(3) BRIGHTNESS CONTROL (at back)

Figure 4-9. Leica PLM (Model DM LSP) designed for student use (courtesy of Leica Inc.).

Aperture Diaph → controls cone of light

Field Diaph

Adjustments of a Microscope

Change magnifications by grasping the gnurled portion of the nosepiece ring (*but not by grasping and pulling on an objective* because this may de-center the objective and put strain on the objective's housing). [Note the objective-centering screws in the holes where they are stored. These, inserted into the holes in the gnurled ring (above each objective), allow each objective to be individually centered.]

Setting up the microscope. Turn the light on (1), look through ocular (2) and adjust the interpupillary distance to suit your eyes. Also, even before putting a specimen on the stage, adjust the brightness control (3) to a comfortable level while using the 10× objective. With a specimen on the stage, bring it into sharp focus using the coarse adjustment knob (4). Use the fine adjustment knob to clarify the specimen's smallest details. Using the 40× objective, fine-focus further on these details.

Adjusting the field diaphragm. Using the 10× objective, gently constrict the field diaphragm (5) to its smallest size. If necessary, adjust the height of the condenser by turning knob (6). Now use the condenser's two centering screws (7) to bring the field diaphragm's image to the center of the field of view. Switch to the 40× objective and open the field diaphragm (5) until its image just barely leaves the field of view. If this reveals that the field diaphragm is not quite centered, use screws (7) to center it.

Adjusting the aperture diaphragm. Remove the ocular (2). Look down the empty tube to see the back of the objective. Adjust the aperture diaphragm (8) until its image reduces the radius of the circle of light from the objective by about 25%.

5

OPTICAL EXAMINATION OF
ISOTROPIC SUBSTANCES

OVERVIEW

The degree to which a transparent colorless grain (refractive index: n_g) is visible when immersed in a colorless medium (index: n_o) is called **relief**. If n_g almost equals n_o, the relief will be low (and the grain almost invisible). If n_g differs greatly from n_o, **high relief** results (and the grain stands out like a sore thumb). Relief is arbitrarily called **positive**, if $n_g > n_o$, but **negative** if $n_o > n_g$.

The **immersion method** determines n_g for a solid by successively immersing grains of it in oils whose indices (n_o) are known. For each such grain-oil mount, one can use the Becke line method; oblique illumination; and/or dispersion staining to determine whether $n_g > n_o$ or $n_g < n_o$ and, ultimately, the oil of match ($n_g = n_o$).

Becke lines form along grain edges as a medium-power objective (10×) is raised upwards from sharp focus (Fig. 5-3). In such case, a bright line, called the Becke line, *always moves toward the material having the higher refractive index.*

Oblique illumination results if an opaque stop is partly inserted into the light path (Fig. 5-6). This causes the grains to display shadowed edges on their sides *opposite from* the stop's shadow if $n_g < n_o$ (Fig. 5-5A) but *toward it* if $n_g > n_o$ (Fig. 5-5B)—or, sometimes, *vice versa.* Check using a grain of known index in an oil of known index.

A material's refractive index (n) has different values for the various wavelengths (λ) composing white light. Consequently, a plot of n versus λ yields a **dispersion curve** on ordinary graph paper but, usually, a straight line on Hartmann dispersion net paper. Commonly, a dispersion curve or line (Fig. 5-7A) slopes downward as wavelength increases (= **normal dispersion**). The intersection of the two lines at 550 nm in Figure 5-7A marks λ_m, the wavelength of match (where $n_o = n_g$.). Note that, because, as is usual, the oil has the steeper slope, $n_o > n_g$ for $\lambda < 550$ nm, but that $n_g > n_o$ for $\lambda > 550$ nm. As a result, two oppositely-moving, colored Becke lines occur. One (Fig. 5-7B), a bluish amalgam of wavelengths <550 nm, enters the oil, whereas the other, a reddish amalgam of wavelengths >550 nm enters the grain.

Coloration of Becke lines (or oblique shadows) indicates that the dispersion curves of grain and oil intersect in the visible range.

The usual goal is to determine the grain's refractive index for $\lambda = 589.3$ nm (Fraunhofer's D line). This can be done by (1) using a sodium lamp to illuminate the grain-oil mount and finding an oil for which $n_o = n_g$, or (2) almost as well, even if white light is the illuminant, by estimating λ_m from the colors of the Becke lines. Figures 5-9 and 5-10 summarize how ($n_{D,g} - n_{D,o}$)—the grain's index for D-light minus the oil's—can be estimated from the colors of the Becke lines or oblique shadows. This difference, if added algebraically to $n_{D,o}$ for the oil enveloping the grain, yields $n_{D,g}$, an index that can be confirmed (or refined) by immersing the grain in an oil whose $n_{D,o}$ index precisely equals $n_{D,g}$.

Dispersion staining is achieved by using a special objective that contains, at its back focal plane, either a clear disk with an opaque 4 mm-diameter dot at its center

(= **central stop** or **CS**) or an opaque disk containing a ~3 mm hole, either at its center (= **annular stop** or **AS**) or slightly off-center (= **unilateral masking** or **UM**). If the dispersion curves of oil and grain cross in the visible, CS, AS, and UM dispersion-staining impart edge-colors to the grains. These edge-colors permit λ_m, the wavelength of match where the dispersion curves cross, to be estimated to within 30 or 40 nm. If λ_m is thus determined from two oil mounts—to obtain $\lambda_{m,1}$ and $\lambda_{m,2}$ —then n_D for the grain (and oil) can be determined using Su's equation (Eqn. 5-5). This technique minimizes the number of oil mounts needed to estimate n_D for a grain.

CS dispersion-staining facilitates needle-in-the-haystack searches for a minor component (of known dispersion) among a multitude of other grains. If the powder is immersed in an oil whose dispersion curve crosses those of the sought-for grains, these grains exhibit edge-colors that stand out from the dark field background produced by CS illumination. Stray asbestos fibers can be detected this way.

For each Cargille liquid, the label's index (n_D) is for 25°C. At the time of grain-oil match, however, the oil is likely to be at room temperature, T_R, not at 25°C. In such case, n_{DM}, the oil's index at match, must be corrected for temperature. Thus,

$$n_{DM} = n_D + (T_R - 25°)\frac{dn}{dt}$$

where dn/dt, usually about -0.0004, is stated on the label.

INTRODUCTION

As previously discussed, the refractive index (R.I.) of a substance differs for different wavelengths of light; hence, n_C, n_D, and n_F may all be measured in detailed studies. Commonly, however, the only index sought is n_D or n. Whereas n_D indicates a material's R.I. either measured using sodium light or estimated to be n_D from dispersion colors, n indicates that white light was the illuminant during the measurement. Either value may suffice to identify an unknown material but n tends to be the less accurate. However, according to Emmons and Gates (1948), if the colors into which the grain edges disperse the white light are properly interpreted, values of n that differ from n_D by less than ±0.002 may be obtained.

The following discussions will therefore center on the measurement of n_D either directly or indirectly as n. It will be tacitly understood that n_C or n_F could be measured instead of n_D by substituting for the sodium light source either a suitably filtered hydrogen discharge tube, a monochromator set to emit wavelengths 656.3 nm (C) or 486.1 nm (F), or appropriate narrow-band interference filters.

REFRACTIVE INDEX MEASUREMENT IN LIQUIDS

The Abbé refractometer has become the standard instrument for the measurement of n_D in liquids. Depending upon the model, the range of the refractive indices measurable may be 1.30 to 1.71 or 1.45 to 1.84 with a precision of ±0.0002. A sodium vapor lamp or a monochromator set for 589.3 nm is the usual illuminator.

Numerous alternative methods of refractive index measurement of liquids exist; in general, however, methods of increased accuracy also require increased time. Fisher (1958) recommends use of a minimum amount of oil for increased accuracy during calibration of the Abbé refractometer with test plates of known indices.

REFRACTIVE INDEX MEASUREMENT IN SOLIDS

Duc de Chaulnes Method

This method permits measurement of the refractive index of transparent plates with only fair accuracy. It is included here briefly to point out the inverse relationship between a transparent plate's refractive index and its apparent thickness. The latter value represents the apparent depth of the plate's bottom surface below its top surface as viewed looking down through the plate. The three steps of the method are: (1) Focus a medium-power objective (N.A. 0.25) on the upper surface of a glass slide placed on the microscope stage (Fig. 5-lA) and read the calibrated fine-adjustment drum; (2) carefully place the plate of unknown index on this glass slide and then rack upward (using the fine-adjustment drum only) until the upper surface of the unknown plate is in sharp focus (Fig. 5-lB) the difference between this second reading on the fine-adjustment drum and that obtained in step (1) indicates t, the true thickness of the unknown plate; (3) Now carefully focus downward through the unknown plate until the upper surface of the supporting glass slide is once more in sharp focus (Fig. 5-lC) the difference between this fine-drum reading and that obtained in step 1 is a measure of the apparent thickness, t_a, of the unknown plate.

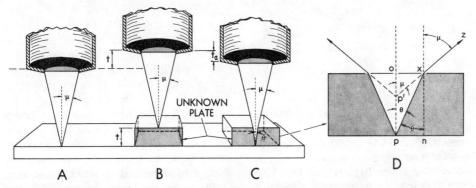

Figure 5-1. The three steps in the Duc de Chaulnes method of measuring the refractive index of an unknown glass plate. (A) Focus on slide surface; (B) Focus on upper surface of unknown; (C) Focus on slide surface *through* unknown. In (D), an enlarged view of a portion of (C), the rays of light in air (xz, etc.) appear to have emanated from point p' although they actually originated from point p. Thus op' appears to be the thickness of the plate as measured by focusing through it. The angles θ and u have been exaggerated for illustrative purposes.

The Duc de Chaulnes equation for the unknown plate's refractive index is then

$$n = \frac{t}{t_a} \qquad \text{(Eqn. 5-1)}$$

where t and t_a respectively signify true and apparent thickness. The differential drum readings obtained in steps 2 and 3 above are respectively proportional to t and t_a and may be substituted directly into Equation 5-1 to obtain the refractive index of the unknown plate.

Derivation of Equation 5-1, following Figure 5-1D, is as follows:

$$\tan u = \frac{ox}{op'} \quad \text{and} \quad \tan \theta = \frac{ox}{op}$$

but op' and op respectively equal t_a and t; thus

$$\frac{\tan u}{\tan \theta} = \frac{op}{op'} = \frac{t}{t_a}$$

42 Chapter 5

However, since rays px and xz obey Snell's law,

$$n = \frac{\sin u}{\sin \theta}$$

For small angles, the ratio of their sines approximately equals that of their tangents; consequently

$$n = \frac{\sin u}{\sin \theta} \cong \frac{\tan u}{\tan \theta} = \frac{t}{t_a}$$

Immersion Methods

One of the most convenient methods of measuring the refractive index of a transparent solid is by immersing fragments of it in a series of liquids ("oils") of known refractive index. Criteria, which will be discussed in the following sections, can then be applied, to determine whether the refractive index of the unknown fragments is within 0.002 or 0.003 of that of the surrounding oil. The immersion liquids used should at least span the refractive index range between 1.430 and 1.740 at intervals of 0.004 or 0.005. Such sets of immersion media are obtainable commercially or can be prepared in the laboratory.

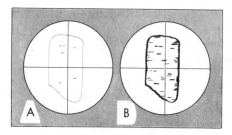

Figure 5-2. Low relief (A) and high relief (B) of a grain immersed in oil.

Relief. The depth of shadows along a grain's borders—that is, the degree of relief—grossly indicates how close the value of the grain's refractive index is to that of the oil. In a close match, the grain shows little or no relief if viewed in the oil; that is, it is almost completely invisible (Fig. 5-2A). To the extent that the indices of the oil and grain differ, however, the relief increases from low through moderate, high, and (ultimately) to extremely high. Extremely high relief (Fig. 5-2B) is characterized by the presence of heavy shadows on the grain surfaces. The shadow effects that cause the grain to stand out in relief in the oil may arise because (1) the grain's index is less than that of the oil (**negative relief**) or (2) its index is greater than that of the oil (**positive relief**). Unfortunately, positive and negative relief cannot be distinguished through routine observation.

The Becke Line Method.[1] A grain in oil, viewed with the microscope objective focused slightly above the position of sharpest focus, will usually display two thin lines (one dark and one bright) concentric with its border. The brighter of these is always closest to the material having the higher refractive index (Fig. 5-3, F_2F_2 fields of view) and, moreover, *always moves* (as shown by hollow arrows in F_2F_2 fields) *toward the medium having the higher refractive index, if viewed as the microscope objective is raised steadily upward above correct focus*—that is, from a focus upon plane F_1F_1 to F_2F_2. This line, which represents a concentration of light because of refraction and/or reflection at the grain-oil boundaries, is called simply the Becke line in most works. In this text, however, it will be called the bright Becke line to distinguish it on occasion from its dark companion, which, although usually nameless, will here be called the dark Becke line. The Becke lines become particularly obvious as the substage iris diaphragm is closed down (gently).

The Becke lines are generally attributed to (1) refraction at the lenslike edge of the grain and/or (2) total reflection at the grain-oil boundaries. Their explanation by refraction

[1] Sometimes called the method of central illumination

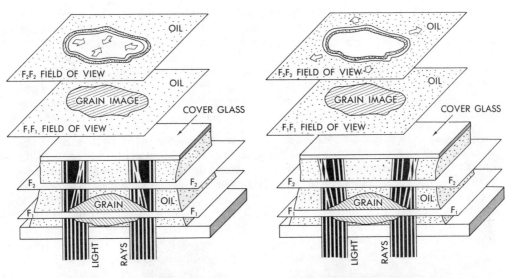

A. GRAIN INDEX GREATER THAN OIL'S   B. GRAIN INDEX LESS THAN OIL'S

Figure 5-3. The disposition and movement of Becke lines. Field of view F_1F_1 is that observed if the microscope is focused upon plane F_1F_1 to produce the sharpest grain image; here the Becke lines are not too obvious. However, if observed while the objective is raised upward toward a focus on plane F_2F_2, the Becke lines become increasingly apparent, the brighter line moving (as indicated by the hollow arrows in field of view F_2F_2) toward the medium having the greater refractive index. The grain cross sections indicate the dispersionally produced "crowns" of darkness and of brightness (ray concentrations) that occur above grain-oil boundaries and give rise to the Becke line effects. The dark and bright crowns change position according to whether the grain has a greater index (A) or a lesser index (B) than the oil.

presumes that a grain whose index is greater than the oil's acts as a converging lens (Fig. 5-3A) whereas a grain whose index is lower acts as a diverging lens (Fig. 5-3B). Consequently, the bright Becke line, observed as the microscope is raised upward from a sharp focus at F_1F_1 to F_2F_2, appears to move toward the grain (Fig. 5-3A) or toward the oil (Fig. 5-3B), whichever has the higher index. Total reflection at near-vertical grain-oil boundaries (Fig. 5-4) similarly deflects the near-parallel rays from the illuminator toward the medium of higher index and thus offers an equally plausible (and often preferred) explanation for the origin of the Becke lines. Note that certain rays within the grain are incident at angles equal or greater than their critical angle—for example, ray *a* in Figure 5-4. Both effects, refraction and total reflection, undoubtedly occur at the edges of grains in oil and are therefore probably jointly involved in the development of the Becke lines.

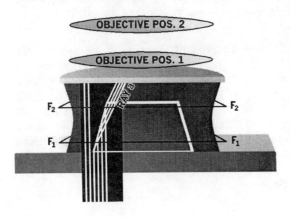

Figure 5-4. The role of total reflection at a near-vertical boundary in producing the Becke line effect. As the objective is raised upward from its focus on plane F_1F_1 to a focus on plane F_2F_2 (that is, from position 1 to position 2), the Becke line moves toward the grain's center since, in this case, the grain has a larger index (N) than the oil (n). For simplicity, light rays on the right half of the grain and to the rear are omitted.

The sensitivity of the Becke line method is increased if the substage iris diaphragm is sufficiently closed so as to make the Becke lines distinct. Many authorities prefer the high-power (about 45×) objective for observing the Becke line effect, although Saylor (1935) cites a 10× objective as permitting increased accuracy. The sensitivity of the method is also affected by the size and shape of the fragments as well as by the intensity of the light source. A near-vertical crystal-oil boundary generally permits greatest sensitivity. According to Saylor, more reliable results are obtained if the observed crystal-oil boundary is oriented parallel to the privileged direction of the polarizer.

Oblique Illumination Method.[2] Used with monochromatic light, this method permits detection, according to Wright (1913), of differences as small as 0.001 between the refractive index of a grain and that of its surrounding oil. Thus, utilizing white light and a set of immersion media calibrated in steps of 0.005 or less, a grain's index of refraction can be estimated to an accuracy of ± 0.003.

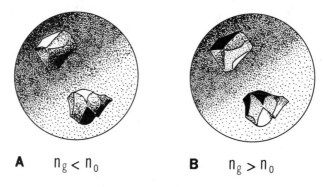

A $n_g < n_0$ B $n_g > n_0$

Figure 5-5. Shadows and, opposite to them, bright areas as produced on a grain by oblique illumination. The opaque stop producing oblique illumination has been inserted until its shadow has encroached upon approximately half the field of view. For most points of insertion of the opaque stop, the situation of the grain in (A)—*namely, (grain's) shadow away from (encroaching) shadow*—indicates that $n_g < n_o$, whereas that of the grain in (B)—*namely, shadow toward shadow*—indicates that $n_g > n_o$. For other points of insertion of the opaque stop, the significance of (A) and (B) may be reversed, so it is well to check this, for the microscope and experimental placement of the opaque stop to be used, using a grain of known index in a liquid of known index.

In essence, the method involves the gradual insertion of an opaque stop into the optical light path and observation of the grain in the field of view of the microscope as the shadow of the stop approaches it. Usually, a grain whose refractive index is higher than that of the oil will become shadowed on the edges nearest the approaching shadow but bright on the opposite border (Fig. 5-5A); if the grain's index is lower than that of the oil, this will be reversed (Fig. 5-5B).

For certain microscopes (and for different locations of insertion of the opaque stop into the optical light path), "shadowed toward shadow" (Fig. 5-5A) may indicate the grain's index to be lower than that of the oil rather than greater. For such microscopes, "shadowed away from shadow" (Fig. 5-5B) will indicate the grain to have a higher refractive index than the oil. Consequently, for any microscope it is wise to check the significance of "shadowed toward shadow" and "shadowed away from shadow" by means of a grain of known index immersed in an oil of known index or, more simply, by a Becke line test on a grain already examined by oblique illumination.

---

[2] Occasionally called the Schroeder van der Kolk method.

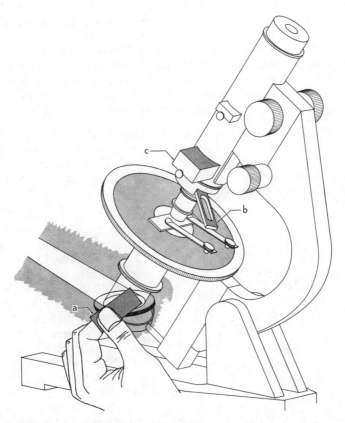

Figure 5-6. Convenient production of oblique illumination by partly blocking light with cardboard at *a*, with the metal frame of the accessory at *b*, or with the frame of the (partly inserted) analyzer at *c*.

Oblique illumination may be produced by several ways, of which the following are most convenient: (1) slow insertion of a cardboard (or one's finger) into the light path below the polarizer (Fig. 5-6a); (2) partial insertion of an accessory into the accessory slot until its metal frame intercepts the light (Fig. 5-6b); or (3) partial insertion of the analyzer until its frame intercepts the light (Fig. 5-6c). Saylor (1935) suggests that a low-power objective increases the sensitivity of the method. The advanced worker may wish to use Saylor's "double diaphragm" method of oblique illumination, which significantly increases the accuracy of the technique.

Dispersion Colors. If n_D of the grain is close in value to n_D of the surrounding oil, the bright and dark Becke lines (as well as the bright and shadowed areas produced by oblique illumination) will be observed to possess distinctive colorations if white light is the illuminant. Evidently, the white light is dispersed at the grain boundary into its spectrum (much as a prism disperses the Sun's rays). Close observation of these dispersion colors helps to determine whether n_D of the grain is greater than, equal to, or less than n_D of the oil. Consequently, n_D of the mineral can be estimated with accuracy better than $\pm$ 0.002 (Emmons and Gates, 1948) even though white light rather than sodium light is the source.

Although *n* plotted versus wavelength λ yields a dispersion curve (Fig. 2-6), these same data plotted on Hartmann dispersion net paper, will usually yield a straight line. Such Hartmann graph paper is based on the following empirical equation for dispersion:

$$n = A \frac{C}{(\lambda - B)^D}$$

where A, B, C and D are constants. For most materials D can be taken to equal 1.0 and, if λ is given in nanometers, one can conveniently set $C = 10^5$ nm and $B = 200$ nm, to obtain

$$n = A + \frac{10^5 \text{nm}}{(\lambda - 200)\text{nm}} \qquad \text{(Eqn. 5-2a)}$$

By substitution of x for $(\lambda - 200)^{-1}$, Equation 5-2a becomes a simple linear equation

$$n = A + 10^5 x \qquad \text{(Eqn. 5-2b)}$$

Thus, Hartmann paper[*] allows n to be plotted linearly against $(\lambda - 200)^{-1}$, that is, x—although the abscissa is labeled λ.

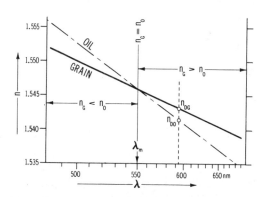

Figure 5-7A. Dispersion curves (on Hartmann paper) of a typical oil and grain whose indices $(n_o$ and n_g, respectively) are equal for light of wavelength λ_m (550 nm). Note that, as is commonly the case, the slope of the oil curve is greater than that of the grain.

A Hartmann plot of an oil's and crystal's dispersion curve (Fig. 5-7A) usually yields lines that slope downward toward the longer wavelengths. Significantly, the oil line slopes more steeply than that for the crystal. This will be especially true for the high dispersion oils (Series E) supplied by Cargille. In general, the greater the difference in slope between grain and oil, the more sharply their dispersion curves intersect at λ_m, the wavelength of match for which the oil and mineral have the same index. In Figure 5-7A, for example, λ_m equals 550 nm and the refractive index of oil and crystal for light of this wavelength is a bit over 1.546.

Consider next, grains of this mineral mounted in this oil. If, as is commonly the case, the crystal is thinner at its edge than at its center, any white light incident at this edge will be dispersed into a spectrum (Fig. 5-7B). For light of wavelengths longer than λ_m, the grain's refractive index is higher than the oil's, thus the grain acts as a miniature condensing lens, serving to converge these rays. For light of wavelengths shorter than λ_m, the grain's refractive index is less than the oil's; thus the grain acts as a diverging lens for these shorter wavelengths. Light of wavelength λ_m, on the other hand, passes through oil and grain without deflection. As a result of these dispersional effects, the Becke lines rimming the grain are now definitely colored—although the novice may at first have difficulty in seeing these colors. Consequently, if observed as the objective is being racked upward from F_1 (the position of sharpest focus) to F_2 (Fig. 5-7B), a red or reddish-orange Becke line is observed to move toward the grain's center whereas a violet blue or blue Becke line will move outward from the grain-edge into the oil. As may be deduced from Figure 5-7A, the reddish Becke line is composed of wavelengths longer than 550 nm, the bluish Becke line of wavelengths shorter than 550 nm. A general rule thus becomes apparent: A *colored Becke line*, viewed as the microscope is focused upward, *moves toward the medium having the higher refractive index for the light wavelengths composing it.*

---

[*] Available from Cargille Laboratories, 55 Commerce Road, Cedar Grove, New Jersey 07009 U.S.A.

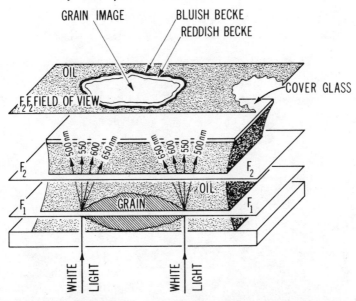

Figure 5-7B. The dispersion of white light at the edges of the grain in the oil of Figure 5-7A. Field of view F_2F_2 is that seen with the microscope no longer focused for sharpest grain detail on plane F_1F_1 but rather, above it, on plane F_2F_2. Angles between the rays for the different wavelengths are exaggerated.

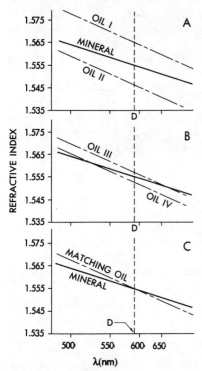

Figure 5-8. Explanation of the movements and colors of the Becke lines according to whether (and where) the dispersion curves of the grain and oil intersect within the visible spectrum.

Interpretation of Becke Lines. In the process of refractive index determination by the immersion method, the grain may be placed in an oil whose refractive index differs so greatly from the grain that the dispersion lines do not intersect in the visible range (Fig. 5-8A). Consequently, whether in oil I or oil II, there would be no color observed in the Becke lines at this grain's edges. When in oil I, a very intense white Becke line would enter the oil as the objective is raised above true focus. For the grain in oil II, the results would be reversed, the bright white Becke line entering the grain. *Lack of color in the Becke line thus indicates that the dispersion curves of grain and oil do not intersect within the visible spectrum.*

Consider grains of this mineral to be respectively immersed in two oils (III and IV in Fig. 5-8B) whose dispersion lines intersect that of the grain, but only at the opposite extremities of the visible spectrum. The Becke lines will now tend to develop slight colorations, although the bright Becke line will be still much more intense than the dark one. For the grain in oil III, a bright bluish-white Becke line will enter the oil as the microscope is racked up; simultaneously a dark reddish Becke line will enter the grain. In oil IV, on the other hand, a bright, yellowish-white Becke line will enter the grain whereas a less intense, dark

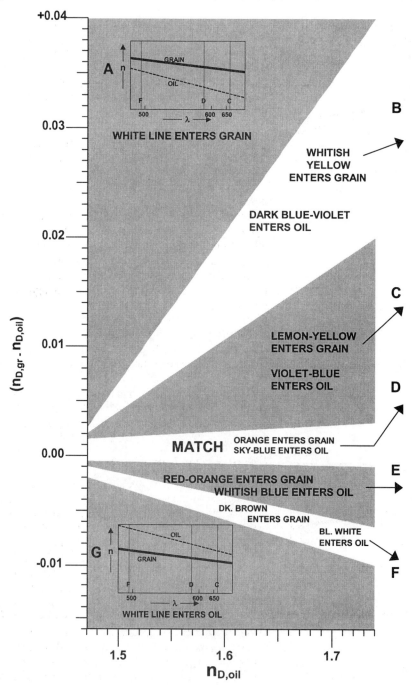

Figure 5-9. Use of the colors observed for the Becke lines or oblique illumination shadows to determine the amount by which n_D for the solid exceeds n_D for the liquid (if Cargille Series A or B liquids are being used). The Becke line movements are those observed when the objective is raised upward from sharp focus. The color observed depends upon the wavelength (λ_m) where—as shown to the right—the dispersion curves of liquid and solid intersect within the visible range. To correct the colors cited to your own perceptions of color, observe grains of salt $(n_D = 1.544)$ mounted in liquids for which n_D equals 1.570, 1.560, 1.550, 1.544, 1.540, and 1.530. [Figure continued on facing page.]

DISPERSION CURVES THAT CROSS IN VISIBLE RANGE

B

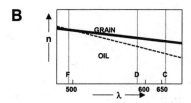

C

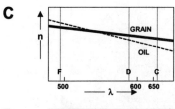

D

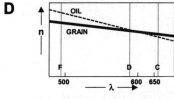

E

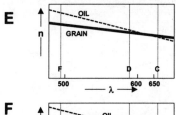

F

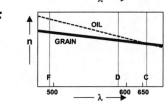

Note that $[n_{D(solid)}$ minus $n_{D(liquid)}]$ values, if positive, disclose the amount whereby the next liquid's n_D value should exceed that of the liquid in use (in order to achieve a matching wavelength λ_m close to 589 nm).

violet Becke line enters the oil. In either case the bright Becke line enters the medium whose refractive index is higher for the majority of wavelengths of light. The particular Becke lines indicate by their markedly unequal intensities, that the dispersion lines of grain and oil intersect only at the outer fringe of the visible spectrum.

DETERMINATION OF $N_{D,g}$ BY BECKE LINES OR OBLIQUE ILLUMINATION

To determine the R.I. of a grain for sodium light—that is, $n_{D,g}$—microscopists successively immerse the grains in oils whose R.I. for sodium light—$n_{D,o}$—are precisely known. When a matching oil is found, that is, when $n_{D,g} = n_{D,o}$, the grain's index becomes known. The accuracy of the determination of $n_{D,g}$ will depend upon the criteria for recognizing a precise match. If sodium light is the illuminant, the criterion will be the total disappearance of the Becke line, the grain (if uncolored and transparent) becoming completely invisible within the oil. If white light is the illuminant, the colors of the Becke lines (or oblique-illumination shadows) usually disclose if $n_{D,g} = n_{D,o}$. Usually, for such a match, the Becke line entering the grain (as the objective is raised above precise focus). will be an orange-tinged yellow (some say orange) whereas that entering the oil will be a green-tinged blue .

Use of Becke Line Colors

For near-matches, the colors of the Becke lines or oblique-illumination shadows (Fig. 5-9, opposite page) allow estimation of $(n_{D,g} - n_{D,o})$, the difference between the R.I. of grain and oil for sodium light. These color interpretations presume the source of illumination to be a white tungsten bulb equipped with a blue "daylight" filter. As an example of the use of Figure 5-9, assume that as the objective is raised upward from its position for sharp focus, a white Becke line is observed to enter an unknown mineral grain that is immersed in an oil of index 1.700, The figure suggests that the grain's index probably exceeds the oil's by 0.038 or more. The oil chosen for the next mount should then be at least of index 1.738. If so, the grain's Becke lines should be colored and will either indicate that a precise match has been obtained or guide the choice of the next oil.

The boundaries between the Becke line colors drawn in Figure 5-9 are, of course, only approximate. Indeed, Figure 5-9 holds only to the extent to which the dispersion coefficient of the mineral being examined, $n_F - n_C$, approaches in value 0.015, the assumed average upon which the figure was based. Moreover, because color perception is highly subjective, it may be advisable to calibrate Figure 5-9 by observing grains of known indices immersed within oils of known indices.

Use of Oblique Illumination Colors

Under oblique illumination, whenever the dispersion curves for a grain and surrounding liquid cross within the visible, colored shadows (fringes) appear on opposite sides of the grain. These colors resemble those cited for the oppositely moving Becke lines in Figure 5-9. Thus, on one side of the grain, they will be blue, green, or violet (and colors in-between). On the opposite side, they will be yellow, orange, red, or brown (and colors in-between). Stoiber and Morse (1994), who discuss the oblique illumination method with gratifying thoroughness and clarity, successfully employ only the colors of the yellow-orange-red-brown fringes to estimate the value of $(n_{D,sol} - n_{D,liq})$ for solids immersed in Cargille liquids (Fig. 5-10). Again, a personal calibration of this chart using grains and oils of known indices is recommended.

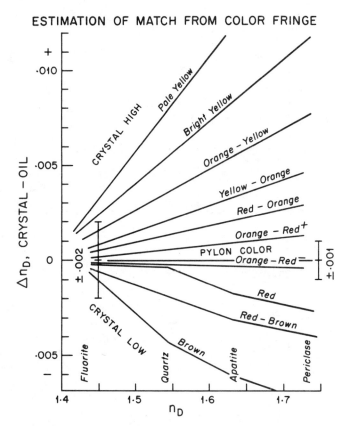

Figure 5-10. Use of yellow-orange-red-brown oblique illumination fringes to estimate the value of $(n_{D,sol} - n_{D,liq})$ for solids immersed in Cargille liquids. Stoiber and Morse (1994) observe that: a yellow fringe signifies $n_{D,sol} > n_{D,liq}$; an orange-red one (their pylon color, as for the plastic pylons used to divert auto traffic) signifies $n_{D,sol} \approx n_{D,liq}$; whereas a brown fringe signifies $n_{D,sol} < n_{D,liq}$.

When using this chart to decide the amount whereby the solid's index for sodium light exceeds (yellow fringe), equals (pylon color), or is less than (brown) that for the liquid, note that, as Stoiber and Morse observe: "...the sensitivity of match decreases with rising refractive index ... because oils of higher index have higher [steeper] slopes, and hence show...[the same] color over a greater range of refractive index [differences]." For example, a red-orange fringe in a 1.625 liquid occurs for $(n_{D,sol} - n_{D,liq})$ values within ±0.002, whereas this same color in a 1.500 liquid indicates $(n_{D,sol} - n_{D,liq})$ within ±0.001.

Whenever the pylon color indicating $(n_{D,sol} \approx n_{D,liq})$ is not obtained, this figure will guide the choice of the next liquid (which should then yield the pylon color). [The observed fringe colors are based on the minerals cited.]

This figure, courtesy of R.E. Stoiber and Stearns A. Morse, 1994, *Crystal Identification with the Polarizing Microscope*, Chapman & Hall, New York, is a slight modification of their Figure 3-15.

Effect of Temperature. The refractive indices of immersion oils decrease rather readily as temperature is increased, whereas those of inorganic solids are little affected. An instructive experiment is to place a grain in an oil whose index is sufficiently high so that its dispersion curve does not quite intersect that of the grain at room temperature (Fig. 5-11).

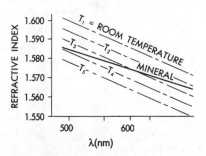

Next gently warm the oil mount on a hot plate (do not boil) until a temperature such as T_5 has been attained; the oil's dispersion curve will have shifted translationally (from T_1 to T_5 in Fig. 5-11) whereas the grain's curve will hardly have shifted at all. Microscopic observation of the grain edges while the mount cools to room temperature—that is, while the oil's dispersion curve steadily shifts back from T_5 to T_4 ... to T_1—will reveal the gamut of dispersion colors summarized in Figure 5-9 or Figure 5-10.

Figure 5-11. The shift in the dispersion curve of an oil as its temperature is increased from room temperature up to T_5. In contrast, the dispersion curve of a mineral immersed in the oil undergoes no significant shift when subjected to the same temperature increase.

The change of refractive index with temperature, dn/dt, varies for different oils. For immersion media of index about 1.633, dn/dt usually approximates -0.0004; in other words, the oil's refractive index decreases 0.0004 for each 1°C rise in the oil's temperature. For oils in the 1.739 range, dn/dt is usually about -0.0007. The value dn/dt is generally stated on the label of each oil in the commercially available sets. Precise values for particular Cargille oils are listed in Appendix I.

DETERMINATION OF $N_{D,G}$ BY DISPERSION STAINING

Dispersion Staining

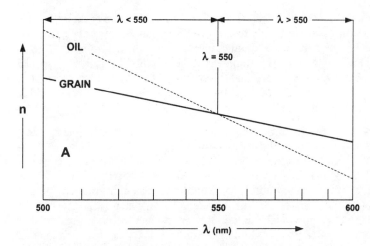

Figure 5-12A. The dispersion curves for a grain and oil are here shown to cross at 550 nm (= wavelength of match, λ_m).

Assume that a grain is immersed in an oil such that $\lambda_m = 550$ nm (in other words, their dispersion curves intersect at 550 nm). If white light traveling parallel to the microscope's axis passes through the grain's edges, its components for which $\lambda < 550$ nm are diverged at the grain's edges (Fig. 5-12B) whereas those for which $\lambda > 550$ nm are converged (see Fig. 5-12D). By contrast, those for which $\lambda \approx 550$ nm continue to travel parallel to the microscope's axis (Fig. 5-12C)—as do all rays that never passed through the grain at all. As previously discussed (Fig. 3-3A), all lens-axis-parallel rays will be refracted by the lens so as to pass through its principal focus. Consequently, the wavelengths of match—550 nm in this case—will be refracted by the

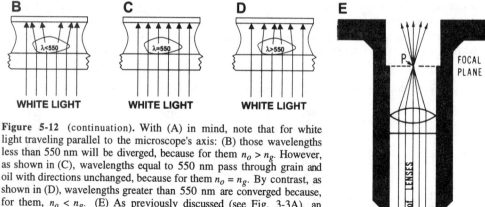

Figure 5-12 (continuation). With (A) in mind, note that for white light traveling parallel to the microscope's axis: (B) those wavelengths less than 550 nm will be diverged, because for them $n_o > n_g$. However, as shown in (C), wavelengths equal to 550 nm pass through grain and oil with directions unchanged, because for them $n_o = n_g$. By contrast, as shown in (D), wavelengths greater than 550 nm are converged because, for them, $n_o < n_g$. (E) As previously discussed (see Fig. 3-3A), an objective focuses all rays that travel along its axis so that they pass through its principal focus P. Consequently, those rays that missed the grain in (B) and (D), as well as the matching 550 nm rays in (C)—because *all* continued to travel parallel to the microscope's axis *after* passing through the grain-oil mount—are focused by the objective so as to pass through its principal focus P.

objective lens so as to pass through P, its principal focus (Fig. 5-12E). The non-matching wavelengths ($\lambda < 550$ nm and $\lambda > 550$ nm) will not. Now, if a circular cover glass with an opaque dot at its center is inserted at the objective's focal plane, the dot will block out the matching wavelengths. As a result, the grain's edges will be illuminated by only the non-matching wavelengths and thus appear colored, the color being that of white light with $\lambda \approx 550$ nm subtracted from it. And if an opaque disk with a central hole were inserted in place of the circular cover glass—so that the central hole locates at P (Fig. 5-12E)—the grain's edges will be illuminated only by the matching wavelengths (~550 nm) and thus appear greenish.

The foregoing modifications of the objective lens constitute the basis for a marvelous technique—called **dispersion staining** by Crossmon (1949) but **focal screening** by Cherkasov (1960). The technique permits a semiquantitative means of determining n_D for a grain in oil even if white light is the illuminant. The method requires a special 10× dispersion-staining objective (DSO) obtainable commercially (McCrone Associates: 800-622-8122) or by modification of an ordinary 10× objective, provided a metal-turning lathe is available (Delly and Sirovatka, 1988).

Figure 5-13A shows an objective convertible to a DSO by inserting a **central stop (CS)**, an **annular stop (AS),** or a **unilateral mask (UM)** at its focal plane (Fig. 5-13B). The central stop, essentially an opaque circle about 3 mm in diameter, if correctly centered on the objective's principal focus, will block out all lens-axis-parallel rays. These include   (1) all rays that miss the grains entirely, or do not pass through grain edges, and (2) of those passing through the grain edges, the wavelengths of match ($\lambda_m \approx 550$ nm in the example). Consequently, as previously noted, the grain-edge colors (Fig. 5-13C) consist of the non-matching wavelengths ($\approx$ white light minus λ_m). By contrast, an annular stop, in essence an opaque disk with an approximately 3-mm hole at its center, if correctly centered (Fig. 5-13D), allows only lens-axis-parallel rays—or those nearly so—to pass through the objective. Thus, grain-edge colors largely consist of λ_m, the wavelength of match.

A central stop is preferred to an annular stop because it blocks out not only the λ_m wavelengths that pass through grain edges but also *all rays of white light that do not pass through grain edges at all* (Fig. 5-14A). Thus, central-stop grain-edge colors (white minus λ_m) are seen against a black or dark-field background. Annular-stop grain-edge colors, on the other hand, although a purer mix of wavelengths at (and near) λ_m, appear against a white (bright-field) background (Fig. 5-14B) that makes their hues more difficult to observe and judge.

Central-stop dispersion staining permits needle-in-the-haystack searches for, say,

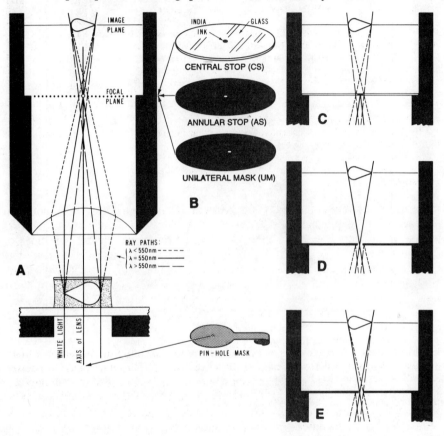

Figure 5-13. (A) The grain and oil whose dispersion curves cross at 550 nm are here drawn with the grain modified in shape (and over-sized by at least 50× relative to the objective lens). A pin-hole mask or a closed-aperture diaphragm located at the conjugate focus *below* the microscope stage ensures that the rays of white light that enter the oil mount will travel closely parallel to the axis of the lens. After passage through the grain edges, only the wavelengths of match λ_m = 550 nm) continue to travel parallel to the lens axis. Consequently, only λ_m is focused by the objective so as to pass through its principal focus, here shown as the hollow dot lying on its focal plane. The other wavelengths intersect the focal plane at distances from the principal focus that are proportional to the extent that their wavelengths differ from 550 nm. (B) Perspective drawings of three masks that, if placed at the objective's focal plane, produce "focal masking." The central stop (CS) consists of an opaque dot centered on a clear transparent disk. Its opposite, the annular stop (AS), consists of a small hole in the center of an opaque disk. The unilateral mask (UM) resembles the annular stop except that the small hole is off-centered. The top half of the objective in (A) is here re-drawn with (C) a central stop in place, with (D) an annular stop in place, and with (E) a unilateral mask in place. For CS illumination note that the grain will be outlined by the color that results if the λ_m wavelengths are subtracted from white light. For AS illumination the grain's outline consists of λ_m wavelengths and wavelengths close thereto. For UM illumination the colors somewhat resemble those seen for oblique illumination. In other words the opposite sides of the grain will be illuminated by complementary hues, the hue on one side consisting of wavelengths shorter than λ_m, that on the opposite side consisting of wavelengths that are longer.

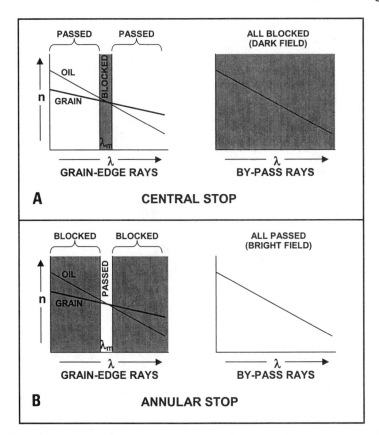

Figure 5-14. Comparison of the effect of a central stop (CS) and an annular stop (AS) on the edge colors of a grain, illuminated by white light, in an oil whose dispersion curve crosses the grain's within the visible. Also, their effect on the rays that by-pass the grain to illuminate the field around it. If a central stop is in place, the grain's edge colors will consist of white light from which λ_m wavelengths (and wavelengths close thereto) have been blocked out. Note that all rays that miss the grain and pass only through oil are also blocked out (because they continue to travel parallel to the objective's axis after passing through the oil mount). The advantage of this is that the edge colors are viewed against a black (dark-field) background. If an annular stop is in place, the grain's edge colors will consist of λ_m wavelengths (and wavelengths close to λ_m), these being the wavelengths that continue to travel parallel to the objective's axis after passing through the oil mount—but so do the rays of white light that by-pass the grains and comprise the background illumination. A disadvantage of this is that the edge-colors are viewed against a white (bright-field) background.

grains of a material whose dispersion curves are known. Simply immerse the powder in an oil whose dispersion curve crosses that of this material. In such case, even if only one grain out of a thousand consists of the searched-for material, its edge-colors leap out from the darkfield background produced by central-stop illumination. The technique is often used for detecting the presence of asbestos fibers.

Particularly useful are DS objectives that allow rapid conversion from central-stop (CS) to annular-stop (AS) illumination or to unilateral masking (which somewhat resembles oblique illumination). This versatility enhances the precision by which λ_m—the wavelength of match between grain and oil—can be estimated from edge-colors (Table 5-1). The movement of the central-stop colors as the objective is raised above clear focus will also be useful. The colors may vary somewhat depending upon (1) the spectral composition of the illumination and (2) the dispersion curves of oil and grain. Use of the

Series *E* (high dispersion) oils available from Cargille also enhances this precision.

After estimation of λ_m from the CSDS and/or ASDS colors—that is, from the CS- and/or AS-produced dispersion-staining colors—Figure 5-15, as discussed in its caption, will guide the choice of the oil for the next grain mount, an oil for which λ_m should be much closer to 589 nm.

Table 5-1. Estimated relationship of λ_m to the edge-colors observed with central-stop and annular-stop illumination.

1	2	3	4	5	6	7	8
Matching Wavelength (nm)	**Central Stop** *Dark Field*			**Annular Stop** *Bright Field*	**Unilateral Masking** *Gray Field*		n_D **of Grain**
	At Focus	Raising Focus Moving In	Moving Out		One Edge	Opposite Edge	
660	bright greenish blue	---	bright greenish blue	red	very dark red	pale greenish azure	
625	sky blue	---	sky blue	orangish-red	dark red	greenish blue	Lower than oil
600	blue	faint dark red	greenish blue	orange	red	light greenish blue	
589	deep violet	weak red	strong blue	orangish-yellow	orangish-red	green	Same as oil
575	purple	red	blue	yellow	reddish-orange	bluish-green	
540	reddish purple	orange-red	bluish-violet	green	orange	blue	
505	orange-red	orange	weak blue violet	bluish green	canary yellow	dark blue	Higher than oil
480	orange	yellow	weak violet	blue	yellow	dark blue-violet	
465	bright gold	bright gold	---	violet	bright yellow	dark violet	

Su's Equations for Determining $n_{D,sol}$ from Edge-Colors

The Two-Liquid Method. S.C. Su (1993) developed an ingenious method for determining $n_{D,sol}$—a solid's refractive index for sodium light—from edge-colors produced by dispersion staining. In application, assume a solid to have been immersed in two oils—Oil **L** and Oil **S**—whose dispersion curves cross the solid's within the visible range, namely at λ_L and λ_S where λ_L is longer and λ_S is shorter than 589 nm (Fig. 5-16). Dispersion staining then produces edge-colors (top, Fig. 5-16) that allow the wavelengths of match—λ_L for Oil **L** and λ_S for Oil **S**) to be estimated to within 30 or 40 nm (Su, personal communication). To be specific, assume that in Oil **L** the edge-colors—blue for CS and orange for AS—suggest $\lambda_L \approx 630$ nm to be the wavelength of match whereas for Oil **S** the edge-colors—purplish red (CS) and green (AS)—indicate $\lambda_S \approx 510$ nm. To calculate n_L, the value of the index of match between Oil **L** and the solid, insert the value for λ_L (630 nm) and oil **L**'s Cauchy constants—$c_1, c_2,$ and c_3 (as supplied by Cargille in Appendix I)— into the Cauchy equation:

$$n = c_1 + \frac{c_2}{\lambda^2} + \frac{c_3}{\lambda^4} \qquad \text{(Eqn. 2-8).}$$

Similarly, n_S , the index of match for Oil **S** results if this oil's Cauchy constants and λ_2 (510 nm) are substituted into Equation 2-8.

With λ_L, n_L, λ_S, and n_S known, the solid's index for D-light ($n_{D,sol}$) can now be calculated. To clarify this calculation, a horizontal and a vertical dotted line are added to Figure 5-16 so as to define a large triangle having a vertical side equal to Δ ($= n_S - n_L$) and a horizontal side equal to $(x_S - x_L)$. Within this large triangle a smaller, similar triangle has a vertical side Δ_D ($= n_{D,sol} - n_L$) and a horizontal side $(x_D - x_L)$. From similar triangles there

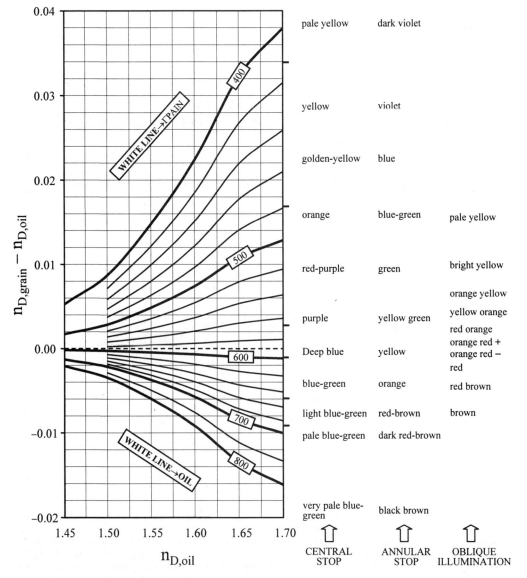

Figure 5-15. Use of λ_m—the wavelength of match determined by dispersion staining—to estimate ($n_{D,sol} - n_{D,liq}$), the difference in refractive index between solid and liquid for sodium light.

results

$$\frac{n_{D,sol} - n_L}{n_S - n_L} = \frac{x_D - x_L}{x_S - x_L}$$

which becomes

$$n_{D,sol} = n_L + (n_S - n_L)\left(\frac{x_D - x_L}{x_S - x_L}\right) \qquad \text{(Eqn. 5-3)}$$

For simplicity, let

$$k_D = \left(\frac{x_D - x_L}{x_S - x_L}\right) \qquad \text{(Eqn. 5-4)}$$

So that Equation 5-3 becomes

$$n_{D,sol} = n_L + (n_S - n_L)k_D \qquad \text{(Eqn. 5-5)}$$

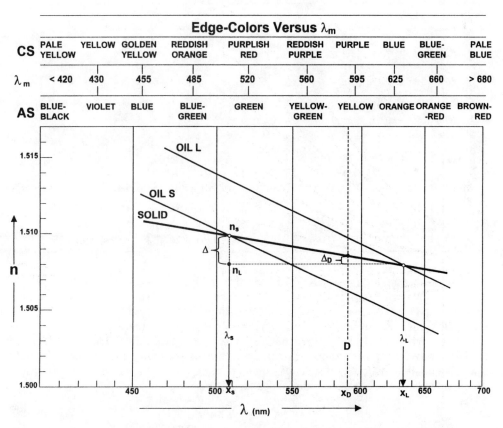

Figure 5-16. Grains of a solid have been placed in two successive oils whose dispersion curves are known. In Oil **L** the grain-edge colors are determined to be blue, using a central stop but orange using an annular stop. From these colors the wavelength of match (λ_L) is estimated to be 630±30 nm. In Oil **S** the observed edge-colors—purplish red (CS) and green (AS)—permit the wavelength of match (λ_S) to be estimated to be 510±30 nm. From the oils' dispersion curves the corresponding indices of match—n_L and n_S—can be determined from λ_L and λ_S. These four values define a triangle whose vertical side, labeled Δ, equals $n_S - n_L$ and whose horizontal side equals x_L (= λ_L) minus x_S (= λ_S). From similar triangles one can determine Δ_D, the amount that n_D for the solid exceeds n_L, by using Equation 5-3.

As discussed previously, the x values for Hartmann dispersion nets actually represent $(\lambda - 200)^{-1}$ *where λ is in nanometers.* Consequently, the value of k_D can be calculated, because x_D equals $(589.3 - 200)^{-1}$, $x_L = (\lambda_L - 200)^{-1}$, and $x_S = (\lambda_S - 200)^{-1}$. Once the values for λ_L and λ_S become known, all values on the right-hand side of Equation 5-5 become known, and thus $n_{D,sol}$ can be calculated. Table 5-2, modified from Su (1998), permits the values observed for λ_L and λ_S to be directly converted to k_D values.

In general, the closer λ_L and λ_S are to 589 nm, the more accurate $n_{D,sol}$ will be.

To determine the solid's index for a wavelength other than 589.3, say, λ_i, substitute for x_D in Equation 5-4 the value $(\lambda_i - 200)^{-1}$ instead of $(589.3 - 200)^{-1}$.

Table 5-2. Converting λ_m to k_D for the Two-Liquid Method (modified from Su, 1998).

		Shorter Matching Wavelength (nm)												
		400	450	500	520	540	560	580	600	620	640	660	680	700	750
Longer Matching Wavelength (nm)	450	-1.43													
	500	-0.46	-1.15												
	520	-0.30	-0.64	-2.67											
	540	-0.18	-0.35	-0.95	-2.03										
	560	-0.09	-0.17	-0.38	-0.60	-1.28									
	580	-0.03	-0.05	-0.09	-0.13	-0.20	-0.43								
	600	0.03	0.05	0.08	0.11	0.16	0.25	0.52							
	620	0.07	0.12	0.20	0.25	0.34	0.47	0.75	1.58						
	640	0.11	0.17	0.28	0.35	0.44	0.59	0.82	1.30	2.73					
	660	0.14	0.22	0.34	0.42	0.51	0.65	0.86	1.21	1.91	4.00				
	680	0.17	0.25	0.39	0.47	0.57	0.70	0.89	1.16	1.63	2.56	5.36			
	700	0.19	0.28	0.43	0.51	0.60	0.73	0.90	1.14	1.49	2.09	3.27	6.82		
	750	0.24	0.34	0.50	0.57	0.67	0.78	0.92	1.10	1.33	1.65	2.11	2.83	4.13	
	800	0.27	0.39	0.54	0.62	0.71	0.81	0.93	1.08	1.26	1.49	1.78	2.16	2.71	5.95

The One-Liquid Method. Results from this method will be less accurate than from the Two-Liquid Method. However, such accuracy may be sufficient to ascertain the presence (and type) of asbestiform minerals present in a bulk sample (see Chapter 13). The One-Liquid Method can be used if: (1) The solid's dispersion coefficient—$(n_F - n_C)_S$—is already known, and (2) The dispersion curves of the liquid and solid intersect at λ_m, a matching wavelength within the visible range. Once λ_m becomes known through Becke line, oblique illumination, or dispersion-staining colors, the R.I. of the solid for any visible wavelength λ_i—namely, $n_{i,sol}$—can be calculated from:

$$n_{i,sol} = n_{i,liq} + [(n_F - n_C)_L - (n_F - n_C)_S] \, k_i \qquad \text{(Eqn. 5-6)}$$

because, assuming Cargille liquids were used, $n_{i,liq}$ can be calculated from the liquid's Cauchy constants (Eqn. 2-8), $(n_F - n_C)_L$ will be known (see Appendix I), and $(n_F - n_C)_S$ was known to begin with, and k_i can be calculated because

$$k_i = \frac{x_0 - x_i}{x_F - x_C} \qquad \text{(Eqn. 5-7)}$$

where x_0, x_i, x_F and x_C are defined by replacing λ in the expression $(\lambda_i - 200)^{-1}$ with, respectively, λ_m, λ_i, 486, and 656. Table 5-3 (Su, 1998) allows k_i to be determined from the values λ_m, λ_i, 486, and 656. Usually, the solid's index for 589 (D) is desired. In other words λ_i is taken to be 589 and thus k_i is read from the column headed D in Table 5-3.

Table 5-3. Converting λ_m to k_D for sodium light or to k_i at selected wavelengths (i) for the One-Liquid Method (modified from Su, 1998).

Matching Wavelength λ_m (nm)	Wavelengths of Selected Fraunhöfer Lines and Lasers (nm)						
	F 486.1	*E* 508.6	*e* 546.1	*D* 589.3	*HeNe* 632.8	*C* 656.3	*Ruby* 694.3
300	4.99	5.18	5.45	*5.70*	5.90	5.99	6.12
320	3.71	3.91	4.17	*4.42*	4.62	4.71	4.84
340	2.80	2.99	3.26	*3.51*	3.71	3.80	3.93
360	2.11	2.31	2.58	*2.82*	3.02	3.11	3.24
380	1.58	1.78	2.04	*2.29*	2.49	2.58	2.71
400	1.15	1.35	1.62	*1.86*	2.06	2.15	2.28
420	0.81	1.00	1.27	*1.52*	1.71	1.81	1.93
440	0.51	0.71	0.98	*1.23*	1.42	1.51	1.64
460	0.27	0.46	0.73	*0.98*	1.18	1.27	1.40
480	0.06	0.25	0.52	*0.77*	0.97	1.06	1.19
500	-0.12	0.07	0.34	*0.59*	0.78	0.88	1.00
520	-0.28	-0.09	0.18	*0.43*	0.62	0.72	0.85
540	-0.42	-0.23	0.04	*0.29*	0.48	0.57	0.70
560	-0.55	-0.35	-0.09	*0.16*	0.36	0.45	0.58
580	-0.66	-0.47	-0.20	*0.05*	0.25	0.34	0.47
600	-0.76	-0.57	-0.30	*-0.05*	0.15	0.24	0.37
620	-0.85	-0.66	-0.39	*-0.14*	0.05	0.15	0.27
640	-0.94	-0.74	-0.47	*-0.23*	-0.03	0.06	0.19
660	-1.01	-0.82	-0.55	*-0.30*	-0.10	-0.01	0.12
680	-1.08	-0.89	-0.62	*-0.37*	-0.17	-0.08	0.05
700	-1.15	-0.95	-0.68	*-0.44*	-0.24	-0.15	-0.02
720	-1.21	-1.01	-0.74	*-0.50*	-0.30	-0.21	-0.08
740	-1.26	-1.06	-0.80	*-0.55*	-0.35	-0.26	-0.13
760	-1.31	-1.12	-0.85	*-0.60*	-0.40	-0.31	-0.18
780	-1.36	-1.16	-0.89	*-0.65*	-0.45	-0.36	-0.23
800	-1.40	-1.21	-0.94	*-0.69*	-0.49	-0.40	-0.27

COMPARISON OF METHODS

According to Saylor (1935) the Becke line method is more sensitive than the ordinary oblique illumination method (but less so than his double diaphragm modification of oblique illumination). Saylor's results (Table 5-4) indicate that the medium-power objective (10×, N.A. 0.25), which he apparently terms a "low-power objective," yields the greatest accuracy in refractive index determination, being the best compromise between increased magnification and lowered aperture.

Dispersion staining, because it does not require a match at a specific λ, minimizes the number of oil mounts required to estimate n_D. Using Su's method, n_D for an isotropic solid can be estimated from just two oil mounts, provided the wavelength of grain-liquid match,

Table 5-4. After Saylor (1935, Fig. 6).

| Objective | Error in measuring refractive index of glasswool | | |
| | by Becke line | By oblique illumination | |
		± 0.0006	double diaphragm
10×, N. A. 0.25	± 0.0005	± 0.0005	< ± 0.0005
20×, N. A. 0.40	± 0.0009	± 0.0010	± 0.0005
45×, N. A. 0.85	± 0.0012	> ± 0.0020	

λ_m, is in the visible for each oil. Professor Ann Wylie (personal communication) notes that estimated n_D is "most accurate when at least one λ_m is greater and one less than 589.3 nm." She further observes that "...for anisotropic crystals [discussed in subsequent chapters], measurement of λ_m can be made for more than one principal index of refraction in the same oil. Another advantage is that dispersion-staining colors change very quickly as λ_m approaches 589.3 nm. Therefore, chemical inhomogeneity, manifested as slight variations in index of refraction within a grain—or among grains—is very obvious when n-grain and n-oil are close in magnitude."

Among the disadvantages of dispersion staining, Wylie observes that for very small grains, "dispersion-staining colors may be difficult to see and interpret." And, "when λ_m is not in the visible one cannot determine whether n-grain is less than or greater than n-oil (without resort to the Becke line or oblique illumination techniques.)"

Determinations of n_D more precise than those obtainable by dispersion staining can be made by the **single variation method**. Using this method, the wavelength of the light is varied—by use of a monochromator or variable interference filter—until, when using oblique illumination, the shadow "hops" from one side of the grain (Fig. 5-5A) to the other (Fig. 5-5B). This method offers greater precision than determination of λ_m from the edge-colors of dispersion-stained grains. If this is done for two different oils so as to obtain two λ_m values that bracket 589.3 nm, Su's calculation (Eqn. 5-3) will yield n_D for the grain. Use of Cargille's high dispersion (series E) oils will enhance the precision of the method.

PRACTICAL PROCEDURES

An excellent procedure for determining the refractive index of an unknown is to use the oblique illumination technique in the preliminary oil mounts, and the Becke line method for the final determinations when grain and oil are close in index. Here the advantages of oblique illumination (rapidity and almost simultaneous testing of all grains within the field of view) are combined with that of the Becke line (higher accuracy than ordinary oblique illumination). But note that Stoiber and Morse (1994), using their figure (here reproduced as Fig. 5-10), achieve an accuracy for oblique illumination that is comparable to that for Becke lines.

Preparation of Mount

The unknown crystal is first pulverized and the 100 to 200 mesh size is isolated by sieving. (In the case of powdered unknowns, of course, this has already been done). The immersion oil selected should be of refractive index equal to that of the suspected identity of the crystal; if there is no clue as to identity, an oil of index 1.53 may be used. Place a drop of the oil on a clean slide, dislodging the drop from the glass dropper by tapping it. [The dropper should never directly touch the slide, because the immersion media may become contaminated by stray mineral grains that adhere to the dropper on contact.] Replace the bottle of immersion oil, *with cap tightly in place*, in the case immediately.

Dust a few dozen grains of the unknown crystal onto the oildrop and cover it with a cover glass about 0.6 × 0.6 cm in size.

Microscopic Observations

The grains of the slide mount can now be examined between crossed polarizers, using the low-power objective. If the grains are truly isotropic, they will all remain black—that is, extinct—even if observed while the stage is being rotated a full 360°. If the grains brighten, they are anisotropic and present problems of index measurement that will be discussed later. A slightly more sensitive test for anisotropism is to insert the first-order red accessory plate while conducting the preceding observation. The grain is anisotropic if, during rotation, its color varies from the violet background color produced by the plate for the surrounding oil.

After the grain has been verified to be isotropic, oblique illumination may be used to determine whether the grain's index is greater or less than the oil's. An exact match probably will not be obtained the first time, making it necessary to select a second immersion oil and prepare a second mount (on the same glass slide). It is wise to sketch the slide in your notebook (Fig. 5-17) and label each mount with the indices of the oil used. Observations can later be rechecked, for at room temperatures the oils of the mounts (*if under cover glasses*) do not change significantly in index, even after a time lapse of several hours.

After the grains have been mounted in a closely matching oil, the relative intensities and dispersion colors of the Becke lines may be utilized to determine the refractive index of the grain for sodium light to within ±0.002, provided the index of the matching oil is corrected for temperature as described in the following section.

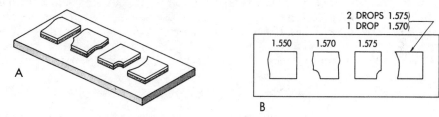

Figure 5-17. (A) Glass slide with cover glasses over oil mounts. (B) Plane view of slide as sketched in notebook. For each mount the refractive index of the oil used (as given on its label) is recorded. Note that the final matching oil is a mixture of two media of the set.

Temperature Correction of Index

The label on a bottle of immersion oil usually contains the following information: n_D, its refractive index for sodium light; T, the temperature at which the oil possesses this index; and dn/dt, the amount the index changes per °C change in temperature. The date when the index was measured is, although not often stated, a useful addition to the data on the label. Normally, unless the light source is allowed to heat up the slide mount over an extended period of time, the temperature of the oil in the powder mount will equal room temperature, T_R. If T_R equals T, the index of the oil in the powder mount will be the same as that (n_D) stated on its label. If the two are not equal, then the index of the oil in the powder mount, n_{DM}, must be calculated:

$$n_{DM} = n_D + (T_R - T)\frac{dn}{dt}$$
(Eqn. 5-8)

As an example of the use of Equation 5-2, assume a mineral has been matched in index to a particular oil ($n_D = 1.530$, $T = 20°C$, $dn/dt = -0.0003$), the room temperature at the time of the match being 25°C. The actual refractive index of the oil (and therefore of the mineral) at the time of the match is

$$n_{DM} = 1.530 + (25° - 20°)\left(\frac{-0.0003}{1°}\right) = 1.5285$$

The index reported for the mineral is then rounded off to 1.528 or 1.529; reporting the grain's index as 1.5285 implies a greater accuracy than is attainable by the immersion method (± 0.002). Wilcox (1959) believes that under favorable circumstances—that is, sodium light, small intervals in refractive index spacings of the media, and close attention to temperature corrections—accuracy of ± 0.001 may be attainable with Becke line methods. Advanced techniques such as the double variation method of Emmons (1943) permit accuracy to ± 0.0002.

In addition to measurement of the refractive index, other observations should be made. The color transmitted by the grains should be recorded. Inclusions within the grain—such as empty bubbles, liquid-filled bubbles tiny crystals, cavities where tiny crystals once were (that is, negative crystals), or crystallites—should be searched for, using high-power magnification. Linear parallelism of elongated inclusions or of bubble trains should be noted. The nature of the cleavage or fracture of the crushed grains may also yield information valuable in identification of the mineral. Figure 5-18 illustrates the grain shapes typical of the different types of breakage observable for isotropic crystals.

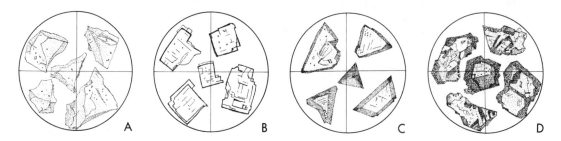

Figure 5-18. Breakage types commonly seen on crushed isotropic grains: (A) conchoidal fracture but no cleavage; (B) cubic cleavage {100}—that is, three mutually perpendicular directions of equal ease of cleavage; (C) octahedral cleavage {111}—that is, four directions of equal ease of cleavage that are parallel to the faces of an octahedron; (D) dodecahedral cleavage {110} that is, six directions of equal ease of cleavage parallel to the faces of the dodecahedron. Note that for dodecahedral cleavage the fact of six "competing" directions for cleavage makes it unlikely that a particular direction will be extensively developed; instead, the breakage surface alternately follows one and then another of these six directions. The relief of these grains in oil varies as follows: (A) low, (B) moderate, (C) high, (D) very high.

RECOMMENDED READINGS

STOIBER, R.E. and MORSE, S.A. (1994) *Crystal Identification with the Polarizing Microscope*. Chapman & Hall, New York & London, pp. 49-73.

SU, Shu-Chun (1998) Dispersion staining: principles, analytical relationships and practical applications to the determination of refractive index. *The Microscope 46-3:*123-146.

WILCOX, R.E. (1983) Refractive index determination using the central focal masking technique with dispersion colors. *American Mineralogist 68:*1226-1236.

6 OPTICAL INDICATRICES AND ELLIPSES

OVERVIEW

Light travels as transverse vibrations that are perpendicular to the **ray path** (RP) in isotropic media (Fig. 6-1A) but not necessarily so in anisotropic media (Fig. 6-1B). For closely neighboring rays, nearest points that always vibrate in the same direction (and amount)—for example, a, b, c, d and e in Figure 6-2A—are said to be **in phase**. By definition, the surface connecting such in-phase points constitutes a **wave front** (WF) and the direction perpendicular to it is called a **wave normal** (WN). The RP and WN always coincide in direction for isotropic media (Fig. 6-2A). For anisotropic media they usually do not (Fig. 6-2B). In isotropic media both the RP and WN obey Snell's Law (Eqn. 2-2). In anisotropic media just the WN obeys Snell's Law. The RP usually does not.

The optical indicatrix is an imaginary surface connecting the tips of radii, drawn outward from a common center, whose lengths are drawn proportional to the crystal's refractive index (R.I.) for light vibrating parallel to that radius. Because isotropic materials exhibit the same R.I., regardless of vibration direction, the isotropic indicatrix is a sphere (Fig. 6-3).

By contrast, tetragonal and hexagonal crystals—all characterized by a single 4, $\overline{4}$, 3, $\overline{3}$, 6, or $\overline{6}$ axis of symmetry called the c-axis—exhibit a unique R.I. symbolized as ε, for light vibrating parallel to this crystallographic c-axis (Fig. 6-10A). For light vibrating along any direction *perpendicular* to c, they exhibit an index symbolized as ω. For vibrations at a random angle θ to the c-axis, they exhibit an index between ε and ω, customarily symbolized as ε', with a value such that

$$\varepsilon' = \frac{1}{\sqrt{\dfrac{cos^2\theta}{\varepsilon^2} + \dfrac{sin^2\theta}{\omega^2}}} \qquad \text{(Eqn. 6-3)}$$

Their optical indicatrix, an **ellipsoid** (Fig. 6-10B,C), contains a single **circular section** whose radius equals ω. The direction perpendicular to this circular section, actually the crystal's c-axis, is called the **optic axis**. This indicatrix is called a **uniaxial indicatrix** because it contains a single optic axis.

By convention, uniaxial crystals are said to be **negative** in optic sign if $\varepsilon < \omega$ (Fig. 6-11A), but **positive** if $\varepsilon > \omega$ (Fig. 6-11B).

Within a tetragonal or hexagonal crystal, the uniaxial indicatrix can be moved anywhere in the crystal, provided its optic axis remains parallel to the crystal's c-axis. Thus, in Figure 6-15, the indicatrix has been moved until its center falls on faces c, q and m, respectively. Face m intersects the indicatrix in a **principal section** that, by definition, lies parallel to the optic axis and hence cuts through the indicatrix as an ellipse whose semiaxes equal ε and ω. Face c, being perpendicular to the optic axis, intersects the indicatrix in a **circular section** (of radius ω). Face q intersects the indicatrix in a **random section**, namely an ellipse whose semiaxes equal ε' and ω.

Under ordinary illumination, the light from a microscope's polarizer consists of wave normals that are essentially perpendicular—and associated wave fronts that are parallel—to the microscope stage. For normal incidence ($i = 0°$) on a grain in a matching oil, these wave normals pass through the grain undeviated ($r = 0°$), and thus their associated wave fronts remain parallel to the stage while traveling through the grain. *The nature of the intersection between the crystal's optical indicatrix and these stage-parallel wave fronts controls how the crystal will affect the light that enters it.*

Case I: The intersection is a circle. This case occurs for all isotropic materials, because their indicatrix is a sphere, and for any uniaxial crystal oriented with its optic axis perpendicular to the microscope stage (Fig. 6-16). Such a circular intersection indicates that light will pass through without change in its state of polarization. In other words the incident light, whether unpolarized (Fig. 6-16B) or E-W polarized (Fig. 6-16C), remains so after entering the crystal. Thus, an isotropic material exhibits the refractive index n, whereas a uniaxial crystal, so oriented, exhibits the refractive index ω.

Case II: The intersection is an ellipse. This case occurs for any uniaxial crystal whose optic axis is not perpendicular to the microscope stage (Fig. 6-16D,E). The semiaxes of the ellipse of intersection—*OW* and *OE*—constitute the crystal's **privileged directions** or **vibration directions** because the light, upon entering the crystal, *must* vibrate along one (or both) of these directions [but never along any in-between direction]. For light vibrating along *OW*, which lies in the indicatrix's circular section, the crystal will exhibit the index ω. For light vibrating along *OE*, the crystal will exhibit the index ε', if oriented with its optic axis at a random angle θ to the microscope stage (Fig. 6-16D), but true ε if its optic axis lies parallel to the microscope stage (Fig. 6-16E). The value of ε' depends upon that of θ (see Eqn. 6-3).

For Figures 6-16D,E, if *OE* lies E-W and the microscope has an E-W polarizer, *all* the light entering the crystal will vibrate along *OE*—and none along *OW*. However, if we rotated either the microscope stage or its polarizer so that privileged direction *OE* is at an angle τ relative to *OP*, the polarizer's privileged direction (Fig. 6-18), then amplitude *OP* would be resolved into two amplitudes (*OE* and *OW*) whose relative magnitudes would be

$$OE = OP\cos\tau \quad \text{and} \quad OE = OP\sin\tau$$

REVIEW OF TERMINOLOGY

A ray of light represents the path by which a continuous, infinitely thin, straight-line stream of energy travels outward from a source. The energy travels along this ray as a series of vibrations that in isotropic media are perpendicular to the ray path (Fig. 6-1A) but in anisotropic media generally are not (Fig. 6-1B). A wave normal direction (WN in Fig. 6-1) may be defined as one that (1) lies in the same plane as the ray path and vibration direction and (2) is perpendicular to the vibration direction. Only for light traveling in isotropic media do the wave normal and ray directions invariably coincide; within anisotropic media they generally do not.

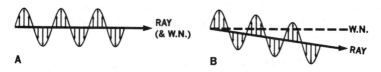

Figure 6-1. Geometric relationships between ray path (heavy arrow), wave normal (dashed line), and vibration directions (small arrows). (A) For light in isotropic media; (B) for light in anisotropic media. All lines are in the plane of the paper. The wave normal (W. N.) is perpendicular to the vibration directions.

To speak in terms of one ray is, of course, unrealistic. The thinnest pencil of light one can isolate will not be infinitely thin; rather it will consist of numerous rays. The points on these rays that, at a precise moment of time, are in the same stages of vibration (for example, points a, *b, c, d,* and *e* of Fig. 6-2A) are said to be in phase with each other. A surface connecting such points for numerous rays constitutes a wave surface or wave front. The vibration directions of the rays are always parallel (or tangent) to this wave front; the wave normal is perpendicular to it. Ray paths are generally not perpendicular to the wave front except in isotropic media and special cases in anisotropic media wherein they happen to coincide with the wave normal.

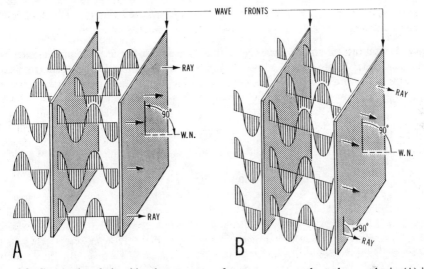

Figure 6-2. Geometric relationships between wave fronts, wave normals, and ray paths in (A) isotropic media and (B) anisotropic media. For simplicity only polarized light is considered. In (B) the ray paths are not perpendicular to the wave fronts.

GENERAL CONCEPT OF THE INDICATRIX

The optical indicatrix illustrates how the refractive index of a transparent material varies according to the vibration direction of the light wave in the material (monochromatic light assumed). Consider an infinite number of vectors radiating outward in all directions from a common point within the crystal. Each vector is drawn proportional in length to the crystal's refractive index for light vibrating parallel to that vector direction. The indicatrix is a surface connecting the tips of these vectors. The vectors themselves are generally omitted when this connecting surface is drawn, but in Figure 6-3 a few are shown for illustration. The indicatrix is purely a method of rationalizing optical phenomena. As such, it furnishes an orderly framework whereby the optical phenomena associated with transparent crystals may be interpreted, remembered, and predicted. It is particularly useful for anisotropic crystals. For isotropic media, however, indicatrix theory is not particularly advantageous, chiefly because of the simplicity of their optical behavior. We discuss the theory here because it serves as an introductory step in the development of the highly important anisotropic indicatrices.

THE ISOTROPIC INDICATRIX

Description

In isotropic media, by definition, the index of refraction does not change with the

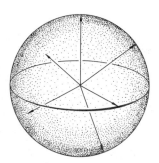

Figure 6-3. Isotropic indicatrix of a crystal for sodium light. The crystal's refractive index for sodium light (n_D) remains constant regardless of the direction in which the light is vibrating; the indicatrix is therefore a sphere.

vibration direction of the light. Consequently, all the vectors relating refractive index to vibration direction are of equal length, and therefore all isotropic indicatrices are perfect spheres (Fig. 6-3). Transparent glasses, liquids, and isometric crystals—not under strain—are characterized by such indicatrices.

As discussed under the topic of dispersion, the index of an isotropic substance varies according to the wavelength of light used. Sodium chloride, for example, possesses the indices $n_C = 1.541$, $n_D = 1.544$, and $n_F = 1.553$. Technically, therefore, a slightly different-sized indicatrix exists for each wavelength of light. Figure 6-4 illustrates sodium chloride's indicatrices for C-, D-, and F-light, respectively. For intermediate wavelengths the indicatrices would be intermediate to those shown.

Figure 6-4. Comparison of the optical indicatrices of crystalline sodium chloride for C, D, and F wavelengths. Dimensional changes between the three spheres are exaggerated for illustrative purposes.

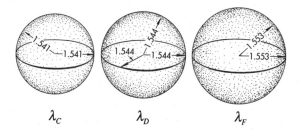

$$\lambda_C \qquad \lambda_D \qquad \lambda_F$$

Application

The incidence of light upon the surface of an isotropic material makes few demands on the indicatrix theory. The crystal surface in question is assumed to pass through the indicatrix center, and the resultant intersection between surface and indicatrix is a circle of radius proportional to the crystal's refractive index for the light. In indicatrix theory such a circular section indicates that the crystal "permits" the entering light to vibrate within the crystal in the same direction(s) as it did prior to entry; that is, the light is not required to vibrate parallel to a particular direction in order to pass through the crystal. Thus, after entry into the crystal, unpolarized light (Fig. 6-5A) remains unpolarized whereas polarized light (Fig. 6-5B) maintains its same plane of polarization.

Since isotropic materials cannot alter the direction of polarization of the entering light, an isotropic grain, viewed between crossed polarizers, always appears extinct (that is transmits no light), even during a 360° rotation of the stage.[1] This property thus serves as a test for isotropism. The following explanation will clarify: The light from the polarizer passes through the crystal with its E-W vibration direction unchanged (Fig. 6-6B). At the analyzer, however, which is usually set to transmit only N-S vibrating light, all this light is absorbed, the analyzer acting as though opaque to this light. The situation is

---

[1] The possibility of optical activity is here disregarded.

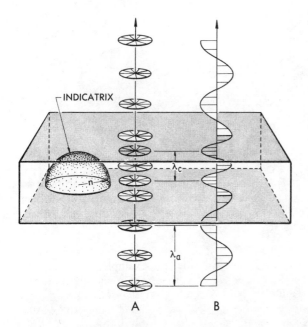

Figure 6-5. The effect of an isotropic plate upon (A) a normally incident unpolarized ray and (B) a polarized ray. The lower crystal surface intersects the spherical isotropic indicatrix in a circle whose radius, n, equals that of the sphere, n being thus the refractive index of the plate. Changes in amplitude due to reflectional losses at interfaces, etc., are not considered in the drawing. Note that the wavelength of the light while in the crystal (λ_c) is smaller than its wavelength in air (λ_a).

considered vectorially in Figure 6-6B. Here OP represents the amplitude and direction of the light vibrations from the polarizer that have passed through the crystal. However, vector OP has no component parallel to $A'A'$, the direction of light vibration transmitted by the analyzer. Consequently, not even the smallest component of the light energy vibrating parallel to OP is transmitted by the analyzer. Rotation of the stage changes neither the polarizer's privileged direction $P'P'$ nor the analyzer's privileged direction $A'A'$. Thus the vectorial relationships shown in Figure 6-6B remain the same, regardless of the position of the stage.

On the other hand, if either the polarizer or analyzer is rotated so as to change ϕ (phi), the angle between $P'P'$ and $A'A'$ (Fig. 6-6C), to a value other than 90°, the isotropic grain will no longer appear extinct between the two polarizers. Instead, a vector component of OP (OA in Fig. 6-6C) will be transmitted by the analyzer. Note that the amplitude of OA may be graphically determined from that of OP by dropping a perpendicular from point P to line $A'A'$; expressed mathematically the relationship is

$$OA = \cos\phi \cdot OP \qquad \text{(Eqn. 6-1)}$$

The greater the amplitude of vibration of the light, the brighter the light. In the case of Figure 6-6C, the light passing through the crystal (amplitude OP) is brighter than that passing through the analyzer (amplitude OA). Only when the angle ϕ of Equation 6-1 equals 0° will OP and OA be equal and therefore represent equal brightnesses.

THE UNIAXIAL INDICATRIX

Historical Origin

Description and discussion of all the steps that prefaced the elucidation of the indicatrix theory by Fletcher (1891) cannot be included here. We will, however, present in the following sections a few of the major discoveries that indicated the existence of other than isotropic materials (and, subsequently, the need of more than Snell's law to explain their optical behavior).

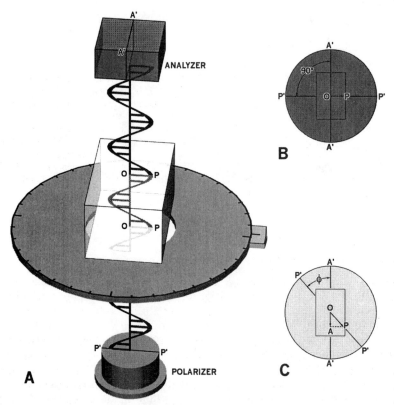

Figure 6-6. (A) Passage of light in an isotropic plate on the stage of a polarizing microscope. The vibration direction of light from the polarizer (represented by the vector *OP)* remains unchanged after passage through the plate. At the analyzer, therefore, the light is entirely absorbed. (B) The grain in the field of view thus appears black (extinct) when viewed between crossed polarizers. Vectorially *OP* represents the amplitude and direction of vibration of light from the polarizer both before and after passage through the crystal. *OP* has no component parallel to *A'A'*, the privileged direction of the analyzer, if the polarizers are crossed. Thus no light is transmitted through the analyzer. (C) If either the analyzer or polarizer is rotated in its holder so as to cause ϕ, the angle between their privileged directions, to be other than 90°, then there is a component of *OP* (that is, *OA*) that is parallel to *A'A'*, the privileged direction of the analyzer. Consequently, the analyzer transmits a component of the light, and the crystal no longer appears extinct.

Discovery of O and E Rays. Erasmus Bartholinus in 1669 reported that a dot on paper (or a ray of light) gave rise to two images when viewed through a rhomb of calcite. Thus a normally incident parent ray (for example, *PO* in Fig. 6-7) produced not only ray OP_O but also ray OP_E, the two rays following different paths within the crystal. Ray OP_O was called the **ordinary ray** or *O* **ray** (since its path was predictable by Snell's law) whereas ray OP_E was called the **extraordinary ray** or *E* **ray** (because its path was an obvious contradiction of Snell's law). This contradictory nature of path OP_E was obvious since $\angle r$ did not equal 0° as required by Snell's law.

Fresnel and Arago (1811) showed that the *O* and *E* rays in calcite were polarized at right angles to each other. The light composing the *O* ray was always observed to vibrate at right angles to the plane containing both the *O* ray path and the *c* axis (that is, it vibrated perpendicular to the shaded plane in Fig. 6-7). The light composing the *E* ray, on the other hand, was always observed to vibrate *within* this plane. Moreover, whenever a parent ray is normally incident on the surface of an anisotropic crystal, the vibrations of the refracted rays entering this crystal are always parallel to this surface. Thus, in Figure 6-7, the *E* and

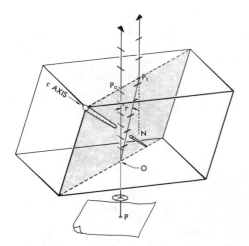

Figure 6-7. Double refraction of an unpolarized ray, *PO*, by a rhomb of Iceland spar (clear calcite) to produce two rays, OP_O and OP_E. If the rhomb is viewed from above, two images of point *P* are seen, one from rays emergent at P_O, the second from rays emergent at P_E. The angle between rays OP_O and OP_E is exaggerated for illustrative purposes. The construction line, NP_E, is perpendicular to the upper face of the rhomb.

O vibrations are both parallel to the underside of the rhomb.

Limitations of Snell's Law. Although Snell's law cannot correctly predict the *E*-ray path, it does correctly predict that of its associated wave normal direction. Figure 6-8 is a cross-sectional view of an unpolarized ray *PO* passing from an isotropic medium (refractive index: n_i) into an anisotropic medium thus to form two refracted rays, ordinary ray OP_O and extraordinary ray OP_E. The vibration directions of the light for both rays are shown, those associated with OP_E as short lines and those for OP_O as dots (since the latter represent vibrations precisely perpendicular to the cross-sectional plane). As will be later discussed more fully, the crystal exhibits different indices of refraction for these two different vibration directions, an index of ω for the *O*-ray vibrations and of ε' for the *E*-ray vibrations. Snell's law holds for the ordinary ray, thus

$$n_i \sin i = \omega \sin r_O$$

but it does not for the extraordinary ray since

$$n_i \sin i \neq \varepsilon' \sin r_E'$$

However, if the angle of refraction is measured as r_E—that is, with respect to direction OW_E in Figure 6-8 rather than to the *E*-ray path—Snell's law holds:

$$n_i \sin i = \varepsilon' \sin r_E \qquad \text{(Eqn. 6-2)}$$

OW_E is, of course, the direction perpendicular to those vibration directions marked off along OP_E; thus it is the *E*-wave normal.

Figure 6-8. Cross-sectional view of the passage of a ray of unpolarized light *PO* from an isotropic medium (shaded) into a uniaxial crystal to form an ordinary ray OP_O and an extraordinary ray OP_E. The *E*-wave normal OW_E is a direction perpendicular to the vibration directions drawn along OP_E; to emphasize this, one of these vibrations is extended by dotted lines.

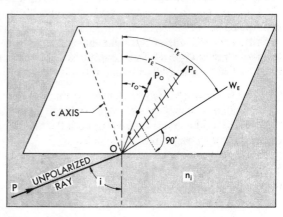

The limitations in the applicability of Snell's law may now be summarized. Snell's law predicts ray paths correctly only if such paths happen to coincide with their wave normals; in the prediction of wave normal directions the law is infallible. Such coincidence of ray path and wave normal occurs if the light composing the ray vibrates perpendicular to the ray's path; this situation occurs for (1) all rays in isotropic media and (2) the ordinary ray in uniaxial media but generally not for (3) the E ray in uniaxial media. Thus the E-ray path in uniaxial media rarely follows Snell's law; however, its associated wave normal always does.

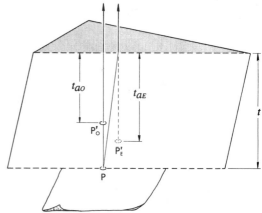

Figure 6-9. The front half of the rhomb of Figure 6-7 has been removed to expose the shaded plane shown therein. P'_O and P'_E represent the apparent positions of the O- and E-ray images of dot P as seen by an eye looking through the rhomb. The apparent thickness of the rhomb for the O- and E-ray images of P (that is, t_{aO} and t_{aE} respectively) are compared with the rhomb's true thickness, t.

Birefringence. If a calcite rhomb 2 cm thick or more is placed over a dot on a sheet of paper (Fig. 6-9), the dot image P'_O formed by the O rays appears to be shallower than P'_E the dot image formed by the E rays. Thus the rhomb's apparent thickness for the O ray (that is, t_{aO}) is less than that for the E ray (that is, t_{aE}). Symbolizing the crystal's refractive index for the O ray as ω and that for the E ray as ε', it is apparent from the Duc de Chaulnes equation (Eqn. 5-1) that $\omega = t/t_{aO}$ and $E = t/t_{aE}$, where t signifies the true thickness. Consequently, the calcite rhomb has two indices of refraction, the larger being associated with the O ray. Possession of more than one index of refraction is known as **birefringence**; only birefringent crystal plates are capable of producing double refraction—that is, doubling of images.

If a clear calcite rhomb is available, the reader is invited to verify the above observations and conclusions as an exercise. As a first step, the O dot may be recognized since it remains stationary even if viewed as the crystal is rotated on an axis parallel to PP'_O (Fig. 6-9). The relative depths of the E and O dot images may be qualitatively determined by viewing them while moving the head from side to side, cobra-like. Because of the effect of parallax, the shallower O-dot image will appear to move from side to side with respect to the E-dot image, the direction of its apparent motion being opposite to that of one's head. (The principle of parallax can be quickly demonstrated by lining up two vertically held pencils, one 10 inches from your eyes, the other at arm's length. If you now move your head to either side of this alignment, the closer pencil appears to move with respect to the more distant one, its motion being opposite to that of the head.)

The vibration directions for the O and E dot (of Fig. 6-7) can be determined by viewing them through a sheet of polaroid while rotating the rhomb around axis PP'_O (Fig. 6-9). Each dot will disappear when its vibration direction is at 90° to the privileged direction of the polaroid.

Description and Discussion

In anisotropic media the index of refraction actually varies according to the **vibration**

direction of the light in the crystal. Consequently, the optical indicatrix for anisotropic media is not a sphere but an ellipsoid. Of the two types of anisotropic optical indicatrices, the uniaxial indicatrix will be discussed first, since it is simpler.

Crystals of the hexagonal and tetragonal systems exhibit, for monochromatic light vibrating parallel to the c axis, a unique index of refraction customarily symbolized as ε. In Figure 6-10A, therefore, a vector proportional in length to the value of ε has been drawn parallel to the c axis to indicate this. On the other hand, for all vibration directions at 90° to the c axis, the crystal's refractive indices all equal a common value symbolized as ω.[2] By constructing vectors proportional in length to ω along these vibration directions, a circle of radius ω is defined (Fig. 6-10A); this circular section is, of course, always perpendicular to the c axis.

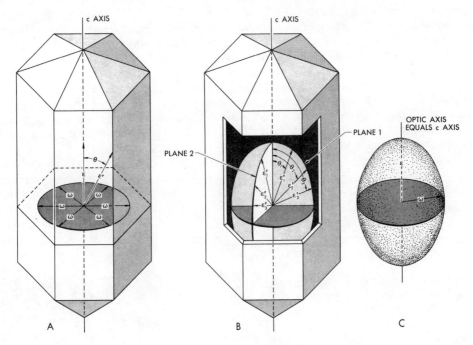

Figure 6-10. (A) Angular relationships to the c axis of the vibrations corresponding to indices ε, ω, and of one particular value of ε'. All ω vibrations lie in the plane perpendicular to the c axis. (B) Vector lengths in planes 1 and 2 indicate the variation in index ε' of the crystal for light vibrating parallel to them. Their tips outline identical ellipses in planes 1 and 2 and in all planes through the c axis. (C) The uniaxial indicatrix for the crystal.

For light vibrating at a random angle θ to the c axis (Fig. 6-10A), the crystal exhibits a refractive index somewhere between ω and ε in value; these intermediate indices are symbolized as ε'. The value of ε' can be computed from the formula

$$\varepsilon' = \frac{\omega\varepsilon}{\sqrt{\omega^2\cos^2\theta + \varepsilon^2\sin^2\theta}} = \frac{1}{\sqrt{\dfrac{\cos^2\theta}{\varepsilon^2} + \dfrac{\sin^2\theta}{\omega^2}}} \qquad \text{(Eqn. 6-3)}$$

---

[2] Other symbols sometimes used for ε and ω are

ε: n_ε; N_ε; E; n_E; N_E

ω: n_ω; N_ω; O; n_O; N_O

Plane 1 in Figure 6-10B indicates by the vector lengths how, as θ (for a vibration direction) varies from θ_1 to θ_3, the corresponding crystal index varies from ε_1' to ε_3'. The tips of all such vectors within plane 1 fall along an ellipse (for which Eqn. 6-3 is the equation in polar coordinates). Similarly, within any other plane containing the crystal's c axis (for example, plane 2) the vectors describing the ε' values fall along an ellipse identical with that for plane 1. Thus the ellipse of plane 1 can be rotated about the c axis as a hinge to coincide with any of these identical ellipses. As a result an ellipsoid of rotation (Fig. 6-10C) is formed. The length of any radius of this ellipsoid indicates the crystal's refractive index for light vibrating parallel thereto. Figure 6-10C is called the indicatrix or, more precisely, the uniaxial indicatrix (since there is only one axis in it that is perpendicular to a circular section).

The indices ω and ε represent the maximum and minimum—or minimum and maximum—refractive indices measurable in a tetragonal or hexagonal crystal. Collectively they may be referred to as the crystal's principal indices. Uniaxial materials fall naturally into two categories: **uniaxial positive**, in which by definition the value $(\varepsilon - \omega)$ is positive in sign (that is, $\varepsilon > \omega$), and **uniaxial negative** crystals, in which $(\varepsilon - \omega)$ is negative in sign (that is, $\varepsilon < \omega$). If the indicatrix for each of these two types is drawn in its customary orientation—that is, with the c axis vertical (Fig. 6-11)—the positive indicatrix (a prolate spheroid) may be mnemonically linked to the vertical stroke of a + sign and the negative indicatrix (an oblate spheroid) to a – sign. Note that regardless of sign, there is only one circular section in a uniaxial indicatrix; its radius is always equal to principal index ω, and it lies in a plane normal to the c axis.

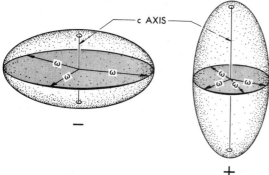

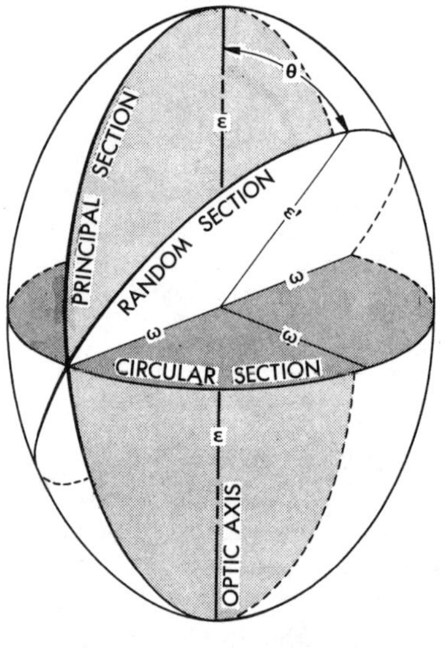

Figure 6-11 (above). Comparison of the positive and negative uniaxial indicatrices. The circular section for each is shaded dark gray.

Figure 6-12 (right). Illustration of the three types of central sections through a uniaxial indicatrix.

Directions and Central Sections

Terminology. The direction in the uniaxial indicatrix that coincides with the crystal's c axis is called the **optic axis** (heavy vertical line in Fig. 6-12). With reference to it, three types of sections may be cut through the indicatrix center: (1) **a principal plane, principal section, or principal ellipse** (that is, one which contains the optic axis and therefore intersects the indicatrix as an ellipse whose semiaxes[3] are equal to ε and ω);

---

[3] The term semiaxes is used here to refer collectively to the semimajor and semiminor axes of an ellipse. For convenience, a brief summary of the nomenclature, properties, and constructions associated with ellipses, pertinent to optical crystallography, is given in Appendix II. This section, particularly where it deals with the concept of conjugate radii of an ellipse, should be well understood before reading the following paragraphs.

(2) the previously mentioned **circular section** (that is, a section cut normal to the optic axis); and (3) a **random section** (that is, the intersection of the indicatrix with a plane cut at a random angle (θ) to the optic axis). A random section always intersects the indicatrix in an ellipse whose semiaxes are ω and ε'; the precise value of ε' can be calculated from Equation 6-3, if the value of the angle (θ) is known.

Wave Normals, Ray Paths, and Vibration Directions

For a random wave normal direction in a uniaxial indicatrix (for example OW in Fig. 6-13A), the two associated vibration directions lie in the plane perpendicular to this wave normal. This plane, extended outward from the indicatrix center, intersects the indicatrix in an ellipse (stippled) whose major and minor axes (OV_E and OV_O) constitute the only two vibration directions associable with wave normal OW. Consequently, light with a random wave normal direction such as OW would be constrained to vibrate parallel to OV_O or OV_E (or both) while passing through a uniaxial crystal. One of these two vibration directions, OV_O, will always be perpendicular to the optic axis, being the intersection of the stippled plane normal to OW with the circular section (shaded dark gray in Fig. 6-13A) and thus a radius of the circular section. The second of these vibration directions, OV_E, always lies within the same plane (shaded gray in Fig. 6-13B) as the optic axis and the wave normal OW.

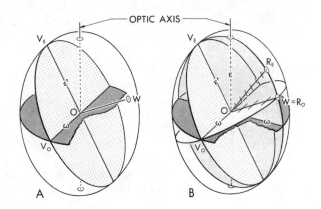

Figure 6-13A,B. (A) Relation of a random wave normal OW to the only two vibration directions, OV_O and OV_E, that are associable with it. The stippled plane perpendicular to OW intersects the indicatrix in an ellipse for which OV_O and OV_E are semiaxes. (B) The location of OR_E, the only ray path associable with OW and OV_E. All three lie in the same plane (shaded gray). Similarly, ray path OR_O, the only path associable with OW and OV_O, lies in the same plane (unshaded) with them; OR_O coincides with OW in this instance. In both (A) and (B) the circular section is shaded dark gray.

Only one ray path can be associated with a given combination of wave normal and vibration direction. All three (path, normal, and vibration direction) lie within a common plane that usually intersects the indicatrix in an ellipse. Within this ellipse the ray path and vibration direction represent conjugate radii—an important point to understand. To illustrate, the ray path associated with wave normal OW and vibration direction OV_E also lies in the ellipse shaded gray in Figure 6-13B, being OR_E, the radius conjugate to OV_E in this ellipse. Similarly, the ray path associated with wave normal OW and vibration direction OV_O, lies in the unshaded ellipse in Figure 6-13B. For this unshaded ellipse, OV_O is a semiaxis. Hence, OR_O, the ray path (and radius conjugate to it), is perpendicular to OV_O.[4] Consequently, OR_O coincides with wave normal OW, which in turn is always perpendicular to vibration direction OV_O. Thus, ray OR_O, since it vibrates perpendicular to and coincides in path with its wave normal direction, is an ordinary ray and obeys Snell's law. Ray OR_E, however, does not conform to this and is thus an extraordinary ray whose path does not obey Snell's law. The significance of the subscripts E and O used in the

---

[4] The radius conjugate to one semiaxis of an ellipse is the other semiaxis, the semiaxes thus constituting the only pair of conjugate radii in an ellipse that are mutually perpendicular. The reader should confirm this.

preceding discussions (and that to follow) becomes apparent. Subscript E refers to the vibration direction and ray path of the extraordinary ray; subscript O to those for the ordinary ray.

The ray path and wave normal direction for light in a uniaxial crystal coincide only if their associated vibration direction is perpendicular or parallel to the optic axis. A vibration direction thus oriented will correspond to a principal index, ω or ε. In consequence, this vibration direction will be the longest or shortest radius (that is, a semiaxis) for all elliptical cross sections of the indicatrix in which it may lie. The case for a vibration direction that is perpendicular to the optic axis has already been illustrated, vibration direction OV_O in Figure 6-13B having been associated with a ray path (OR_O) and wave normal (OW) that coincided in direction.

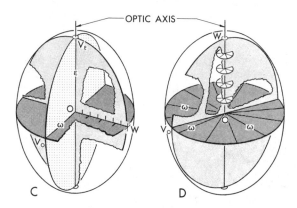

Figure 6-13C,D. (C) For OW, a wave normal perpendicular to the optic axis, the associated vibration directions are OV_O and OV_E, and the ray path associated with OW and OV_E (or with OW and OV_O) coincides in direction with OW. (D) For OW, a wave normal parallel to the optic axis, the associated vibration direction will be any one (or all) of the vibrations labelled ω. Moreover, any ray path associated an ω vibration will invariably coincide in direction with OW.

The directional relationships of ray paths and vibration directions to wave normals that are at the special angles of 90° or 0° to the optic axis may be determined in a manner similar to that for a random wave normal. For example, if wave normal OW is at 90° to the optic axis (Fig. 6-13C), the two vibration directions are OV_O and OV_E (for which the indices are ω and ε, respectively). Unlike the random case, however, the E-ray path now also coincides with its associated wave normal OW (since its vibration direction OV_E and wave normal OW are conjugate radii within the gray shaded ellipse). On the other hand, if the given wave normal coincides with the optic axis (Fig. 6-13D), the indicatrix section perpendicular to OW is a circular section. Consequently, no particular privileged directions are associable with this wave normal; instead, a wave traveling along the optic axis may vibrate parallel to any one of the innumerable radii of the circular section—or to all of them if the incident ray was unpolarized. Only the index ω can be associated with this ray, and its path coincides with the wave normal OW. The coincidence of ray path and wave normal for each vibration in Figure 6-13D is readily understood if a principal ellipse (shaded gray) is drawn through one of them (for example, OV_O). Note that OV_O and OW are semiaxes of this ellipse and therefore conjugate radii; consequently, OW represents a ray path as well as a wave normal direction.

In summary, it may be noted from Figure 6-13B that, with respect to a wave normal at a random angle to the optic axis, either of two mutually perpendicular vibrations and, therefore, either of two ray paths may be associated. Both possible ray paths lie within the principal plane containing the wave normal (shaded gray in Fig. 6-13B). One of these rays, the O ray, vibrates normal to this principal plane; the second, the E ray, vibrates within this principal plane along the radius of the ellipse that is conjugate to its path. An important corollary of this is: *Rays (or wave normals) traveling within a principal plane must vibrate (1) within or (2) perpendicular to this principal plane.*

Application to Light Incidence on Crystal Surfaces

Types of Incidence. A light ray entering a uniaxial crystal defines a plane of incidence that is either parallel or at an angle to the crystal's optic axis. Rays 1 and 2 in Figure 6-14 illustrate the first case; both lie in a plane of incidence that parallels the optic axis. Ray 1 is further specialized since it coincides with the normal to the crystal face; it therefore represents what is called the case of **normal incidence** upon this crystal face. Ray 2, on the other hand, is at an angle of i_2 to the normal. Ray 3 illustrates the more general case since it defines a plane of incidence (heavily shaded) that is at an oblique angle to the crystal's optic axis. Only if the optic axis is parallel to the crystal face upon which incidence occurs can the angle between the plane of incidence and the optic axis ever equal 90° (*cf.* the plane of incidence containing ray 4 in Fig. 6-14).

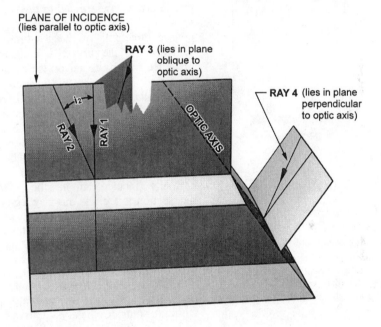

Figure 6-14. The various types of angular relationships between the optic axis of a uniaxial crystal and the planes of incidence defined by light rays entering it. The plane of incidence containing rays 1 and 2 is parallel to the optic axis. The plane of incidence containing ray 3 represents the general case, being at an angle other than 0° or 90° to the optic axis. The plane of incidence containing ray 4 is at 90° to the optic axis; this 90° angle can occur only for incidence upon a crystal surface parallel to the optic axis.

Rays 1, 2, 3, and 4, after entering the crystal, will generally form an O and E ray that travel along different paths within the crystal. For all four cases the O-ray path may be readily determined since (1) it always lies within the plane of incidence and (2) it follows Snell's law. The path of the E ray is rather difficult to determine for ray 3, moderately so for ray 2, and simpler for ray 4 as well as for normal incidence (ray 1). In this text, the method of locating the E-ray path will be discussed only for the cases represented by ray 1 (the case of normal incidence), by ray 2, and by ray 4. The case of normal incidence in particular is most important to understand in the routine practice of optical crystallography and will therefore be next discussed in greatest detail.

Normal Incidence. Prescribed geometrical relationships exist between the ray path, wave normal, and vibration direction of a given light energy traveling within a uniaxial

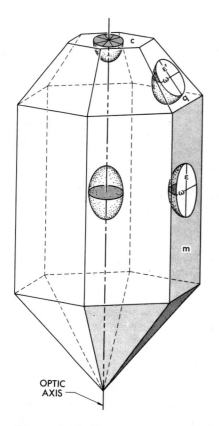

crystal. Thus a refracted ray path in a uniaxial crystal can be determined if its associated wave normal and vibration direction can be located. For normal incidence ($i = 0°$), the wave normals of the rays entering the crystal remain perpendicular to the crystal surface upon which the incidence occurs (since for the revised Snell's law, if $i = 0°$ for the incident wave normal, then $r = 0°$ for all refracted wave normals). Therefore, because vibrations are invariably perpendicular to wave normals, *the vibration directions for the rays entering the crystal are always parallel to the crystal surface upon which normal incidence occurs*. The precise directions of these vibrations can be visualized if the crystal's indicatrix can be imagined with its center on the crystal face. As illustrated in Figure 6-15, the intersection between the indicatrix and crystal face is either an ellipse (*cf.* faces *m* and *q*) or a circle (*cf.* face *c*), depending upon the angle between the face and the optic axis. If the intersection is an ellipse, its semiaxes mark the vibration directions, after entry into the crystal, of light normally incident upon the face. If the intersection is a circle, no privileged directions exist; thus, as for isotropic media, light normally incident on this face will vibrate in the same direction(s) after entry into the crystal as it did prior to entry.

Figure 6-15. The types of intersection between the faces of a crystal and its indicatrix. The heavy radii of the ellipse (or circle) indicate the crystal's privileged directions for light entering by normal incidence on this face.

Figure 6-15 further illustrates that it is permissible to draw the indicatrix *anywhere* within (or outside) the crystal just so long as its optic axis is maintained parallel to the crystal's *c* axis. Thus the indicatrix has a specific orientation but not a specific location within the crystal.

*Section perpendicular to the optic **axis.*** A section cut perpendicular to the optic axis of a uniaxial crystal (plane *c* in Fig. 6-15) intersects the indicatrix in a circle of radius ω. The situation is thus analogous to that described for an isotropic plate; that is, the light entering into the crystal may be considered to vibrate, with equal ease, parallel to any (or all) radii of the circle of intersection. Consequently, unpolarized light normally incident on the plate will remain unpolarized (for example ray *BB'* in Fig. 6-16) whereas a plane-polarized ray (for example, *CC'* in the figure) will retain its same direction of polarization.[5] Thus, like the isotropic plate (and for the same reasons), this plate viewed between crossed polarizers would remain completely extinct, even if observed during rotation of the stage, particularly if the substage iris diaphragm is closed down to a small aperture.

The analogy between this particular section and an isotropic plate may be carried even

---

[5] The possibility of rotatory polarization is disregarded here.

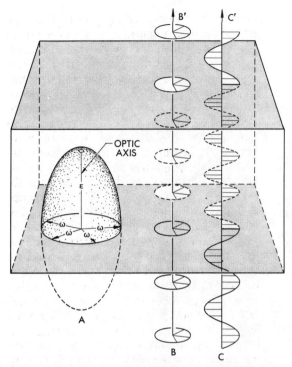

Figure 6-16. Normal incidence of light upon the under surface of a crystal that was cut perpendicular to its optic axis. The orientation of the crystal's optical indicatrix to this surface is shown at *A*. The passage through the crystal of an unpolarized ray, *BB'*, and of a polarized ray, *CC'*, is illustrated.

further since it too lacks birefringence, exhibiting only one index, ω, for normally incident light. (All other types of sections through the indicatrix, we shall soon see, do exhibit birefringence.) Furthermore, the rays *BB'* and *CC'* act as ordinary rays since they coincide with their wave normal directions (or, stated alternatively, since their associated vibration directions are perpendicular to their path). Thus these rays follow Snell's law, even in its unrevised form. Such isotropic-like phenomena are observed in a uniaxial crystal whenever a ray travels along the optic axis (that is, the *c* axis) of the crystal. For this reason the optic axis is sometimes called the **axis of isotropy.**

Section parallel to the optic axis. In this case (Fig. 6-17) the uniaxial indicatrix, if centered on the crystal's boundary plane, intersects this plane in an ellipse whose semimajor and semiminor axes equal ε and ω, the two extremes of refractive index (that is, principal indices) that a uniaxial crystal can exhibit. These semiaxes also represent the two mutually perpendicular directions (that is, privileged directions) parallel to which the light is constrained to vibrate while passing through the crystal. Consequently, an unpolarized light ray normally incident upon the plate (*A* in Fig. 6-17) will, after entry, be resolved into two different rays. They travel, in this case, along a common path but vibrate perpendicular to each other. For the ray vibrating parallel to the ω privileged direction, the crystal exhibits the index ω, for the ray vibrating parallel to the ε privileged direction, the crystal exhibits the index ε. Thus, this plate is birefringent, exhibiting *both* principal refractive indices—ε and ω.

Plane-polarized light normally incident on this same crystal plate (Fig. 6-17) will be differently affected according to the angle between its plane of polarization and the privileged directions of the plate. If the incident light is plane polarized parallel to one of the privileged directions, the crystal transmits only one ray; this single ray vibrates parallel to this particular privileged direction only. Examples are rays *B* and *C* in Figure 6-17, ray *B*

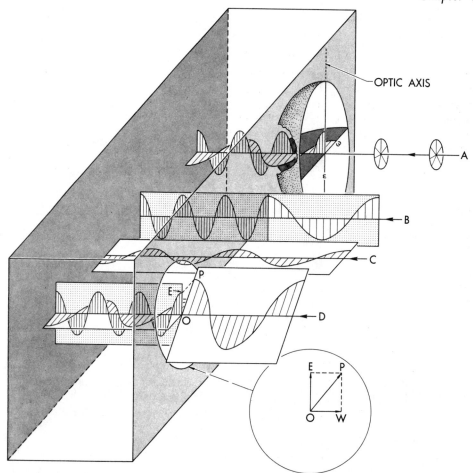

Figure 6-17. Normal incidence of an unpolarized ray, A, and of polarized rays, B, C, and D, on a crystal face cut parallel to the optic axis. Circular inset: enlarged, face-on view of the resolution of vector OP upon entering the crystal.

vibrating parallel to the ε privileged direction, ray C to the ω privileged direction; in each case the crystal exhibits only one refractive index (ε for ray B, ω for ray C).

If, however, the incident light is plane polarized parallel to neither privileged direction (ray D in Fig. 6-17), it is resolved vectorially into two rays upon entering the crystal, each ray vibrating parallel to a privileged direction. Figure 6-18 illustrates in greater detail the resolution of the incident light's amplitude (OP) into the two amplitudes (OE and OW) associable with these two rays. The relative magnitudes of these amplitudes are

$$OE = OP\cos\tau$$
$$OW = OP\sin\tau$$

where τ (tau) is defined as the angle between OP and the privileged direction OE for the extraordinary ray in the crystal.

The light intensity of a ray is proportional to the square of its amplitude. Thus in Figure 6-18

I is proportional to OP^2

I_E is proportional to $OP^2 \cos^2 \tau$

I_O is proportional to $OP^2 \sin^2 \tau$

where I, I_E, and I_O respectively represent the intensities of the incident, extraordinary, and ordinary rays. As may be seen in the figure, the rotating stage of a polarizing microscope permits τ to be varied between 0° and 90°. Consequently, all the incident light energy may alternatively be concentrated in the extraordinary ray or in the ordinary ray, or be divided equally between them $\tau = 45°$) or in any proportion. [What is the intensity ratio of the extraordinary ray to the ordinary ray if $\tau = 30°$?]

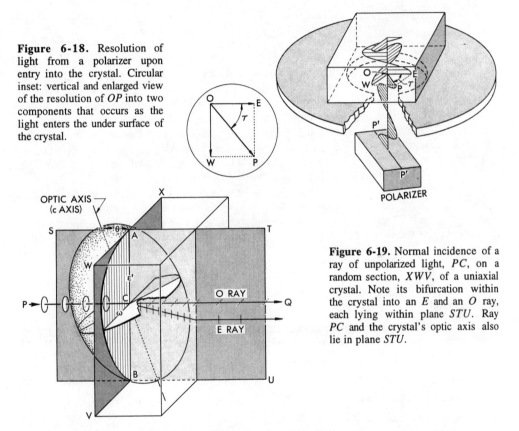

Figure 6-18. Resolution of light from a polarizer upon entry into the crystal. Circular inset: vertical and enlarged view of the resolution of *OP* into two components that occurs as the light enters the under surface of the crystal.

Figure 6-19. Normal incidence of a ray of unpolarized light, *PC*, on a random section, *XWV*, of a uniaxial crystal. Note its bifurcation within the crystal into an *E* and an *O* ray, each lying within plane *STU*. Ray *PC* and the crystal's optic axis also lie in plane *STU*.

Section cut at a random angle (θ) to the optic axis. For this orientation if the crystal's indicatrix is centered on the boundary plane (darkest shading in Fig. 6-19), their intersection is an ellipse (vertically ruled) whose major and minor axes mark two privileged directions corresponding to indices ω and ε' in the crystal plate. As shown, the normally incident, unpolarized, light ray *PC* is separated into an *O* and an *E* ray vibrating parallel to the ω and ε' privileged directions, respectively. These two ray paths, for normal incidence, always lie within the same principal plane (STU in Fig. 6-19). This plane also contains (1) the normally incident ray, (2) the crystal's optic axis, and (3) the crystal's ε' (or ε) privileged direction, these three directions being always coplanar; consequently, this plane is easy to define if two of these three directions are known.

The plane STU, drawn enlarged in Figure 6-20, is thus a key plane in determining graphically the E-ray path and the precise value of ε' for its associated vibration. To do this

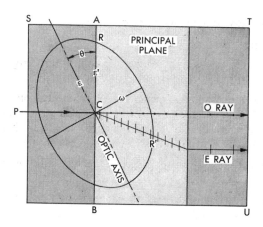

Figure 6-20. Unobstructed view of plane *STU* in Figure 6-19. The intersection between plane *STU* and the indicatrix produces the ellipse shown, its major axis coinciding with the crystal's optic axis.

one must know the actual values of ε, ω, and θ—the last being the angle between the crystal's optic axis and the crystal face upon which normal incidence occurs. Construction details for Figure 6-20 (and similar graphic solutions) are: (1) Construct an ellipse with ω and ε drawn to scale along the semiaxes so as to represent the intersection between plane STU and the indicatrix in Figure 6-19; (2) through its center and at an angle θ to its ε semiaxis (the optic axis of the crystal), draw the line AB, representing the line of intersection in Figure 6-19 between plane STU and the crystal surface VWX; (3) perpendicular to AB draw the normally incident ray and extend it into the crystal to obtain the *O*-ray path; the *O* ray's associated vibrations, since they are always perpendicular to the principal plane, are shown as dots; (4) CR, the radius of the ellipse that is parallel to AB, represents both the vibration direction and, by its length, the refractive index ε' for the *E* ray; (5) draw the radius conjugate to CR (*cf.* Appendix II) to obtain CR′, the *E*-ray path.

SUMMARY

1. The optical indicatrix indicates how refractive index changes with vibration direction in a crystal.

2. The isotropic indicatrix is spherical, indicating that isotropic materials exhibit the same refractive index, regardless of vibration direction of light.

3. For uniaxial crystals the indicatrix is either a prolate spheroid (positive crystals) or an oblate spheroid (negative crystals).

4. All central sections through the indicatrix, except one, are ellipses.

5. The one exception is the circular section.

6. The direction normal to the circular section is called the optic axis. This optic axis always coincides with the *c* axis of hexagonal and tetragonal crystals.

7. A principal section through the indicatrix is one that contains the optic axis. It intersects the indicatrix as an ellipse whose semiaxes equal to ε and ω.

8. The *O* ray always vibrates *perpendicular* to the principal plane containing its path.

9. The *E* ray always vibrates *within* the principal plane containing its path.

10. Within this principal plane, the *E* ray's path is not necessarily perpendicular to its vibration direction. Instead its path and vibration directions are conjugate radii of the ellipse formed by the intersection of this principal plane with the uniaxial indicatrix.

11. A wave normal direction is always perpendicular to its associated vibration directions.

12. The *O*-wave normal direction and the *O*-ray path always coincide.

13. The *E*-wave normal and *E*-ray path generally do not coincide.

14. The two possible vibration directions associable with a given wave normal are at right angles to it and to each other.

15. Given a wave normal, its associated vibration directions lie within the plane perpendicular to it. More particularly, this plane generally intersects the indicatrix in an ellipse whose major and minor axes represent the only two privileged directions (that is, possible vibration directions) that may be associated with the given wave normal.

16. If this plane intersects the indicatrix in a circle, no privileged directions exist with respect to the given wave normal.

17. For anisotropic crystals, Snell's law must be redefined to apply to wave normal directions rather than ray paths.

18. For normally incident light entering a uniaxial crystal plate from air, the vibration directions are parallel to the crystal boundary both before and after entry (*cf.* revised Snell's law).

19. More specifically, the vibrations after entry are parallel to the major and/or minor axes of the ellipse of intersection which results if the uniaxial indicatrix is translated until its center falls on the crystal's boundary plane.

7 THE INTERFERENCE OF LIGHT

OVERVIEW

For monochromatic light, isotropic crystals exhibit a single refractive index (n), whereas uniaxial crystals may exhibit two (either ω and ε or ω and ε') and, accordingly, are said to be **birefringent**. Of the pair of indices exhibited by a birefringent crystal, let N represent the larger and n represent the smaller—and let ON and On symbolize their corresponding vibration directions while in the crystal. A crystal is said to be "45° off extinction," if oriented with its privileged directions, ON and On, at 45° to those of the polarizer and analyzer (Fig. 7-3). As previously discussed (Fig. 6-18), if light of amplitude OP enters this crystal, it is resolved into one component vibrating along ON and another vibrating along On. As a result, two waves ascend through the crystal (Fig. 7-3). The slower is associated with index N (and vibration direction ON); the faster with n (and vibration direction On).

At the instant the slow wave emerges from the crystal, it lags behind the already emerged fast wave by a distance called the **retardation** (Δ). This distance may be expressed in nanometers (*e.g.*, = 1100 nm) or wavelengths of the light in use (e.g., if $\lambda = 550$ nm, then $\Delta = 2\lambda$). As derived in the text, $\Delta = t\left(N - n\right)$, where t equals thickness (in nanometers) and $(N - n)$ equals the crystal's **birefringence**.

For a transparent crystal (Fig. 7-3) being observed between **crossed polarizers** (= privileged direction of analyzer at 90° to that of polarizer), if Δ equals 0, 1λ, 2λ ... or $n\lambda$, monochromatic light of wavelength λ undergoes total **destructive interference** upon entering the analyzer (Fig. 7-4A). The crystal thus appears black (= extinct) when viewed through the ocular. By contrast, if Δ should equal $\frac{1}{2}\lambda$, $\frac{3}{2}\lambda$, $\frac{5}{2}\lambda$, the slow and fast waves **constructively interfere** at the analyzer and the crystal appears bright (Fig. 7-4B).

These efforts would be reversed—e.g., 1λ causes constructive interference and $\frac{1}{2}\lambda$ causes destructive interference—if the privileged direction of the analyzer were oriented parallel to that of the polarizer (= **parallel polarizers**).

Figure 7-6 illustrates how percent of light transmitted by the analyzer, for a crystal 45° off extinction, varies according to whether the crystal's retardation Δ equals $n\lambda$ or $\frac{2n+1}{2}\lambda$—or values in between.

Illuminated by white light ($\lambda = 380$ to 780 nm), anisotropic crystals display **interference colors** between either crossed or parallel polarizers. The hues of these colors closely depend upon Δ for the crystal. Should Δ equal 550 nm, the crystal will appear reddish violet between crossed polarizers because only the wavelengths that increasingly differ from 550 nm (curve A, Fig. 7-7) will be transmitted by the analyzer. On the other hand, should Δ equal 800 nm, the crystal will appear green (curve B, Fig. 7-7) between crossed polarizers.

The interference colors associated with particular values of Δ—as seen between crossed polarizers—are reproduced in Figure 8-13. By custom, these colors are subdivided into first-order ($\Delta = 0$ to 550 nm), second-order (550-1100 nm), third-order (1100-1650 nm) colors, etc. The top of each order is marked by a red interference color: first-order red (550 nm), second-order red (1100 nm) ... etc.

A bluish-white color, called **first-order white** occurs for Δ equal 200 nm. A creamier white, **high-order white**, occurs for very high values of Δ (see Fig. 7-8).

During rotation of the microscope stage, a crystal's interference color becomes brightest at 45° off extinction but dims to blackness (= extinction) as the crystal's privileged directions become increasingly parallel to those of the polarizers (see Fig. 7-9).

Under **orthoscopic illumination** (Fig. 7-10A), the wave normals dominantly travel along the microscope's axis before entering the crystal. By contrast, under **conoscopic illumination** (Fig. 7-10B)—see Table 7-1—a cone of wave normals enters the crystal and only the central WN travels parallel to the microscope's axis.

Viewed between crossed polarizers (under orthoscopic illumination), a crystal exhibits its highest order colors where thickest (Fig. 7-11) and successively lower ones toward its edges (where t approaches zero). All points of equal thickness along a grain's tapered edges will display precisely the same interference color. Thus, the crystal will be rimmed by **isochromes** (= lines of identical interference colors).

Viewed conoscopically between crossed polarizers, the images of anisotropic crystals are supplanted by highly informative patterns of interference colors called **interference figures**. Thus, the interference figure from a uniaxial crystal, oriented with its optic axis perpendicular to the microscope stage (Fig. 7-12) consists of concentric circular isochromes plus a black cross consisting of two intersecting black bars called **isogyres**. The common center of the circular isochromes and the isogyre-cross—called the **melatope** (= black spot)—marks where the wave normal that traveled along the optic axis crops out in the field of view.

Any wave normal that does not coincide with the optic axis (O.A.)—for example, WN_2, WN_3 ... WN_5 in Figure 7-13A—together with the O.A. defines a principal plane. Of the two associated vibration directions that are perpendicular to this WN, one lies *perpendicular to this principal plane* and corresponds to the index ω. The second lies *within this principal plane* and corresponds to an index ε' or, in the case of WN_5 (Fig. 7-13A), to true ε. Alternatively considered, the two vibration directions associated with a wave normal will invariably coincide with the semiaxes of the ellipse of intersection between the wave normal's associated wave fronts (WF) and the crystal's optical indicatrix.

The origin of the isogyres and circular isochromes in a uniaxial interference figure is discussed (Figs. 7-13 to 7-15) as are the three types of figures—centered O.A. (Figs 7-14, 7-16), off-centered O.A. (Fig. 7-17) and flash figure (Fig. 7-19). An important point to note is that whenever a principal plane emerges along an E-W or N-S direction, a straight isogyre will mark its outcrop in the field of view.

If a crystal's O.A. is so highly tilted that the melatope lies outside the field of view, rotation of the microscope stage (Fig. 7-18) reveals which end of the isogyre is the homodrome end and which the antidrome. The homodrome end of the isogyre always points toward the O.A. For flash figures the direction of the optic axis can be located as discussed in Figure 7-19 or 7-20.

WAVES POLARIZED IN THE SAME PLANE

We have described light waves as being transverse waves. Thus light energy streams along its path in a given medium by means of vibrations of its photons, the vibrations being perpendicular to the path of energy travel. Figure 7-1A represents, in essence, a

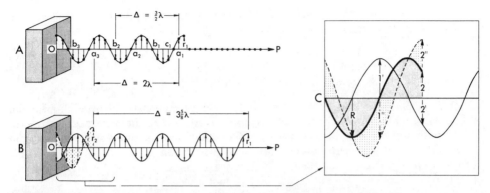

Figure 7-1. (A) Transmission of a plane-polarized light wave of amplitude r_1 from O toward P by means of transverse displacement of particles from their rest positions (black dots) on OP. (B) A similar "photograph" taken an instant later. A second wave motion of amplitude r_2 has entered from the left and is also traveling from O toward P. (C) An enlarged portion of (B) to show in detail the interaction of these two coinciding wave motions to produce a resultant wave motion of amplitude R.

motion-stopping photograph of a plane-polarized wave traveling along OP; the arrows transverse to OP represent the vibrational displacements (from their original rest positions on OP) of a few of the photons taking active part in light transmission. Photons on the same wave train are "in phase" if, at any and all given instants, they are always displaced from their rest position by the same direction and amount. Thus, in Figure 7-1A, points a_1, a_2, and a_3 are all in phase; so are points b_1, b_2, and b_3. Photons such as a_1 and b_1, whose vibrational displacements are equal but opposite in direction, are precisely "out of phase." Points b_1 and c_1 are not in phase since, at a slightly later instant of time, their displacements would be unequal.

The distance between two points on the same wave path is known as their "path difference" and is symbolized as Δ. Since it is a distance, it may be expressed in any convenient units of length; often, however, it is convenient to express path difference in terms of the number of wavelengths of the light being used. We then find that the path difference between all points in phase (for example, a_1 and a_3 in Fig. 7-1A) is always an integral number of wavelengths—that is, 0, 1λ, 2λ, ..., or $n\lambda$—whereas between all points precisely out of phase (for example, a_1 and b_2) it is $\frac{1}{2}\lambda$, $\frac{3}{2}\lambda$, ... or $\frac{2n+1}{2}\lambda$. The path differences between points neither precisely in nor precisely out of phase will be other than these values. Thus, the path difference between two points, if expressed in wavelengths, discloses the extent to which these points are in phase (or out of phase).

In Figure 7-1B, a "photograph" taken an instant later than Figure 7-1A, the original wave (amplitude r_1) has traveled farther to the right and a second wave train, of equal wavelength but of amplitude r_2, has entered from the left. The path difference between the forefronts of these two wave trains is now $3\frac{5}{8}\lambda$. The two waves are thus more nearly out of phase than in phase (since $3\frac{5}{8}$ is closer to $3\frac{1}{2}$ than to 4). These two wave motions simultaneously traveling the same path, do not remain separate entities but rather, as shown in the square inset, they combine (that is, interfere) to produce a composite wave motion (shaded gray) whose amplitude is R. Thus the vibration vectors of the two parent waves, where they coincide in *space* and time, combine vectorially to produce the vibration vectors of the composite wave. For example, the sum of vectors $1'$ plus $1''$ is zero whereas that of $2'$ and $2''$ is vector 2. The form of such composite wave motions depends upon the wavelengths, amplitudes, and path difference of the interfering parent waves. In the common case for optical mineralogy wherein a path difference equal to $x\lambda$ exists between two parent waves of equal wavelengths, the relation between their amplitudes (r_1 and r_2) and the amplitude of the resultant wave (R) is

$$R^2 = r_1^2 + r_2^2 + 2r_1r_2 \cos(x \cdot 360°) \qquad \text{(Eqn. 7-1)}$$

Note that if the two interfering waves are in phase—that is, their path difference is 0, 1λ, 2λ, ... , or $n\lambda$—Equation 7-1 indicates R to equal the sum of r_1 and r_2. In this event *constructive interference* occurs, the resultant wave being of greater amplitude than either parent. If the two interfering waves are exactly out of phase—that is, their path difference is $\frac{1}{2}\lambda$, $\frac{3}{2}\lambda$, ... , or $\frac{2n+1}{2}\lambda$—Equation 7-1 indicates R to equal the difference between r_1 and r_2. In this event, *destructive interference* occurs, the resultant wave being of lesser amplitude than one or both parents. For such a situation, if r_1 should equal r_2, *total destructive interference* would occur, the two wave motions mutually annihilating each other to produce quiescence rather than a wave motion.

Two wave motions can interfere only if polarized in the same plane. Otherwise, they cannot. Physicists, however, find it to be more simple (and to lead to equally correct solutions) to interpret two perpendicularly polarized wave motions as able to interfere and, as discussed next, to form a single wave.

WAVES POLARIZED IN PERPENDICULAR PLANES

For two waves simultaneously traveling along the same path but vibrating within two mutually perpendicular planes (Fig. 7-2), the resultant wave can be represented as the vector sum of the vibrations of the two parent waves for all points along the path. In the case illustrated, wherein the points of zero displacement from the path coincide for both waves, the resultant wave (dark gray in Fig. 7-2) will vibrate in a plane that is at an angle to the plane of vibration of either parent. The vectorial addition at a representative point of the two parent vibrations (hollow arrows) to yield the resultant vibration (solid black arrow) is shown on the imaginary plane in Figure 7-2.

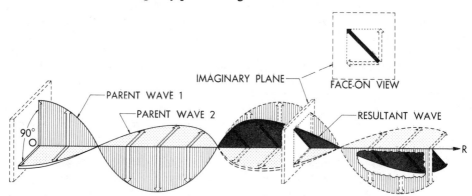

Figure 7-2. Assumed interference between two waves, polarized in mutually perpendicular planes, to produce a resultant wave motion (polarized in another plane). The imaginary plane indicates how, at any point along *OR,* the vibration vectors of the two parent motions (hollow arrows) may be added vectorially to produce the vibration vectors (solid arrows) of the resultant wave.

Calculation of Path Difference or Retardation

Two perpendicularly plane-polarized wave motions like those in Figure 7-2 may be considered to emerge from an anisotropic crystal plate upon which plane-polarized light is incident (Fig. 7-3). As illustrated, this plane-polarized light is resolved immediately upon entering at point O into a slow wave (for which the crystal's privileged direction

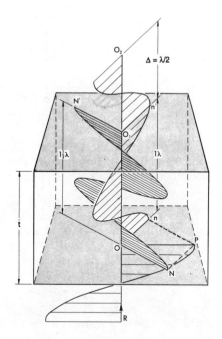

Figure 7-3. Passage of light through a crystal plate that produces a retardation (Δ) of 270 nm. If illuminated by light of wavelength 540 nm, this distance represents $\frac{1}{2}\lambda$. Note that, if a path difference of $\frac{1}{2}\lambda$—or $\frac{2n\pm1}{2}\lambda$ exists, either *ON* or *On*, the light's two vibration vectors upon entry, becomes reversed in direction at its point of exit from the crystal's upper surface (*cf. ON* is reversed to become *ON'*).

and index are *ON* and *N*, respectively) and a fast wave (privileged direction and index, *On* and *n*).[1] At this precise instant the two waves are exactly in phase, no path difference existing between them. However, to pass through the thickness of the crystal, *t*, the slow wave requires the time T_N whereas the fast wave requires only T_n, a lesser amount. Consequently, while "waiting" for the slow wave to emerge, the fast wave travels the distance $c(T_N - T_n)$ in air, *c* being the velocity of light; Figure 7-3, essentially a "photograph" taken at the precise moment when the slow wave is about to emerge into air, shows the fast wave to have emerged by this distance. This distance is the path difference (Δ) between these two perpendicularly polarized wave trains as they travel in air along direction O_1O_2; thus

$$\Delta = c(T_N - T_n)$$
$$= cT_N - cT_n$$

(Eqn. 7-2)

The actual velocities of the slow and fast waves while traveling in the crystal (here symbolized as c_N and c_n, respectively) are, from the familiar distance-per-time-traveled formula,

$$c_N = \frac{t}{T_N} \qquad c_n = \frac{t}{T_n}$$

(Eqn. 7-3)

Solving for T_N and T_n, then substituting the values thus obtained into Equation 7-2, the result is

[1] The symbols *n* and *N* (respectively read "small en" and "large en") will be used here to refer to the smaller and larger refractive indices of any birefringent plate. For the beginning student this appears to be mnemonically superior to the standard practice of using n_1 and n_2 for these indices.

$$\Delta = \frac{ct}{c_N} - \frac{ct}{c_n}$$

$$= t\left(\frac{c}{c_N} - \frac{c}{c_n}\right) \tag{Eqn. 7-4}$$

From the definition of refractive index (p. 5), Equation 7-4 becomes

$$\Delta = t\,(N - n) \tag{Eqn. 7-5}$$

Equation 7-5 indicates that the path difference—that is, retardation of the slow wave behind the fast—is proportional to (1) the plate's thickness and (2) the difference in refractive indices of its two privileged directions.

The term $(N - n)$ is dimensionless; hence path difference, if computed from Equation 7-5, is expressed in whatever units of distance are used for t. Path difference is commonly expressed in nanometers (nm) whereas the crystal thicknesses ordinarily dealt with in optical mineralogy are usually expressed in millimeters (mm). Thus it is necessary to convert the crystal's thickness from mm to nm by means of the conversion factor

$$1\text{ mm } = 10^6\text{ nm}$$

For example, assume a crystal plate 0.03 mm in thickness to possess refractive indices of 1.553 and 1.544 for its two privileged directions. For this plate

$$\Delta = (1.553 - 1.544)0.03\text{ mm}$$

$$= 0.009 \times 0.030 \times 10^6\text{ nm}$$

$$= 270\text{ nm}$$

After their emergence from the crystal in Figure 7-3, the slow and fast wave trains simultaneously travel upward along O_1O_2 as two discrete wave motions. As discussed, these two waves can be considered to mutually interfere and produce a resultant wave motion. Depending upon the path difference between these two interfering wave trains, this resultant wave motion may be plane polarized, circularly polarized, or elliptically polarized. The nature of these types of polarization and their relation to the path difference between the two interfering waves will be discussed next.

Plane Polarization of the Resultant Wave

Assume that the slow wave required two periods, but the fast wave only one, to pass through the crystal of Figure 7-4A.[2] After their emergence, therefore, a path difference of λ exists between the two wave trains. Consequently, as is always the case for path differences of 0λ, 1λ, 2λ, ..., $n\lambda$, the two waves emergent at O_1 are in phase; that is, at any point along O_1O_2 the vibrations of these two waves are either (1) both in the same direction as On and ON or (2) both opposite, On and ON representing the vibrations of the two waves immediately after they entered the crystal at O (when they were exactly in phase).

In Figure 7-4A the two wave trains emerging from the crystal have wave motions as indicated by the dashed curves. However, for convenience, consider their vibrations to be

---

[2] A period is the time required for the series of vibrations necessary to complete one full wavelength. As shown in Figure 7-4A, therefore, the slow wave traced out two wavelengths, the fast wave only one, while passing through the crystal. The period of a wave motion is technically defined as the reciprocal of the frequency and is constant for a given, highly pure color of light.

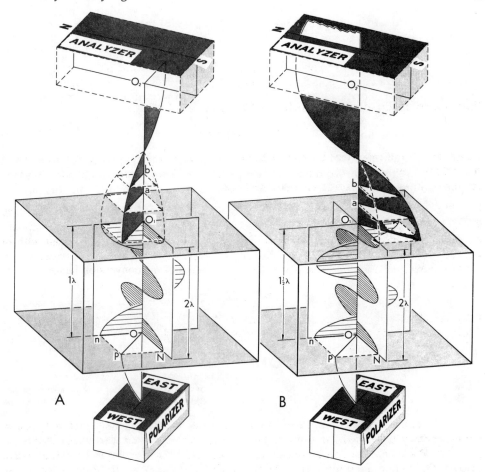

Figure 7-4. The interaction, after their emergence from an anisotropic crystal at 45° off extinction, of what were formerly the slow and fast waves within the crystal. In (A), passage through the crystal has produced a path difference of 1λ between these waves. In consequence their resultant wave motion after exit at O_1 is polarized in the same plane as the light from the polarizer. For (B), where their path difference is $\frac{1}{2}\lambda$, the resultant wave motion after exit at O_1 is at 90° to the plane of polarization of light from the polarizer. Between crossed polarizers, therefore, the resultant light emergent from the crystal is for (A) completely extinguished by the analyzer but for (B) completely transmitted (reflectional and absorptional losses being neglected). Actually, the two wave motions retain their respective identities after leaving the crystal and only interfere, one with the other, after they enter the analyzer and are polarized in the same plane. However, the assumption that they interfere before entering the analyzer allows simpler (and equally correct) interpretations of the analyzer's effect on the light.

vectorially additive—for example, at points O_1, a, and b—and thus to produce the dark-shaded plane-polarized wave that vibrates in precisely the same plane as did the light incident on the crystal (as is always the case for path differences of 0, 1λ, 2λ, ..., $n\lambda$). Note that, if the analyzer is inserted with its privileged direction perpendicular to that of the polarizer (that is, the polarizers are crossed), the analyzer will not transmit any of this light. If, however, its privileged direction is parallel to the polarizer's, it will transmit all of this light.

Next assume the slow wave to require two periods and the fast wave one and one-half to pass through the crystal (Fig. 7-4B). Upon their emergence, a path difference of

$\frac{1}{2}\lambda$ exists between these waves. Consequently, at O_1 one of these waves (but never both) will always be vibrating opposite in direction from On or ON, as the case may be. The resultant of these two wave motions (shown in detail at points O_1, a, and b) thus produces light plane-polarized at 90° relative to the incident light. Thus, the light from this crystal, if viewed between crossed polarizers, will be fully transmitted by the analyzer; if viewed between parallel polarizers, none will be transmitted. Similar results would be obtained for crystals that produced path differences of $\frac{3}{2}\lambda$, $\frac{5}{2}\lambda$, ..., $\frac{2n+1}{2}\lambda$.

Circular Polarization

If the path difference between the two waves emergent from a crystal is $\frac{1}{4}\lambda$ (or $\frac{3}{4}\lambda$, $\frac{5}{4}\lambda$, ..., $\frac{2n+1}{4}\lambda$), their vibrations can be regarded to interfere, where they coincide in space and time, to produce vibration vectors of constant lengths but variable azimuths (arrows in Fig. 7-5A). The resultant wave motion thus consists of vibration vectors that spiral upward and define a surface[3] resembling the thread of a screw. If it could be viewed by looking down O_1P (the direction this wave motion is traveling), this surface, if the two parent waves were of equal amplitudes, would appear circular in outline (Fig. 7-5B); accordingly, this light is said to be circularly polarized.

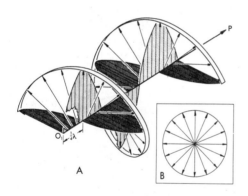

Figure 7-5. (A) Production of circularly polarized light by the interaction of two, mutually perpendicular, plane-polarized waves, of equal amplitude, whose path difference is $\frac{1}{4}\lambda$; O_I represents their point of emergence from a crystal. These wave motions can be regarded to interact to produce spirally distributed vibrations, only a few of which are shown. A ribbon tangent to these arrow tips has been added to emphasize the spiral nature of the surface joining all these resultant vibrations. A perpendicular dropped from any point on this ribbon to O_IP indicates a vibration direction. (B) Outline of the spiral surface joining these vibration directions as seen looking down O_IP.

Elliptical Polarization

From crystals that produce path differences of other than 0, $\frac{1}{4}\lambda$, $\frac{1}{2}\lambda$, $\frac{3}{4}\lambda$, 1λ, ..., $\frac{n+1}{4}\lambda$, the emergent resultant wave motion spirals upward as for circular polarization. Now, however, the vibration vectors no longer maintain a constancy of length. Thus, if viewed as for Figure 7-5B, the spiral surface connecting these vibration vectors is elliptical rather than circular in outline; hence the light is said to be elliptically polarized. Elliptical polarization is the most frequent and general case, circular and plane polarization often being regarded as special cases.

TRANSMISSION BY THE ANALYZER

After its successive passage through (1) the polarizer, (2) a crystal, and (3) the analyzer, the percentage of a monochromatic beam transmitted by the analyzer depends upon (a) ϕ, the angle between the privileged directions of the polarizer and the analyzer; (b) τ, the angle between the polarizer's privileged direction and the crystal's closest privileged direction; (c) Δ, the path difference produced between the slow and fast waves during their transmission through the crystal; and (d) the wavelength (λ) of the light.

---

[3] Known in mathematics as a Riemann surface.

Following Johannsen (1918), the general relationship is

$$L = 100\left[\cos^2\phi - \sin 2(\tau - \phi)\cdot\sin 2\tau\cdot\sin^2\left(\frac{\Delta}{\lambda}\right)180°\right]$$ (Eqn. 7-6)

where L represents the percentage of transmission by the analyzer—that is, the ratio (converted to percent) of the intensity of the light immediately before and immediately after transmission by the analyzer. Equation 7-6 assumes there is no loss of light through reflection or absorption during passage through the crystal or lens system of the microscope.

For the important case in which a crystal is viewed at 45° off extinction between crossed polarizers (that is, τ equals 45° and ϕ equals 90°), Equation 7-6 reduces to

$$L = 100\sin^2\frac{\Delta}{\lambda}180°$$ (Eqn. 7-7)

If the crystal is viewed in this same position between parallel polarizers (that is, τ equals 45° and ϕ equals 0°), Equation 7-6 becomes

$$L = 100\cos^2\frac{\Delta}{\lambda}180°$$ (Eqn. 7-8)

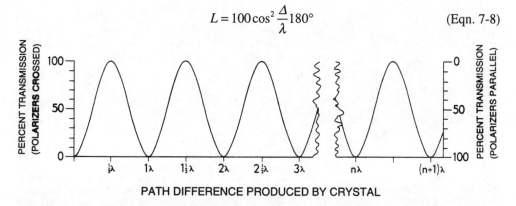

PATH DIFFERENCE PRODUCED BY CRYSTAL

Figure 7-6. Transmission of light by the analyzer according to the phase difference produced in this light by prior passage through a crystal (at 45° off extinction). Use left-hand scale if polarizers are crossed; right-hand scale if they are parallel. The 100 percent value signifies that all the light incident on the crystal from the polarizer also passes through the analyzer (all losses due to reflection and absorption being neglected).

Figure 7-6, based on Equations 7-7 and 7-8, graphically illustrates how L, the percent transmission by the analyzer, varies for a crystal at 45° off extinction according to this crystal's path difference (or phase difference). The left-hand scale cites percentages if the polarizers are crossed; the right-hand scale, those for parallel polarizers.

INTERFERENCE COLORS

Origin

If illuminated with white light, plates of anisotropic crystals viewed (off extinction) between crossed or parallel polarizers will appear colored. These colors, known as interference colors, result from the unequal transmission by the analyzer of the component wavelengths of the white light. The particular wavelengths that the analyzer transmits (or absorbs) depend upon the amount of retardation produced in the light by its prior passage through the crystal. Particular values of retardation produce particular interference colors. For example, suppose that a crystal whose retardation is 550 nm is viewed at 45° off extinction while illuminated by white light. With respect to the 400.0, 440.0, 488.9, 550.0, 628.6, and 733.3-nm wavelength components of this white light, to cite just a few, this 550-nm retardation value respectively represents a path difference of $1\frac{3}{8}\lambda$ (that is, 550/400), $1\frac{1}{4}\lambda$ (that is, 550/440), $1\frac{1}{8}\lambda$ (that is, 550/488.9), 1λ (that is, 550/550), $\frac{7}{8}\lambda$ (that is, 550/628.6), and $\frac{3}{4}\lambda$ (that is, 550/733.3). The percentage of each of these wavelengths which is transmitted by the analyzer for either crossed or parallel polarizers may therefore be quickly determined from Figure 7-6. A plot of the values thus obtained (curve *A* in Fig. 7-7) indicates that only a little of the green and yellow wavelength is transmitted by the analyzer if this crystal is viewed between crossed polarizers, and consequently it appears reddish violet in color; viewed between parallel polarizers, the same crystal (now refer curve *A* to the right-hand scale in Fig. 7-7) would more abundantly transmit green light and thus appear green. The transmission curve for the analyzer may be similarly determined for a crystal of 800-nm retardation (curve *B* in Fig. 7-7) viewed between crossed or parallel polarizers.

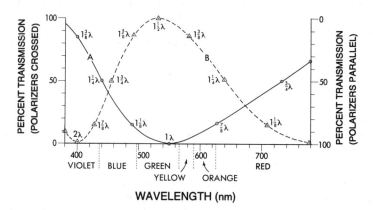

Figure 7-7. Percent transmission by the analyzer of the different wavelengths in a beam of white light that has first passed through a crystal of retardation 550 nm (curve *A*) or of retardation 800 nm (curve *B*), both crystals being at 45° off extinction. For a crystal viewed between crossed polarizers, read the left-hand scale; for parallel polarizers, read the right-hand scale. In case *A*, therefore, the crystal appears reddish violet between crossed polarizers but green between parallel polarizers. In case *B* this is reversed. The path differences developed for a few specific wavelengths of light (by their passage through each crystal) are shown at several points on both curves. For example, light of wavelength 400 nm in the incident white light develops a path difference of 2λ during passage through the crystal associated with curve *B* but a path difference of $1\frac{1}{8}\lambda$ during passage through the crystal associated with curve *A*.

Classification and Nomenclature

The relationships between particular retardation values and the interference colors characteristic of them for crossed polarizers are summarized in Figure 8-13, where a vertical bar of the color appears above the retardation value that produces it. In the figure these interference colors are divided into orders according to whether they result from retardations of 0 to 550 nm (first-order colors), 550 to 1100 nm (second-order colors), 1100 to 1650 nm (third-order colors), and so on. A red interference color, for example, if it results from a retardation of 1650 nm is called third-order red, written more succinctly as 3° red.[4] A red caused by a retardation of 550 nm would thus be written 1° red (and

---

[4] Henceforth, the symbols 1°, 2°, 3°, 4°, ..., will represent the terms "first order," "second order," "third order," "fourth order," .... This convention is particularly convenient in illustrations where space is limited. Confusion with the universal use of the degree symbol for temperature or angular measurement is unlikely.

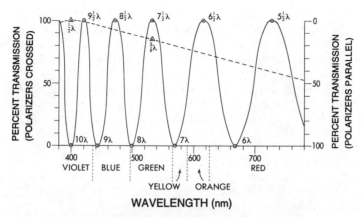

Figure 7-8. Transmission by the analyzer of the different wavelengths in a beam of white light that has first passed through a crystal (at 45° off extinction) of retardation 200 nm (dashed line) or of retardation 4000 nm (solid line). In both cases, the light thus transmitted (for crossed polarizers) is interpreted by the eye as white. The dashed transmission curve represents the first-order white of Figure 8-13; the sinuous curve, a "high-order white." The path differences developed for a few specific wavelengths of light (by their passage through each crystal) are shown at several points on both curves. Note that, if the analyzer's vibration direction were rotated into parallel position with the polarizer, the high-order white would remain white whereas the first-order white observed would give way to a reddish color.

called first-order red). The interference color corresponding to 560 nm, which begins the second order, is readily discriminated by the human eye from the interference colors associable with retardations slightly more or less than 560 nm. Consequently this color is called the *sensitive tint, sensitive violet,* or "tint of passage." The alternating pink and green interference colors associated with retardations increasingly greater than 2300 nm become milkier and milkier until, for very high retardations regardless of their value, the interference color is always white. This white is called a *high-order white* to distinguish it from *first-order white,* which is associated with a retardation of about 200 nm. The analyzer's transmission curve when first-order white is being viewed (dashed in Fig. 7-8) differs strikingly from that obtained when a typical high-order white is being viewed (solid line). Although, superficially, both colors look alike between crossed polarizers, with experience they can be distinguished at a glance since high-order white appears more creamy, whereas first-order white appears more bluish. They are further distinguishable through insertion of an accessory, because it will produce a pronounced change in color for first-order white but not for a high-order white.

Effect of Rotation

Observed during rotation of the stage, the interference color of an anisotropic plate changes in intensity but not in hue. To understand this, consider first those wavelengths of the white light passing through the crystal whose slow waves undergo retardations equivalent to path differences of $1\lambda, 2\lambda, 3\lambda, \ldots,$ or $n\lambda$. Upon emergence from the crystal at 45° off extinction, these wavelengths form resultant wave motions that are plane polarized parallel to the incident light (Fig. 7-4A illustrates this in detail). In Figure 7-9A this is shown less elaborately for a cylinder cut from the crystal of Figure 7-4A, the sinusoidal outlines of the wave motions having been omitted. As for Figure 7-4A, *OP* represents the vibration direction and amplitude of the light from the polarizer; *On* and *ON,* the vibration directions and amplitude of the two light waves into which the incident light is resolved immediately upon entry into the crystal. To indicate in Figure 7-9A that a path difference of $1\lambda, 2\lambda, 3\lambda, \ldots,$ or $n\lambda$ exists between the two waves emerging at O_1, vibrations O_1n_1 and O_1N_1 are drawn to point in the same direction as *On* and *ON*. Study of

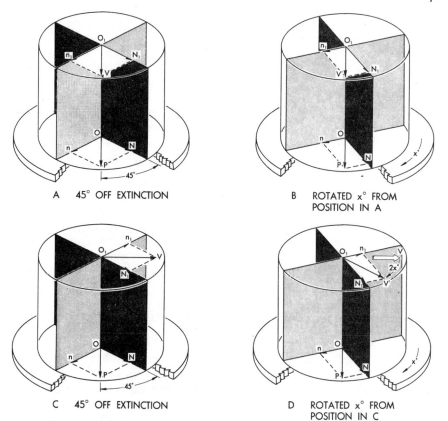

A   45° OFF EXTINCTION

B   ROTATED x° FROM
      POSITION IN A

C   45° OFF EXTINCTION

D   ROTATED x° FROM
      POSITION IN C

Figure 7-9. Effect of rotation on an interference color. (A) Crystal at 45° off extinction with the light undergoing a path difference of 1λ, 2λ, ... or $n\lambda$ during passage through crystal cylinder. The resultant wave motion emerging from the cylinder vibrates parallel to O_1V, whose direction coincides with OP, the polarizer's privileged direction. (B) Crystal rotated x degrees clockwise from position in (A). Despite this rotation, the resultant of On_1 and ON_1—namely O_1V'—continues to coincide with OP, the polarizer's privileged direction. (C) Crystal at 45° off extinction; light undergoing a path difference of $\frac{1}{2}\lambda$, $\frac{3}{2}\lambda$ or $\frac{2n+1}{2}\lambda$ during passage through crystal cylinder. The resultant wave motion emerging from the cylinder vibrates parallel to O_1V which is now at 90° to OP, the polarizer's privileged direction. (D) Crystal rotated x degrees clockwise from its position in (C). The resultant for the wave motion leaving the crystal—that is, O_1V'—now vibrates at $2x°$ relative to the direction O_1V (hollow arrow).

Figure 7-4A illustrates the logic behind this convention. The resultant of O_1n_1 and O_1N_1 is O_1V. Thus the resultant of the light emerging from the crystal vibrates parallel to the incident light. Rotation of the stage through an angle x degrees clockwise (Fig. 7-9B) changes the directions and lengths of On_1 and ON_1, but not of their resultant, O_1V'. Thus, regardless of position of the stage, the resultant light would be completely extinguished by the analyzer (crossed polarizers assumed).

Consider next the wavelengths of the white light whose slow waves undergo retardations equivalent to path differences of $\frac{1}{2}\lambda$, $\frac{3}{2}\lambda$, ..., $\frac{2n+1}{2}\lambda$. Upon emergence from the crystal at 45° off extinction, these wavelengths form resultant wave motions that vibrate at 90° to the vibration direction of the incident light (see Fig. 7-4B). Figure 7-9C, a cylinder cut from the crystal of Figure 7-4B, shows this more simply. To indicate a path difference of $\frac{1}{2}\lambda$, $\frac{3}{2}\lambda$, ..., $\frac{2n+1}{2}\lambda$, On_1 is drawn with its direction reversed from On. Study of Figure 7-4B discloses the logic behind this. Because of this reversal, the resultant of

O_1n_1 and O_1N_1 (that is, O_1V) makes a 90 degree angle to OP. Thus, for the crystal at 45° off an extinction position, the light emergent from the crystal vibrates at 90° to what it did prior to entry. This resultant light would therefore be completely transmitted by the analyzer (crossed polarizers assumed). As the crystal is rotated x degrees clockwise from its position in Figure 7-9C—that is, x degrees from its position at 45° off extinction—the resultant vector O_1V' (see Fig. 7-9D) rotates through an angle of $2x$ degrees from its former direction (O_1V). Since O_1V' *is* no longer parallel to the analyzer's privileged direction (for crossed polarizers), the resultant light is no longer completely transmitted by the analyzer. As the crystal is rotated toward an extinction position, the resultant O_1V' becomes increasingly parallel to OP so that less and less is transmitted by the analyzer.

Thus wavelengths of light that undergo a path difference of 1λ, 2λ, ..., $n\lambda$ "suffer" total extinction at the analyzer regardless of the position of the stage, whereas wavelengths which undergo phase differences of $\frac{1}{2}\lambda$, $\frac{3}{2}\lambda$, ..., $\frac{2n+1}{2}\lambda$ are completely transmitted at 45° off extinction. However, less and less of the latter wavelengths are transmitted by the analyzer as the crystal is turned toward an extinction position. Consequently, if an anisotropic crystal plate is observed between crossed polarizers during a 360-degree rotation of the stage, there will be four positions (representing 45° off extinction) for which the interference color will appear brightest. Similarly there will be four "extinction positions" (at which the plate's privileged directions will be parallel to those of the polarizer and analyzer) for which the interference color will be at zero intensity. The existence of interference colors and the attendant extinction positions as a grain is rotated is a criterion for anisotropy in crystals.

Figure 7-10. Comparison of the ray paths for orthoscopic illumination (A) and conoscopic illumination (B). For the actual situation the rays shown in (A) would be slightly convergent. They become increasingly parallel, however, as the apertures are decreased (for example, by closing down the iris diaphragm or inserting a lower power lens).

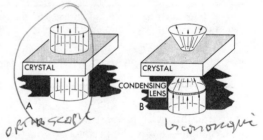

ORTHOSCOPIC AND CONOSCOPIC OBSERVATION
OF INTERFERENCE EFFECTS

In optical mineralogy the interference phenomena produced by the action of anisotropic crystals on light may be observed with the microscope arranged as (1) an orthoscope or (2) a conoscope. The orthoscopic arrangement may be regarded as a normal microscope arrangement in which are inserted the polarizer (below the stage) and the analyzer (above the stage), their privileged directions being mutually perpendicular. The conoscopic arrangement requires, in addition to these, insertion of a Bertrand lens and a substage condensing lens. The latter causes the object on the stage to be illuminated by a cone of light (Fig. 7-10B) rather than by a bundle of near-parallel rays as it is with the orthoscope (Fig. 7-10A). For the orthoscope, therefore, the crystal is illuminated by a series of essentially parallel, normally incident rays all of which travel along the same crystallographic direction within the crystal. For the conoscope, only the central ray within the illuminating cone is normally incident; moreover, the various rays of the cone travel along different crystallographic directions within the crystal. The differences in illumination for the two methods, coupled with the optical effect produced by insertion of the Bertrand lens (or, alternatively, by removal of the ocular) in the conoscopic arrangement, result in entirely different interference phenomena being observed by the two methods.[5] Table 7-1 indicates the microscope set-ups suggested for the two methods.

Table 7-1. Suggested microscope arrangements.

		Orthoscope	*Conoscope*
Bertrand lens		Not inserted	Inserted.* If equipped with iris diaphragm, its aperture may be reduced to sharpen figure (especially for small crystals)
Analyzer		Inserted (Privileged direction at right angle to that of polarizer)	
Objectives		Low, medium, or high according to magnification desired	High-power objective only (N. A. 0.85 preferred)
Substage assembly	Condensing lens	Swing-out lens not inserted	Swing-out lens inserted (or alternative device used to make cone of light illuminating stage more convergent)
	Iris diaphragm	Reduced as needed to sharpen detail	Open; later reduce to sharpen detail
	Polarizer	Inserted	

* *N.B.* If the microscope lacks a Bertrand lens, the conoscopic optical arrangement can still be obtained by substituting a pin-hole eyepiece for the ocular.

ORTHOSCOPIC EXAMINATION OF CRYSTALS

In earlier discussions it was tacitly assumed that the microscope was being used as an orthoscope. In summary, a crystal under orthoscopic examination, if illuminated by white light, will possess an interference color whose hue is dependent upon its retardation—that is, the product of t, its thickness, and $(N - n)$, the difference between the indices for its privileged directions. Along any thinner edges of the grain (Fig. 7-11) the retardation will be less and interference colors will be lower than those at its thick central part. All points of equal thickness on the grain will be marked by the same interference color, the lines connecting these points of identical interference colors being called **isochromes**—that is, lines of equal color (and retardation). When the privileged directions of the grain (ON and On) are at 45° to those of the polarizers, these interference colors are at maximum brightness. As the crystal is rotated toward an extinction position, the intensities of these colors decrease toward zero until, at the extinction position, the crystal becomes black.

CONOSCOPIC EXAMINATION (INTERFERENCE FIGURES)

Viewed with the microscope set up as a conoscope, the images of anisotropic crystals, as seen with the orthoscope, are supplanted by highly informative patterns of interference colors called **interference figures**. These are formed by rays that traveled along different directions while within the crystal being viewed. Accurate observation of interference figures yields a considerable amount of optic data within a minimum of time.

---

[5] The different ray paths involved in the orthoscopic and conoscopic arrangements are discussed in detail by Rinne and Berek (1953, pp. 38-40).

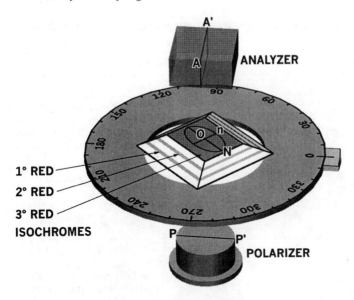

1° RED
2° RED
3° RED
ISOCHROMES

Figure 7-11. Crystal at 45° off extinction on rotatable stage. Its privileged directions, *ON* and *On,* become parallel to either *AA'* or *PP'* four times during a complete rotation of stage. At these times the crystal is at extinction.

For uniaxial crystals, the interference figure consists of two intersecting black bars—or, as they are called, **isogyres**—that form a cross (Fig. 7-12) resembling the Formée cross of heraldry. This cross is concentric with a series of circles that, if monochromatic light is being used to illuminate the crystal, represent alternations of darkness and brightness for this light. If white light is the illuminant, they represent circular distributions of the interference colors in Figure 8-13, the inner circles being marked by increasingly lower order colors. Since each such circle connects points of identical interference colors, the circles are usually called isochromatic curves or, more briefly, **isochromes**. The common center of both the black cross and isochromes is a black spot (**melatope**), which marks in the field of view the outcrop of light rays that traveled along the optic axis while in the crystal.

Origin of the Isochromes;
Cones of Equal Retardation

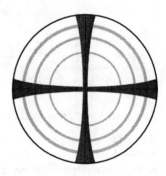

Figure 7-12. Interference figure of a uniaxial crystal oriented so that its optic axis is perpendicular to the plane of the microscope stage. The common center of the isogyre cross (shaded dark) and the isochrome circles (stippled) represents the point of emergence of rays that, when in the crystal, traveled along the optic axis. See the back cover of this book for a color illustration.

Figure 7-13A shows five wave normals—all within a roughly NW-SE principal plane of a uniaxial (+) crystal—whose angles to the optic axis range from 0° (WN₁) to 90° (WN₅). Light traveling along each wave normal necessarily vibrates within the wave front perpendicular to this wave normal. Except for WN_1, each such wave front intersects the indicatrix in an ellipse (minor axis ω and a major axis which is ε'_2 for WN_2, ε'_3 for WN_3, ε'_4 for WN_4, and ε for WN_5). The crystal constrains light traveling along these wave normals to vibrate along the minor and/or major axes of these ellipses of intersection. Wave normal WN_1 is special because it coincides with the optic axis and thus its corresponding wave front intersects the indicatrix in the circular section

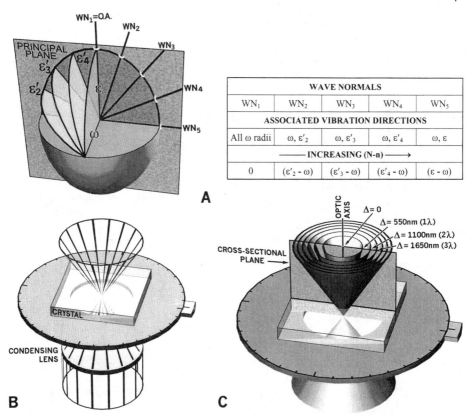

WAVE NORMALS				
WN_1	WN_2	WN_3	WN_4	WN_5
ASSOCIATED VIBRATION DIRECTIONS				
All ω radii	ω, ε'_2	ω, ε'_3	ω, ε'_4	ω, ε
—— INCREASING (N-n) ——→				
0	$(\varepsilon'_2 - \omega)$	$(\varepsilon'_3 - \omega)$	$(\varepsilon'_4 - \omega)$	$(\varepsilon - \omega)$

Figure 7-13. (A) Within the principal plane shaded a mottled gray—one of many that can be passed through the optic axis of the (+) crystal here used as an example—WN_1, WN_2 ... WN_5 represent wave normals whose angles v (nu) to the optic axis range from 0° (for WN_1) up to 90° (for WN_5). As v increases from 0° to 90°, the differences between the refractive indices for the slow and fast waves traveling along these wave normals, as summarized in the table, increases from 0 for WN_1, to $(\varepsilon'_2 - \omega)$ for WN_2, to $(\varepsilon'_3 - \omega)$ for WN_3, and to $(\varepsilon - \omega)$ for WN_5. (B) View of the crystal, oriented with its optic axis perpendicular to the stage, as a cone of light passes through it. (C) This cone may itself be considered to consist of innumerable cones, each such cone containing all the wave normals that are at the same angle (v) to the optic axis. As a result these cones represent cones of equal retardation (Δ). For example, the cones representing retardations of 550, 1100, and 1650 nm. The cone representing a retardation of 0 nm degenerates to a line that coincides with the optic axis.

(radius ω). Consequently, only one wave front—for which the crystal exhibits the refractive index ω—will travel along WN_1. By contrast, *two* wave fronts—for this (+) crystal in which $\varepsilon > \omega$—a fast one (index ω) and a slow one (index ε'_2 for WN_2, ε'_3 for WN_3 ... ε'_4 for WN_4) may simultaneously travel along WN_2 ... WN_5. The retardation Δ of the slow behind the fast wave increases from WN_2 to WN_5 because, as summarized in Figure 7-13A, (N-n) steadily increases in value as the wave normal's angle to the optic axis increases.

Conoscopic illumination causes an entire cone of wave normals to pass through a crystal. If the crystal's optic axis lies perpendicular to the stage (Fig. 7-13B), the retardation (Δ) of the slow behind the fast wave traveling along each wave normal will increase steadily as the angle between the optic axis and wave normal increases. Consequently, there exist, centered about the optic axis, cones of equal retardation, for example, those corresponding to Δ values of 550, 1100, 1650 ... 2750 nm in Figure 7-13C. The crystal's interference figure observed with white light, if we assume only the

550, 1100, and 1650 cones of wave normals enter the objective, would show circular (1°, 2° and 3° red) isochromes (Fig. 7-14).

As a rule of thumb, if the radius of the 1° red isochrome equals r, that of the 2° red equals $\sqrt{2}\ r$, that of 3° red equals $\sqrt{3}\ r$, and that of nth order red equals $\sqrt{n}\ r$.

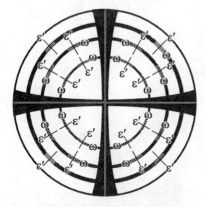

Figure 7-14. Vibration directions of the E and O rays emerging in the field of view of a uniaxial interference figure. Note that all ω vibrations are tangent (whereas all ε' vibrations are perpendicular) to the circular isochromes. And that all ε' vibrations point toward the melatope.

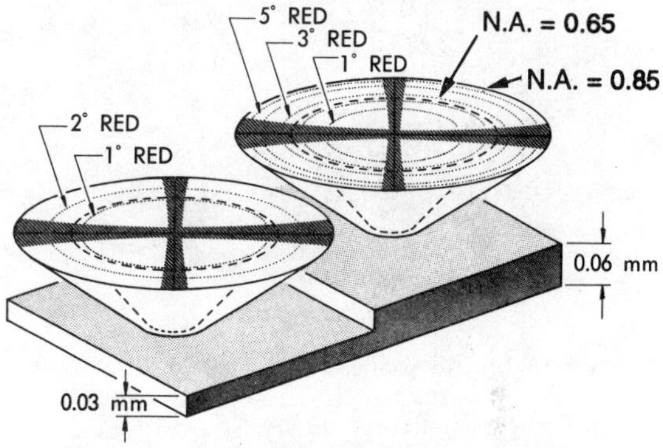

Figure 7-15. Comparison of the number of isochromes seen in the field of view for two different thicknesses of calcite. If an objective of N.A. 0.65 is substituted for the objective of N.A. 0.85, only the portion of the interference figure within the dashed circles will be seen.

Every point in Figure 7-14 marks where a wave normal has emerged and where its slow wave front has interfered with its fast one to produce the color seen there. And any line joining this point to the melatope marks the principal plane that contains this wave normal. As Figure 7-13A may clarify, *ω always vibrates perpendicular and ε′ parallel to this line*. Also, as a consequence, *ω always vibrates tangent to and ε′ along the radius of any circular isochrome present*.

The interference figures for crystals of high birefringence ($\varepsilon - \omega$) possess more isochromes than do those for crystals of low birefringence. This also holds true for a thick section as compared to a thinner section of the same mineral (Fig. 7-15). The higher the numerical aperture of the objective used, the wider the angle of the cone of light from the crystal that enters the objective. The cones drawn above the crystal in Figure 7-15 are those that would enter an objective of N.A. 0.85. If an objective of N.A. 0.65 is used, only the dashed cone of light enters the objective; consequently, only that portion of the interference figure within the dashed circles would be observed. From this standpoint, objectives of N.A. 0.85 are preferable.

Origin of the Isogyres

As discussed earlier: (1) Any plane containing the optic axis of a uniaxial crystal constitutes a principal plane; and (2) all light traveling within a principal plane must vibrate within or perpendicular to this principal plane. Thus, for a crystal with its optic axis oriented perpendicular to the microscope stage (Fig. 7-16A), the light cone passing through it during conoscopic observation consists of innumerable principal planes, all hinged on the optic axis. To emphasize that light must vibrate within or perpendicular to these principal planes, the light's vibration directions are drawn (Fig. 7-16B) along the

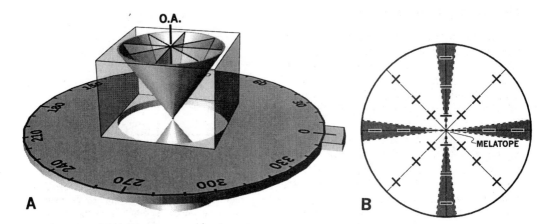

Figure 7-16. (A) A uniaxial crystal oriented with its optic axis perpendicular to the microscope stage will have innumerable principal planes, all hinged on the optic axis, that also lie perpendicular to the stage. The cone of light passing through the crystal under conoscopic observation thus consists of light traveling along each of these innumerable principal planes, a few of which are drawn. (B) Each diameter within the crystal's interference figure contains emerging rays that traveled along the same principal plane and thus must vibrate either along or perpendicular to this diameter. Along the N-S and E-W principal planes that emerge along the ocular's cross hairs, only E-W vibrating rays emerge (assuming an E-W polarizing microscope). Consequently, these rays are entirely extinguished by the analyzer as are, essentially, rays that traveled along principal planes represented by diameters located in the shaded areas. Thus, areas of extinction known as *isogyres*, extend outward from the melatope (like thin wedges of pie).

Rotation of the plane of polarization of the light, caused by reflectance at lens' surfaces, imparts a slight curvature (not shown) to the edges of these wedges. The principal planes at 45° to the cross hairs contain rays vibrating at "45° off extinction" and are thus the sites of the brightest interference colors.

diameters marking where principal planes emerge in the interference figure. All rays emerging along the N-S and E-W diameters—that is, along the cross hairs—will be at extinction between crossed polarizers. Thus, assuming an E-W polarizing microscope, the only rays traveling in these N-S and E-W principal planes will be vibrating E-W and thus be extinguished by the N-S analyzer. This is almost true for rays traveling along principal planes that are *almost* N-S or E-W (and thus crop out between the dashed lines in Fig. 7-16B). Consequently, extending outward from the melatope where the optic axis emerges, are four black wedge-shaped areas, the isogyres. The edges of the wedges are not straight—as drawn in Figure 7-16B—but slightly curved. Such curvature results because reflection at lens surfaces slightly rotates the light's plane of polarization.

Light that traveled along the NE-SW or NW-SE planes in Figure 7-16B is at "45° off extinction." Thus, where such light emerges in the field of view, the interference colors are brightest. However, the brightness slowly decreases for light emerging along principal planes that increasingly approach N-S or E-W in direction.

TYPES OF UNIAXIAL INTERFERENCE FIGURES

The appearance of a uniaxial interference figure depends upon whether the grain rests with its optic-axis direction (1) perpendicular, (2) at an oblique angle, or (3) parallel to the plane of the stage. The types of figures resultant from such orientations are respectively called (1) centered optic-axis figures, (2) off-centered optic-axis figures, and (3) the uniaxial flash figure. Their appearance and means of recognition will be discussed next.

Centered Optic-axis Figures

Centered optic-axis figures have been used previously. Figure 7-14, for example, was a typical, centered optic-axis figure. The unique feature of a centered optic-axis figure is the location of the melatope (which marks the outcrop of the optic axis) at the cross-hair intersection. A necessary corollary is that the N-S and E-W bars of the uniaxial cross will be longitudinally bisected by the N-S and E-W cross hairs respectively. Rotation of the microscope stage will produce no observable change in the appearance of a precisely centered optic-axis figure. Thus, no matter how the stage holding the crystal in Figure 7-17 is rotated, one of the innumerable principal planes that radiate outward from the optic axis (only a few of which are shown) will always intersect the

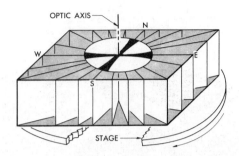

Figure 7-17. Constancy of position of the isogyres (during rotation of the stage) in the interference figure of a crystal whose optic axis is normal to the microscope stage. A few of the innumerable principal planes hinging on the optic axis are shown. Whenever any principal plane, oriented perpendicular to the microscope stage, becomes E-W (or N-S), its emergence in the field of view is marked by an E-W (or N-S) isogyre that is longitudinally bisected by a cross-hair.

field of view along each cross hair and be the site of an isogyre. Regardless of rotation of the stage, therefore, the isogyres will remain in the positions shown in Figure 7-17.

Off-centered Optic-axis Figures

These figures are produced if the optic axis deviates from perpendicularity to the stage by the angle v (Fig. 7-18A). The melatope, consequently, no longer coincides with the cross-hair intersection. Moreover, during a rotation of the stage, the melatope is observed to rotate in the same direction (Figs. 7-18B,C). The isogyres, meanwhile, retain (as always) an approximate parallelism to the cross hairs, their mutual intersection coinciding at all times with the melatope. The isochromes again appear as circles centered on the melatope. The isogyres and isochromes have the same origin as in centered optic-axis figures. The isogyres mark the traces within the field of view of principal planes that are parallel or nearly parallel to the polarizer's privileged directions. Thus (as previously discussed Fig. 7-16) these traces are sites of complete extinction.

Note that if v' represents the angle between the perpendicular to the stage and the path in air of light that in the crystal had traveled along the optic axis (Fig. 7-18A), then from Snell's law

$$\omega \sin v = \sin v'$$

Often, however, the optic axis is so tilted that it falls outside the cone of light that enters the objective from the crystal. For this case, the melatope falls outside the field of view of the interference figure (Fig. 7-19 I). Even if no isochromes are present, the quadrant of the field of view that would contain the melatope, if the field were sufficiently enlarged, can readily be determined. To do so, rotate the crystal counterclockwise and observe the interference figure. An isogyre now enters the field of view as in Figure 7-19 II. With continued counterclockwise rotation of the crystal, the interference figure successively takes on the appearance of Figure 7-19 III, IV, and V. Of the isogyre segments in the field of view, label the end nearest the melatope (*i.e.*, the narrowest end) with the letter H and the end farthest from the melatope with the letter A. During the counterclockwise rotation of the crystal, note how H, one of the isogyre's

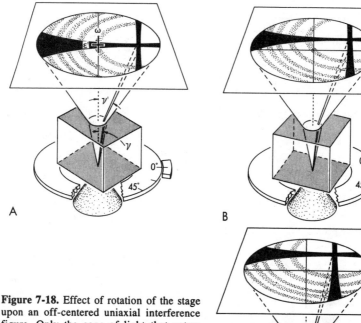

Figure 7-18. Effect of rotation of the stage upon an off-centered uniaxial interference figure. Only the cone of light that enters the objective lens is shown. The dotted line is a perpendicular to the crystal surface. (A) Crystal in an extinction position. Light traveling along the optic axis is at an angle v to the dotted perpendicular while in the crystal and at an angle v' to this perpendicular after emergence. (B) Crystal after a 22.5° rotation counterclockwise. (C) Crystal rotated to the position 45° off extinction.

intersections with the edge of the field of view, also moves counterclockwise (from H_{II} to H_{III} to H_{IV} in Fig. 7-19 IV) whereas the isogyre's opposite end moves clockwise (from A_{II} to A_{III} to A_{IV}). The H end, since it always moves in the same direction as the direction of turn of the crystal, is called the **homodrome end** (Gr., same course or path) of the isogyre; the A end, since it moves opposite to the crystal rotation, is called the **antidrome end** (Gr., opposite path).

A melatope, outside the field of view, is always located in that quadrant which contains the homodrome end of any visible portion of an isogyre. If segments of circular isochromes are present in the field, the melatope will be located in the quadrant containing the center for these circles.

Flash Figures

A flash figure is the interference figure produced from a crystal whose optic axis is parallel (or nearly parallel) to the plane of the microscope stage (Fig. 7-20A). The rays entering the crystal from the illuminating cone travel within an infinite number of principal planes that fan outward from the optic axis; only a few of these planes are shown in the figure. These planes emerge within the plane of the interference figure as a series of parallel traces (dashed lines in Fig. 7-20B). The O rays vibrate perpendicular and the E rays essentially parallel to these traces. The vibration directions for all rays emerging in the field of view are therefore essentially parallel to each other.

Figure 7-19. (I) Crystal that produces an off-centered optic axis figure for which the melatope falls outside the field of view. (II), (III), and (IV) Motion of the E-W isogyre as the crystal is rotated counterclockwise. The opposite ends of this E-W isogyre—that is, H and A—move respectively from H_{II} to H_{IV} and from A_{II} to A_{IV} with rotation. Since H_{II} to H_{IV} involves a motion in the same direction as the crystal was rotated (counterclockwise in this example), the H end is called the homodrome end. The end labeled A is called the antidrome end of the isogyre since the motion of A_{II} to A_{IV} is opposite to the rotation direction of the crystal. *An isogyre's homodrome end always points toward the melatope.* (V) Continued rotation of the stage has caused the melatope to move from position IV to V. Now the N-S isogyre enters the field and its homodrome end (H) again points toward the melatope.

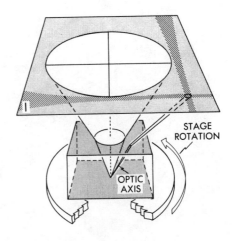

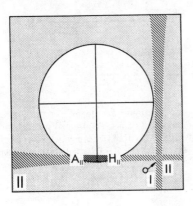

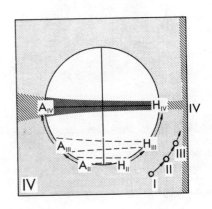

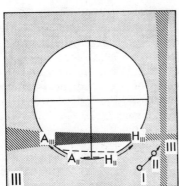

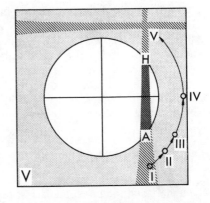

Consequently, if the crystal is rotated until its optic axis is parallel to (or perpendicular to) the polarizer's privileged direction, the field of view is almost completely filled with a diffuse, black cross (Fig. 7-20C). Only at the extreme NE, SE, SW, and NW edges of the field of view is nonextinction observed, an indication that the vibrations for rays emerging within these regions were not parallel to the vibrations of the majority of rays in the field. According to **Lommel's Rule**, upon turning the crystal only a degree or so, the diffuse cross is rapidly resolved into hyperbolic isogyres that leave the field of view within the quadrants containing the optic axis after this rotation (Fig. 7-20D).

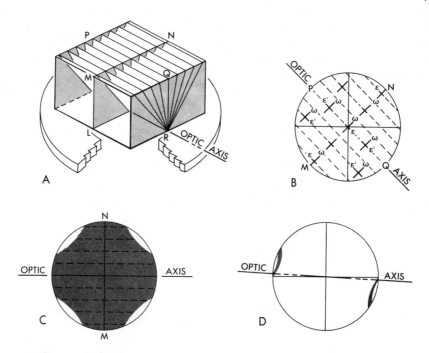

Figure 7-20. Origin of the uniaxial flash figure. (A) Crystal with optic axis ideally oriented to yield a uniaxial flash figure. The planes hinging at the optic axis are principal planes. (B) Mutual parallelism of the traces of these principal planes and, because light invariably vibrates within or perpendicular to a principal plane, of the light vibrations. The optic axis remains at 45° off extinction. (C) Upon rotation of the stage to an extinction position, a diffuse black cross fills the field of view. (D) **Lommel's Rule:** Upon slight rotation off extinction, the cross resolves into hyperbola-shaped isogyres that exit via the quadrants into which the optic axis is being rotated.

The distribution of the isochromes in a uniaxial flash figure at 45° off extinction is shown for a crystal of relatively high retardation (Fig. 7-21A) and for one of low retardation (Fig. 7-21B). The high retardation of the first crystal may be due to its being excessively thick or its having a very high birefringence ($\varepsilon - \omega$). Going outward from the cross-hair intersection in a flash figure at 45° off extinction, the interference colors become increasingly higher in order toward the edges of two quadrants—for example, toward M and N in Figure 7-21B—but lower in order toward the edges of the quadrants in which the optic axis lies—that is, toward P and Q in Figure 7-21B.

To summarize: in uniaxial flash figures at 45° off extinction, retardation always decreases from the center of the field towards the edges of those quadrants containing the optic axis.

To understand the phenomena just described, consider the interference between the E and O rays that emerge from a conoscopically illuminated crystal whose optic axis is parallel to the microscope stage. Within a vertical plane parallel to the optic axis (PQR in Fig. 7-21C), note that the vertical ray a is the result of interference between an O and an E ray that traveled perpendicular to the optic axis. The retardation for this ray is thus $\Delta_a = (\varepsilon - \omega)t$, where t is the crystal thickness. Rays in plane PQR that emerge nearer the edge of the field of view in the interference figure-ray c for example—result from the interference between an E and an O ray that traveled more nearly parallel to the optic axis than did ray a. The retardation between these interfering rays is less than Δ_a because, although they travel a longer distance in the crystal, the difference in their indices, $(\varepsilon_c{}' - \omega)$, is a much smaller value than $(\varepsilon - \omega)$. Thus *PQ*, the trace of plane *PQR* in the interference figure, is the site of interference colors that decrease in order outward from the center. For a plane like *LMN* (Fig. 7-21D), which is perpendicular to the optic axis, all *E* rays traveling within it vibrate parallel to the optic axis and are therefore associated with a refractive index ε. Consequently, the birefringence between all *E*- and *O*-ray pairs

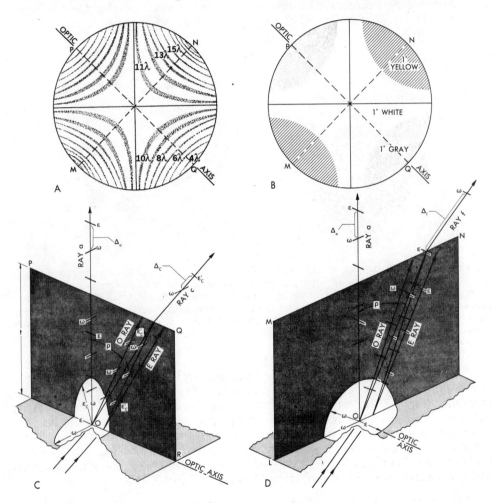

Figure 7-21. In uniaxial flash figures at 45° off extinction, retardation always decreases, outward from the center, toward the edges of those quadrants containing the optic axis. This is illustrated for (A) a crystal of extremely high birefringence illuminated with monochromatic light of wavelength λ and for (B) one of low birefringence illuminated by white light. In (A) the "isochromes" labeled $4\lambda \ldots 15\,\lambda$ are sites of blackness. (Why?)

The reason for the retardation color being lower at *Q* than at *N* is illustrated in (C) and (D), where planes *PQR* and *LMN* represent cross-sections through Figure 7-20A. In both (C) and (D) the refractive index value and vibration direction for each ray is shown by vectors that are either perpendicular to (or lie within) the dark-shaded vertical planes. The intersections of these vertical planes with the crystal's indicatrix are unshaded. In (C), although ray *c* results from a longer path in the crystal than ray *a*, its associated retardation (Δ_c) is less than that for *a* (Δ_a) because its associated birefringence ($\omega - \varepsilon_c'$) is less than for *a* ($\omega - \varepsilon$). In (D), by contrast ray *f* results from a longer path than ray *a*, but is associated with the same birefringence ($\omega - \varepsilon$). Hence $\Delta_f > \Delta_a$

that interfere after their emergence from plane *LMN* of the crystal remains as $(\varepsilon - \omega)$, regardless of their inclination from the vertical. With increased inclination, the path distance of these rays within the crystal, and consequently their retardation, increases. For ray *f* in Figure 7-21D, for example, the retardation is approximately $\Delta_f = (\varepsilon - \omega) \cdot (t/\cos\rho)$, where ρ maybe taken to be the angle of inclination from the vertical of either the *E* or *O* ray that interfere to form ray *f*; the angle between these two rays is usually quite small. Thus Δ_f increasingly exceeds Δ_a in value as the angle ρ increases. Consequently, *MN*, the trace of plane *LMN* in the flash interference figures, is the site of interference colors that increase in order outward from the center.

__Thought question.__ What would Figure 7-14 look like if illuminated by light of $\lambda = 550$ nm instead of white light?

8

OPTICAL EXAMINATION
OF UNIAXIAL CRYSTALS

OVERVIEW

Search the grain-oil mount (crossed polarizers; orthoscopic set-up) for large dark-gray to black grains. These will likely yield interference figures with a melatope in the field of view. For truly uniaxial crystals, the isogyre-cross centered on this melatope will not break up into a hyperbola during rotation of the stage even if observed with a lower power objective (which, so to speak, magnifies the interference figure.) Next, determine the crystal's optic sign by inserting an accessory plate into the microscope's accessory slot. Conventionally, when inserted, the accessory's slow vibration (N_A) will be oriented NE-SW and its fast (n_A) will be NW-SE.

For two accessory plates in common use, the distance their slow wave (index: N_A) lags behind their fast (n_A)—called their retardation, Δ_A—approximately equals 550 nm for the 1° red (or "gypsum") plate and 150 nm for the quarter-wave (or "mica") plate.

For a crystal (retardation: Δ_C) at 45° off extinction, insertion of an accessory plate may increase the observed retardation by **addition**—namely, to $\Delta_C + \Delta_A$—if the crystal's slow vibration N_C lies parallel to the accessory's (N_A, Fig. 8-2A) but decrease it by **subtraction** if N_C for the crystal is at 90° to N_A (Fig. 8-2B). For example, insertion of the 1° red plate (Δ_A = 550 nm) will change a first-order gray crystal (Δ_C = 100 nm) to second-order blue (650 nm) for addition but to yellow-orange (450 nm) for subtraction (because |100-550| = 450 nm). [For subtraction the slow wave in the crystal, behind by 100 nm after passing through the crystal, became the fast wave in the accessory.]

Every point in an interference figure marks the outcrop of a wave normal. And as previously noted (Fig. 7-14), of the two vibrations associable with any given wave normal, the ε' vibration lies along the line joining the melatope to the wave normal's outcrop, whereas ω vibrates perpendicular to this line. As for Figure 7-14, the ω and ε' vibration directions have been drawn at various points in the interference figure for a (+) crystal (Fig. 8-3A) and a (–) one (Fig. 8-3B). Because insertion of an accessory plate affects the entire field of view, those quadrants of the isogyre-cross located SE (and NW) of the melatope undergo subtraction for (+) crystals (Fig. 8-3A) but addition for (–) ones (Fig. 8-3A). Thus, after inserting the 1° red plate, the first-order-gray area SE of the melatope becomes 2° blue for (+) crystals but 1° yellow for (–) ones (Fig. 8-4 and the back cover).

For interference figures where the circular isochromes are numerous, particularly if the melatope lies outside the field of view (Fig. 8-6C,D), slow insertion of a quartz wedge, thin-edge first, will cause the isochromes to move. This is because Δ_A for the wedge increases from 0 to, say, 2200 nm as degree of insertion increases. Invariably, during insertion of the quartz wedge, higher-order isochromes displace lower-order ones for addition (Fig. 8-6C) whereas lower displace higher for subtraction (Fig. 8-6D). Because ε' always vibrates perpendicular to—and ω tangent to—the circular isochromes in a uniaxial interference figure, one can determine whether $\varepsilon' > \omega$ (= crystal +) or $\varepsilon' < \omega$ (= crystal –).

For determining the optic sign from a uniaxial flash figure, see Figure 8-9.

Every uniaxial grain in a powder mount displays the refractive index ω (Fig. 8-7). To orient such grains so as to compare ω to n for the oil, rotate the stage until the N-S cross-hair bisects an isogyre (Fig. 8-8A,B). Assuming an E-W polarizer, switch to orthoscope and remove the analyzer to compare ω to n. Comparing ε to n for the oil is more difficult because only grains whose optic axis lies parallel to the stage, or nearly so (Fig. 8-7D), permit this. The most likely candidates will be the smallest grains displaying the highest order colors. From the flash figures such crystals will exhibit (Fig. 8-9), use Lommel's rule to sort out which vibration is ε, and which is ω. However, if the crystal's optic sign is already known, N for the crystal will be ε, if the crystal is (+) but N for the crystal will be ω if it is (–).

For uniaxial crystals there is dispersion of the indices, ε and ω, and of the birefringence $|\varepsilon - \omega|$. See Figure 8-11.

The angle between a privileged direction, usually N, and an observable linear feature—frequently the trace of a cleavage direction for a crystal in a thin section—is called the crystal's **extinction angle**. In thin sections, uniaxial crystals may exhibit **symmetrical extinction** (Fig. 8-15), **parallel extinction** (Fig. 8-16), or **random extinction** angles.

With the N-S analyzer withdrawn, some crystals exhibit **pleochroism**, that is, they transmit one color if ω is oriented E-W, but another if ε (or ε') is oriented E-W (Fig. 8-18).

Figure 8-13 summarizes the interference colors associated with the various values of the retardation Δ. However, some crystals exhibit abnormal interference colors, which are alien to Figure 8-13, because, imposed upon the normal interference colors may be the effects of pleochroism and/or dispersion of the birefringence $|\varepsilon - \omega|$.

PREPARATION OF THE SAMPLE

The crushed crystals should be sieved to isolate the 100 to 120 mesh fraction for study. Grain thicknesses, as a result, should most frequently fall within the 0.125 to 0.149 mm range. Oil mounts of these crushed grains are prepared as described on p. 61.

ESTABLISHMENT OF UNIAXIALITY

The mineral grains in the oil rest on various fracture surfaces which, unless there is a dominant cleavage, will be at all manner of angles to the optic axis. Those grains for which this surface of rest is most nearly perpendicular to their optic axis will most likely yield an interference figure whose melatope is within the field of view. With the melatope thus visualized, the uniaxial nature of the crystal yielding the interference figure can readily be established since the Formée cross (formed by the isogyre intersection) will remain intact—that is, will not break up into a hyperbola—during rotation of the stage.

The grain most likely to yield such a near-centered optic axis figure can be located by examining the powder mount between crossed polarizers with a low-power objective. Such a grain is characterized by (1) being one of the larger grains, yet (2) possessing a lower interference color at its center or thickest part than the other grains. For such grains, the ε' index will necessarily be close in value to ω. If these values are very close to each other, the grain's center will show a dark gray interference color in all positions of rotation (since $(\varepsilon' - \omega)$ will be minimal). Such a grain most likely rests on a surface nearly parallel to the circular section. Consequently, the melatope of its interference figure will very likely be centered (or nearly centered) in the field of view.

COMPENSATORS AND COMPENSATION

Accessory Plates and Wedges

Three accessories are commonly used in optical mineralogy: (1) the simple quartz wedge (or a variant), (2) a first-order red or "gypsum" plate, and (3) a quarter-wave "mica" plate. Each is designed to slip into the accessory slot of the microscope so as to intercept and transmit all light rays. Like all anisotropic plates, each possesses two, mutually perpendicular, privileged directions. The one corresponding to the larger index N is called the slow direction; the one corresponding to the smaller index n, the fast direction. Generally, only the N privileged direction is indicated on the accessory's metal mount (by an etched line or arrow). Light waves that vibrate parallel to this N direction while passing through the accessory plate travel more slowly than do those that vibrate parallel to the unmarked n direction during their transmission. Consequently, after emergence from the accessory, the slow wave is retarded with respect to the fast wave (see Fig. 7-3).

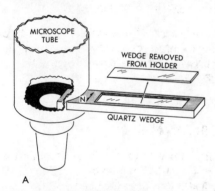

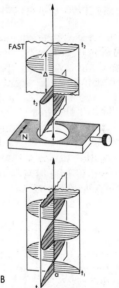

Figure 8-1. (A) Quartz wedge being inserted, thin edge first, into the compensator slot of the microscope. Toward its thick edge the retardation produced by the quartz wedge increases to about 1700 nm for some makes or to about 2800 nm for others. (B) Compensator plate intercepting two perpendicularly polarized light waves. After passage through the plate, the wave that vibrated parallel to the N direction of the plate (double headed arrow) is, at the time t_2, a distance Δ behind the other. If the compensator plate is a first-order red "gypsum" plate, Δ equals approximately 550 nm. If it is a one-quarter wave "mica" plate, Δ equals approximately 150 nm. The double-headed arrow indicating the slow or N direction is sometimes labeled Z or γ by the manufacturers.

A quartz wedge, if gradually inserted, thin end first, into the accessory slot (Fig. 8-1A), produces increasingly higher retardations as its thicker portions successively move into the light path. On the other hand, the first-order red or "gypsum" plate, now also made of quartz, is of constant thickness throughout. Its birefringence $(N - n)$ and thickness are such that it produces a retardation (Δ) of about 550 nm. Consider, for example, two mutually perpendicular waves, precisely in phase at time t_1 in Figure 8-1B. After passing through the plate, they are no longer in phase. At time t_2 the wave that traveled more slowly through the plate lags precisely 550 nm behind the faster wave.

The quarter-wave "mica" plate, once made from a thin cleavage plate of mica, is now a thin plate of quartz of sufficient thickness and birefringence ($N - n$) to produce a retardation (Δ) of about 150 mm (roughly one quarter of the wavelength of sodium light). Thus, if two mutually perpendicular waves are exactly in phase before passage through the plate, the wave that travels more slowly through the "mica" plate is retarded approximately 150 nm behind the fast one after their emergence.

Addition

Suppose that an anisotropic crystal, viewed at 45° off extinction between crossed polarizers, exhibits a first-order gray retardation color ($\Delta = 100$ nm). Insertion of the gypsum plate so that its slow direction (N_A) is parallel to that of the crystal (Fig. 8-2A) changes the observed retardation color to second-order blue ($\Delta = 650$ nm). When insertion of an accessory increases the order of an interference color by an increment comparable to the retardation value of the accessory, the process is called **addition.** The explanation is as follows: After emergence from the crystal, the wave that had vibrated parallel to N_C in the crystal is 100 nm behind that which had vibrated parallel to n_C. Upon entering the gypsum plate, this already retarded wave, since it vibrates parallel to N_A while within the gypsum plate, is retarded an additional 550 nm, finally lagging 650 nm behind the fast ray. If viewed between crossed polarizers, therefore, an interference color

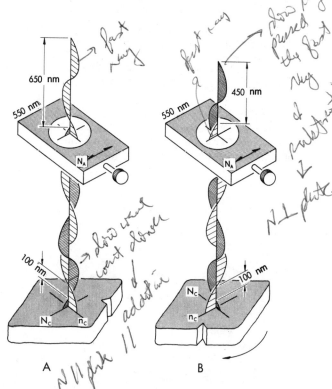

Figure 8-2. Crystal of retardation 100 nm at 45° off extinction in additive position (A) and subtractive position (B) with respect to the first-order-red (550 nm) plate. Note that the finely ruled wave, which traveled slower in the crystal, is further retarded by the gypsum plate in (A). In (B) the wave that traveled faster (coarsely ruled) is retarded by the gypsum plate so that the formerly slow wave has overtaken and passed it by 450 nm.

corresponding to 650 nm (that is, second-order blue) is observed.

Subtraction

Assume the crystal to have been rotated 90° so that its n and N privileged directions have exchanged positions (Fig. 8-2B). The retarded wave that vibrated within the crystal parallel to N_C, the crystal's slow direction, would be, as before, 100 nm behind the fast wave upon emergence from the crystal. Now, however, when it enters the gypsum plate, this formerly slow wave vibrates parallel to the fast direction whereas the formerly fast wave vibrates parallel to the slow direction of the gypsum plate. Consequently, although the coarsely ruled wave (Fig. 8-2B) was 100 nm ahead prior to entering the gypsum plate, the finely ruled wave gained 550 nm to overtake and surpass it while traveling through the gypsum plate. Thus, on emergence from the gypsum plate, the finely ruled wave is ahead by 450 nm (550 nm – 100 nm). The retardation color corresponding to 450 nm—that is, 1° orange—is thus seen. Such a process, produced because the fast wave in the crystal becomes the slow wave in the gypsum plate, is called **subtraction**; the resultant retardation equals the difference between the individual retardation values of the two plates involved.

General Rules

Addition occurs when the N directions of the crystal and of the compensator plate most nearly coincide. Subtraction occurs when the N directions of the crystal and of the compensator are at right angles. Stated conversely, if addition occurs, then N of the crystal and of the compensator must be parallel or nearly parallel. If subtraction occurs, they must be perpendicular to each other or nearly so.

If, after insertion of a 1° red plate or quarter-wave plate or during insertion of a quartz wedge (thin end first)—interference colors of higher order are observed to displace those of lower order, addition has occurred. If lower order colors displace those of higher order, subtraction has occurred.

Where numerous isochromes are seen on the grain or in the interference figure, the quartz wedge is best used to determine addition or subtraction. If only first-order colors occur, the gypsum plate will serve best.

DETERMINATION OF OPTIC SIGN

Principles Involved

The orthographically projected vibration directions of the E and O rays emerging at common points in the field of view are drawn in Figure 8-3 for both a uniaxial (+) and a uniaxial (–) interference figure. By definition, ε' exceeds ω in (+) crystals but is less than ω in (–) crystals. Hence in Figure 8-3, where the relative values of ε' and ω for these rays are schematically illustrated by the lengths of lines indicating their vibration directions, the radial E-ray vibration—that is, the vibration that "points" toward the melatope—is longer than the O-ray vibration for the (+) crystal but shorter for the (–) crystal. Consequently, insertion of an accessory with its N direction as marked in Figure 8-3 produces subtraction in the quadrants to the NW and SE of the melatope for (+) crystals or to the NE and SW for (–) crystals. In the remaining quadrants addition occurs. Useful rules for determining the optic sign are: (1) If the line joining the quadrants of subtraction (dashed in Fig. 8-3) is perpendicular to the N direction of the accessory plate—thus forming an imaginary plus sign the crystal is (+) in optic sign. (2) If this line is parallel—forming an imaginary negative sign—the crystal is (-) in optic sign.

The optic sign can thus be determined by locating the quadrants in which subtraction occurs upon insertion of an accessory whose N direction is known. For interference fig-

Figure 8-3. Angular relationship of N direction of the compensator plate to the N and n vibrations (respectively shown as long and short lines) for rays emerging within the four quadrants into which the uniaxial cross divides the interference figure. These quadrants are labeled with the compass directions usually used to refer to them. In (A) the crystal is positive ($N = \varepsilon'$, $n = \omega$); in (B) it is negative ($N = \omega$, $n = \varepsilon'$). For illustrative purposes, the two quadrants in which subtraction occurs after insertion of the accessory are joined by a dashed line.

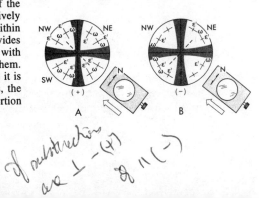

ures in which few isochromes appear, the first-order red (gypsum) plate or the quarter-wave mica plate serve equally well for determination of the optic sign. If the first-order red plate (Δ = 550 nm) is inserted, the 1° gray (Δ = 125 nm) areas adjacent to the melatope become 1° yellow (Δ = 425 nm; that is, 125 – 550 nm) in the quadrants of subtraction but 2° blue (Δ = 675 nm; that is, 125 + 550 nm) in the regions of addition. If the interference figure is viewed after insertion of the quarter-wave mica plate (Δ = 150 nm), however, these same 1° gray areas become 1° black (Δ = 25 nm; that is, 125 – 150 nm) in the quadrants of subtraction but 1° white (Δ = 275 nm; that is, 125 + 150 nm) in the quadrants of addition. Consequently, 1° yellow on opposite sides of the melatope (Fig. 8-4) marks the quadrants of subtraction if a first-order red plate is inserted. If a quarter-wave mica plate is inserted, two black dots (Fig. 8-5) mark the quadrants of subtraction. Thus, following the rules of the preceding paragraph, if the line joining the centers of these two yellow areas or black dots is perpendicular to the *N* direction of the inserted accessory, the crystal is (+) in optic sign. If parallel, the crystal is (–).

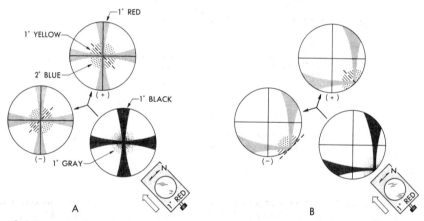

Figure 8-4. Determination of optic sign from the disposition of interference colors after insertion of the 1° red plate. Note that results are similar whether the optic axis is precisely centered (A) or not (B). The heavy dashed line joining the quadrants in which subtraction occurs—that is, those containing 1° yellow—has been added for illustrative purposes. See back cover of this book for color illustrations.

Figure 8-5. Determination of optic sign from the disposition of the two black dots produced by insertion of the quarter-wave mica plate. The two black dots mark the quadrants in which subtraction occurs. A heavy dashed line joining the quadrants in which subtraction occurs has been added for illustrative purposes.

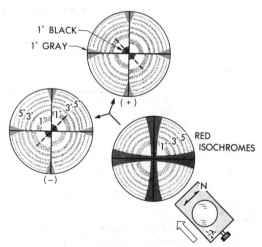

For interference figures containing numerous, closely spaced isochromes, the quartz wedge has certain advantages in optic sign determination, particularly for off-centered figures in which the melatope does not appear in the field of view. Observed while the

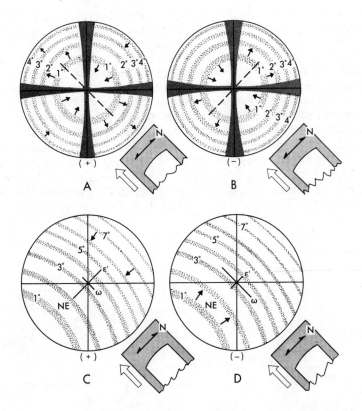

Figure 8-6. Movement of the isochromes if viewed while a quartz wedge is inserted, thin end first. (A) Centered, positive, uniaxial figure. (B) Centered, negative figure. (C) Off-centered, positive figure. (D) Off-centered, negative figure. The NE in (C) and (D) indicates that (C) and (D) compare to the quadrants NE of the melatope for the interference figures shown in (A) and (B). For illustrative purposes the quadrants of subtraction in (A) and (B) are joined by dashed lines.

quartz wedge is being inserted thin edge first, the isochromes move outward from the melatope in the quadrants of subtraction (Fig. 8-6) and inward toward the melatope in the quadrants of addition. If the line joining the quadrants of subtraction on opposite sides of the melatope is perpendicular to the N direction of the wedge, the crystal is (+) in sign (Fig. 8-6A); otherwise (Fig. 8-6B), it is (–).

To determine the optic sign in off-centered interference figures, one needs to determine whether ε' exceeds ω or not. To do this, first rotate the stage until a line connecting the melatope to the cross-hair intersection would be approximately parallel to the N direction of any inserted accessory. The crystal is now oriented with its ε' privileged direction parallel to (and its ω privileged direction perpendicular to) the N direction of the accessory (Fig. 8-6C, D). Insertion of the quartz wedge over the crystal in this position thus produces addition for (+) crystals (since for them ε' exceeds ω) and subtraction for (–) crystals (since for them ε' is less than ω). As Figure 8-6C illustrates, addition in this interference figure is expressed by the higher order isochromes displacing the lower order ones—that is, an inward movement toward the melatope. In Figure 8-6D subtraction is expressed by the lower order isochromes displacing the higher order ones, that is, a movement outward from the melatope. If the movement of the isochromes in the interference figure is hard to observe, it is sometimes preferable to convert to the orthoscopic set-up and observe whether insertion of the quartz wedge causes addition or subtraction with respect to the grain image. Addition is expressed by movement of the isochromes outward from the grain's center (and toward its thinner edges), subtraction by their movement inward towards the grain's center.

In general, during insertion of the wedge, addition causes higher-order isochromes to displace lower-order ones. This causes the isochromes to move *toward* the grain's thinner edges (orthoscopic view) or *toward* the melatope (conoscopic view). This difference, which sometimes puzzles beginners, results because, viewed orthoscopically, a grain's retardation colors decrease towards its (thinner) edges whereas, viewed conoscopically, they decrease towards its melatope. For subtraction, they move *toward* the grain's (thicker) center or, viewed conoscopically, *away* from its melatope.

MEASUREMENT OF REFRACTIVE INDICES

The value of the refractive index ε' of a uniaxial grain depends upon the angle between its optic axis and the plane of the glass slide on which it rests. Figure 8-7 illustrates the variation of ε' and retardation color for four grains of approximately equal thickness of a given uniaxial (+) crystal, the privileged directions being drawn as lengths proportional to the values of ε' and ω for that grain. For grain *b*, whose optic axis is nearly perpendicular to the slide, ε' is close to ω in value, a fact testified to by its relatively low retardation color. The optic axis in grains *c* and *d* is increasingly parallel to the slide; consequently, ε' becomes increasingly closer to ε in value and, as a result, the retardation colors become higher in going from grain *a* to *d*. For grain *d*, the optic axis is parallel to the slide; as a consequence, ε' now equals ε and grain *d* therefore possesses the highest interference color of all the grains (since its birefringence for that position equals $(\varepsilon - \omega)$, the maximum possible).

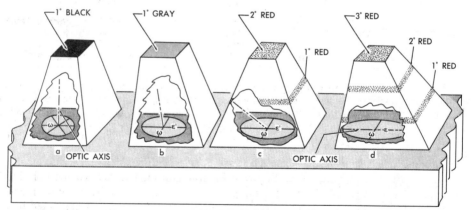

Figure 8-7. Relationship between the orientation of the optic axis (dash-dotted line) and the observed interference color for four grains of equal thickness. Note that, as the optic axis becomes increasingly parallel to the glass slide (from grains *a* to *d*) ε' approaches true ε in value and the retardation attains its highest order for that thickness. Only the red isochromes (stippled) and 1° black and gray are shown.

In a given powder mount, there is usually a multiplicity of grains such as *b* and *c;* measurement of ε' for them is of no particular value. An exception occurs in cases like the rhombohedral carbonates, where a strong rhombohedral cleavage $(10\bar{1}1)$ closely controls the plane upon which the grain will rest. Since, from one mount to the other, grains will rest on this particular cleavage plane, the ε' for such grains (symbolized $\varepsilon'_{10\bar{1}1}$) may be measured and will yield information as to which rhombohedral carbonate is involved.

The indices ω and ε, in contrast to ε', are always definitive values whose determination will aid in identifying the mineral. Their determination, therefore, will be considered in detail.

Measurement of ω

One of the two privileged directions of a uniaxial grain always corresponds to ω (for example, in grains *a-d* in Fig. 8-7). Thus, any grain can be selected for the measurement of ω; however, one of relatively low interference color (for example, grain *a* or *b*) will yield a more readily interpreted interference figure. Rotate the microscope stage until an isogyre of this interference figure is bisected by the N-S cross hair as in Figure 8-8A or B. For illustrative purposes, in each figure the privileged directions that are associated with the central ray of the cone of illumination are shown at this ray's point of emergence at the cross-hair intersection. The path of this central ray and therefore its associated privileged directions within the crystal coincide in direction with those of all the rays that pass through the crystal after conversion of the microscope to the orthoscopic set-up (see Fig. 7-10). Thus, the center of the interference figure discloses both the direction and identity (that is, whether ε' or ω) of the privileged directions possessed by the grains if viewed orthoscopically (Fig. 8-8C).

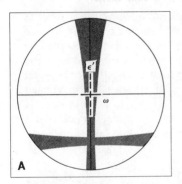 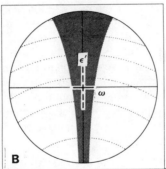 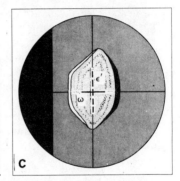

Figure 8-8. (A and B) Correct conoscopic orientations of grains so that their ω privileged direction is oriented E-W. (C) Use of oblique illumination to test the value of ω against the index of the immersion oil for the grain that was conoscopically oriented in (A) or (B). Assuming an E-W polarizer, note that only O rays, for which the crystal's index is ω, are transmitted by the crystal if it is illuminated orthoscopically as in (C). Since no E rays are transmitted in this orientation, the ε' privileged direction is drawn as a dotted line.

Uniaxial grains oriented as in Figure 8-8C transmit only O rays (if the polarizer's vibration direction is E-W). The grain's ε' privileged direction has therefore been drawn as a dashed line, because no light vibrating parallel to this direction is transmitted by the grain when in this orientation. Thus, ω is the only index exhibited by the grain in this orientation. Its value can be measured, after conversion to the orthoscope and removal of the analyzer, by either oblique illumination or the Becke line method in the same manner that n was for isotropic grains.

Measurement of ε'

Occasionally, as previously explained, it may be necessary to measure ε'. The grains of Figure 8-8 would be positioned for this measurement if the stage were rotated until the E-W isogyre was bisected by the E-W cross hair. Conversion to the orthoscope and removal of the analyzer would then permit measurement of ε' by oblique illumination or Becke line observations.

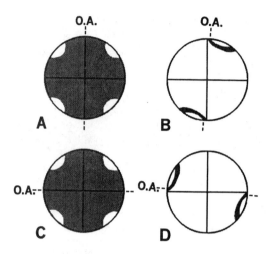

Figure 8-9. A uniaxial flash figure at extinction (A or C) discloses that the optic axis (O.A.) lies parallel to the microscope stage—but not whether it is N-S as in (A) or E-W as in (C). To sort this out, rotate the stage a few degrees, say, clockwise. Now employ Lommel's rule which states: If a uniaxial flash figure is rotated slightly off extinction, the broad diffuse cross resolves into hyperbola-shaped isogyres that leave the field via the quadrants into which the optic axis is being rotated. Thus, if the optic axis had been N-S as in (A), then (B) would have resulted. And, if it had been E-W as in (C), then (D) would have resulted.

Measurement of ε

Unlike ω, ε cannot be measured from every grain. Only a grain whose optic axis lies parallel to the microscope stage (for example, grain *d* in Fig. 8-7) will possess a privileged direction corresponding in index to ε. Grains of this orientation are located by scanning the slide (orthoscope; crossed polarizers; low-power objective) to find the smallest grain possessing the highest retardation color. The high retardation color is an indication that the difference between the refractive indices for the grain's two privileged directions is equal (or very close) to the maximum possible, $(\varepsilon - \omega)$; in other words, its optic axis is parallel or nearly parallel to the microscope stage. An interference figure serves to check this orientation; a flash figure should be obtained if the grain is correctly oriented for measurement of ε.

This flash figure will confirm that the optic axis lies parallel to the microscope stage. However, it does not disclose whether the optic axis is oriented precisely N-S (Fig. 8-9A) or E-W (Fig. 8-9C). To sort this out, rotate the microscope stage a degree or two, say, clockwise. **Lommel's rule** states that this small rotation will cause the broad diffuse cross to break up into hyperbola-shaped isogyres that leave the field of view via the quadrants into which the optic axis is being rotated. The small clockwise rotation would thus produce Figure 8-9B, if the optic axis had been N-S, but Figure 8-9D if it had been E-W.

Alternatively, if the flash figure displays a range in retardation colors when rotated 45° off extinction, then, as already noted, the optic axis must lie in those quadrants for which, at the edge of the field of view, the retardation colors are lowest.

With the optic axis oriented E-W, the grain will exhibit the index ε for a microscope with an E-W polarizer. Consequently, upon converting from conoscope to orthoscope (and removing the analyzer), ε can be compared to *n* for the oil by using Becke lines or oblique illumination.

Optic Sign Determination from Flash Figures

If an optic sign of a crystal has not been previously determined, this can be done as explained in Figure 8-10.

Dispersion

The change of any optical property with wavelength is called **dispersion**. For

Figure 8-10. Determination of optic sign after locating the direction of the optic axis, and thus the ε vibration direction, by applying Lommel's rule. The next step is to rotate the microscope stage until ε is oriented, say, NE. Now switch from conoscope to orthoscope and, with the polarizers crossed, insert the quartz wedge. If higher order isochromes displace lower order ones as in (A), ε coincides with the crystal's slow vibration and the crystal is (+). If the reverse is true, as in (B), the crystal is (−). Note that if the first-order red plate were inserted instead of the wedge, the 1° and 2° red isochromes would respectively change—by addition—to 2° and 3° red in (A) but—by subtraction—to black and 1° red in (B).

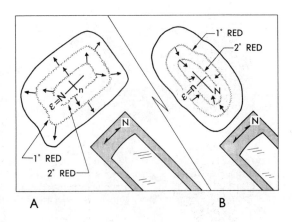

isotropic materials only their single refractive index (n) undergoes dispersion. For uniaxial crystals, their two indices, ε and ω, and thus their birefringence (ε - ω), can each undergo dispersion (Fig. 8-11).

In advanced work the values of ε and ω for a mineral may be measured at different wavelengths of light. Such measurements on quartz (Winchell and Winchell, 1951), for example, indicate $\omega_F = 1.54968$, $\varepsilon_F = 1.55898$; $\omega_D = 1.54425$, $\varepsilon_D = 1.55336$; and $\omega_C = 1.54190$, $\varepsilon_C = 1.55093$. Metatorbernite, $Cu(UO_2)_2P_2O_8 \cdot 8H_2O$, is unusual in this respect since it is uniaxial (−) for violet or blue light ($\omega_F = 1.638$, $\varepsilon_F = 1.636$), isotropic for green light of wavelength 512 nm ($\omega = \varepsilon = 1.6335$), and uniaxial (+) for red light ($\omega_C = 1.618$, $\varepsilon_C = 1.622$). Figure 8-11 illustrates these relationships graphically for metatorbernite.

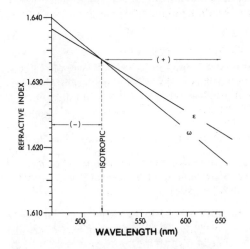

Figure 8-11. Dispersion of the refractive indices of metatorbernite. Note that for one particular wavelength it is isotropic whereas it is optically positive for longer wavelengths and optically negative for shorter wavelengths.

DETERMINATION OF RETARDATION AND BIREFRINGENCE

Estimation from Interference Colors

The absolute value of a mineral's birefringence, ($\varepsilon - \omega$), can be quickly estimated from the highest order interference color observable among the smaller grains in a powder mount. Assuming that the grains in the mount represent the 100 to 120 mesh fraction of a thoroughly sieved sample, all have passed through openings of 0.149 mm

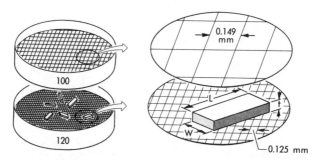

Figure 8-12. *Left:* The 100 to 120 mesh fraction of a crushed mineral as caught on the 120 mesh sieve. *Right:* Enlarged view of a grain to show its length *(L)*, width *(W)*, and thickness *(t)* as it rests in its most stable position—that is, on its surface of maximum area. If sieving was vigorous and complete, its width must exceed 0.125 mm; otherwise it would have passed through the 120 mesh sieve. (Mesh openings not to scale.)

but not through openings of 0.125 mm (Fig. 8-12). Their thickness *(t)* and width *(W)* are therefore undoubtedly less than the 0.149 mm openings. Assuming that the sieving was thorough,[1] the width of the grains as they lie on the glass slide most likely exceeds 0.125 mm; their thickness will, however, in many cases be less than 0.125 mm (particularly for flakes). However, for the narrowest grain showing the maximum interference color (of the hundreds on the slide) two assumptions appear likely: (1) The thickness, *t*, for this grain most closely approaches 0.125 mm (we shall assume it to be 0.12 mm)[2] and (2) its optic axis is parallel to the slide so that the indices for its privileged directions are ε and ω (or, if ε' and ω, then a value of ε' very close to ε). Using Figure 8-13, Δ can be evaluated to within 100 nm from interpretation of the maximum interference color observed. Thus, with Δ known and the thickness *t* approximately known from the minimum sieve opening, $(\varepsilon - \omega)$ can readily be calculated from an adaptation of Equation 7-5; that is,

$$(\varepsilon - \omega) = \frac{\Delta}{t} \qquad\qquad \text{(Eqn. 8-3)}$$

Figure 8-13 permits quick, graphic solutions of Equation 8-3 as follows: (1) Locate on it the vertical color bar that corresponds to the maximum interference color observed in the grains. (2) Next locate the horizontal line corresponding to the crystal thickness, *t*.

Figure 8-13 (folded color insert). Interference colors (vertical bars) and the retardation values (Δ) that produce them. Thin-section thickness along ordinate (in mm; multiply by 10^6 to convert to nm). The dots indicate 0.03 mm, the standard thickness. Radial lines indicate the increase of Δ with thickness for such particular birefringence values $(N - n)$ as 0.002, 0.004. Minerals with comparable birefringences extend outward from these lines with boldface indicating the more important ones. Thus " B– **kyanite** 12-16 " indicates, as discussed later, a biaxial (–) mineral whose birefringence—multiplied by 1000—ranges from 0.012 to 0.016 (because kyanite's composition varies from pure Al_2SiO_5). The 0.009 line corresponds to the birefringence of quartz. In thin sections quartz grains should exhibit, at most, first-order white tinged with yellow (= 270 nm) as indicated by the dot on the 0.009 line. If the grains exhibit greater retardations, the thin section is too thick. Note that for kyanite the dots on the 0.012 and 0.016 lines indicate that the maximum retardation exhibited by kyanite—in 0.03-mm thick thin-sections—may be 360 nm (yellow) or as high as 480 nm (deep orange) depending variations in its composition.

---

[1] If it was not, many very small grains capable of passing through the 0.125-mm openings will remain in the sieved sample.

[2] If the grains of the mount represent the 100 to 200 mesh fraction (as some may prefer), this minimum thickness may be assumed to be about 0.07 mm.

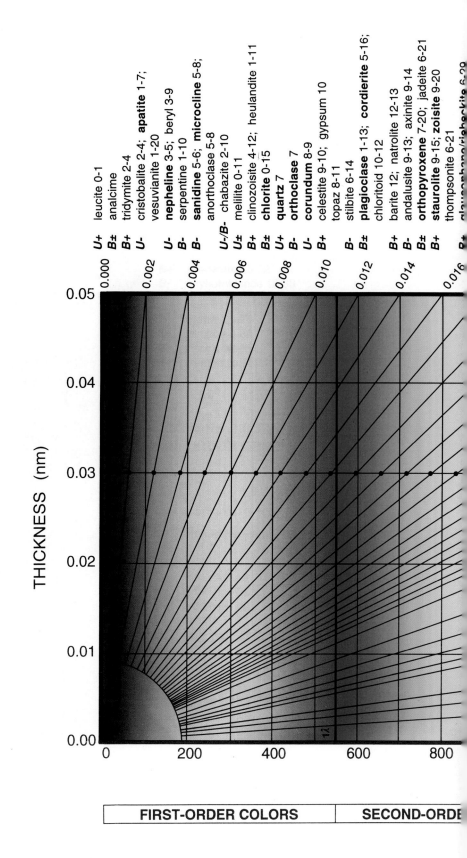

THICKNESS (nm)

U+	leucite 0-1
B±	analcime
B+	tridymite 2-4
U-	cristobalite 2-4; **apatite** 1-7;
	vesuvianite 1-20
U-	**nepheline** 3-5; beryl 3-9
B-	serpentine 1-10
B-	**sanidine** 5-6; **microcline** 5-8;
	anorthoclase 5-8
U-/B-	chabazite 2-10
U±	melilite 0-11
B+	clinozoisite 4-12; heulandite 1-11
B±	**chlorite** 0-15
U+	**quartz** 7
B-	**orthoclase** 7
U-	**corundum** 8-9
B+	celestite 9-10; gypsum 10
	topaz 8-11
B-	stilbite 6-14
B±	**plagioclase** 1-13; **cordierite** 5-16;
	chloritoid 10-12
B+	barite 12; natrolite 12-13
B-	andalusite 9-13; axinite 9-14
B±	**orthopyroxene** 7-20; jadeite 6-21
B+	**staurolite** 9-15; **zoisite** 9-20
	thompsonite 6-21
B±	glaucophane/riebeckite 6-29

0.000
0.002
0.004
0.006
0.008
0.010
0.012
0.014
0.016

0.05
0.04
0.03
0.02
0.01
0.00

0   200   400   600   800

FIRST-ORDER COLORS | SECOND-ORDE

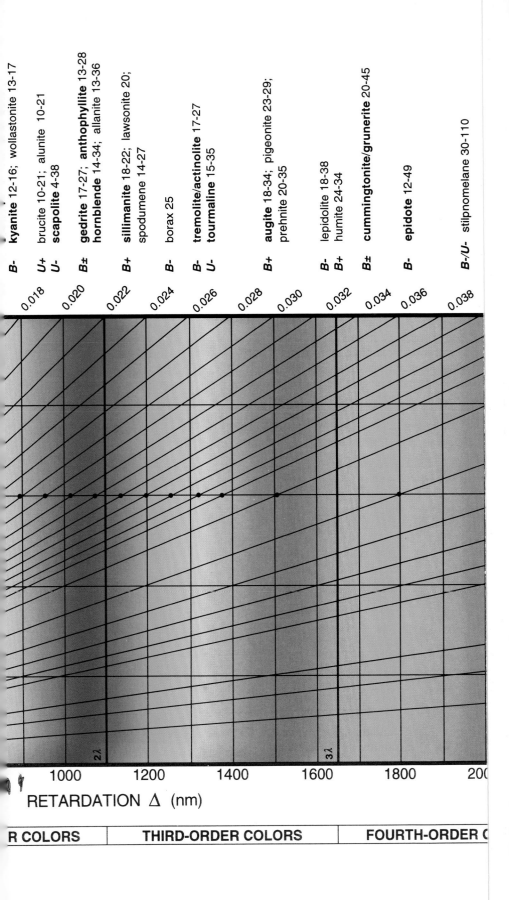

B- kyanite 12-16; wollastonite 13-17

U+ brucite 10-21; alunite 10-21
U- scapolite 4-38

B± gedrite 17-27; anthophyllite 13-28
hornblende 14-34; allanite 13-36

B+ sillimanite 18-22; lawsonite 20;
spodumene 14-27

B- borax 25

B- tremolite/actinolite 17-27
U- tourmaline 15-35

B+ augite 18-34; pigeonite 23-29;
prehnite 20-35

B- lepidolite 18-38
B+ humite 24-34

B± cummingtonite/grunerite 20-45

B- epidote 12-49

B-/U- stilpnomelane 30-110

0.018   0.020   0.022   0.024   0.026   0.028   0.030   0.032   0.034   0.036   0.038

2λ   3λ

1000   1200   1400   1600   1800   200

RETARDATION Δ (nm)

R COLORS | THIRD-ORDER COLORS | FOURTH-ORDER C

(3) The intersection of the vertical color bar and horizontal thickness line marks a point (or small area) in the interior of the color chart. (4) Through or near this point will pass several radial lines emanating from the origin of the color chart. (5) Follow these lines outward to the bold-faced numbers of the $(N - n)$ scale (the birefringence scale) to the top or right of the color chart. (6) The $(N - n)$ value thus indicated is likely to be quite close to $(\varepsilon - \omega)$ for the mineral being studied. By way of example, assume that the 100 to 120 mesh fragments of a powdered unknown (1) represent a maximum thickness of 0.12 mm and (2) exhibit a maximum interference color of 2° green. Using Figure 8-13, the value $(\varepsilon - \omega)$ seems likely to fall within the 0.006 to 0.008 range.

For the sieved crystals of our example, the thickness of the crystal showing a maximum interference color was presumed to be near 0.12 mm. Figure 8-13 is also especially useful for determining the birefringence $(N - n)$ of minerals in thin sections of rocks. Such wafers, cemented onto glass slides for study, are paper thin and generally 0.03 mm in thickness. Thus the intersection of the 0.03 mm thickness line with the vertical color bar of Figure 8-13 that corresponds to the maximum interference color observed (for the mineral in the thin section) would be used. Sometimes, however, thin sections vary in thickness from 0.03 mm, either throughout the section or in various areas; for example, the wafer may be slightly wedge shaped. In such cases the experienced petrographer can determine the thickness of particular areas of the thin section by observing the maximum interference color of any quartz grains ($\varepsilon - \omega = 0.009$) locally present. Thus the intersection of the vertical color bar (corresponding to this maximum interference color) with the radial line corresponding to an $(N - n)$ value of 0.009 falls on the horizontal line corresponding to the thickness of the thin section in Figure 8-13.

The more important of the rock-forming minerals are arranged in Figure 8-13 according to their maximum birefringence. Uniaxial minerals listed are denoted by (U), their birefringence corresponding to $(\varepsilon - \omega)$. For completeness, biaxial minerals (to be discussed in Chapter 10) are also listed and denoted by (B). A (+) or (–) sign, if present behind U or B, indicates the mineral's optic sign. The birefringence $(N - n)$ for biaxial crystals, as Chapter 10 will make clear, corresponds to $(\gamma - \alpha)$. If a mineral's birefringence is included in the list of Figure 8-13, the mineral can sometimes be rapidly identified on that basis alone. On the other hand, a particular value for maximum birefringence—for example, 0.010—may be possessed by several different minerals, some of which may not appear on the list. Consequently, if an initial identification from the list is made, it is wise to test its validity by further comparison of as many additional optical and physical properties as possible. Reference books such as Winchell and Winchell (1951), Tröger (1952; revised by Bambauer *et al.*, 1979), and Phillips and Griffen (1981) contain complete descriptions of minerals with which the properties of the unknown can be compared. The computer database, *MinIdent* (see p. 195), is a readily accessible source of up-to-date information.

Precise Measurement

The retardation Δ of a crystal, a fiber, or a plastic film—and thus its birefringence $(N - n)$, assuming its thickness can be measured—can be quantitatively determined by use of a **compensator**. A Brace-Köhler compensator (Fig. 8-14A) permits precise determination of exceedingly small retardations such as are found in organic objects and glasses of low-strain birefringence. A Sénarmont compensator (Fig. 8-14B), whose use and theory are described by Bloss (1981, p. 266), requires use of a monochromatic light source ($\lambda = 546$ or 589 nm) in conjunction with a rotatable analyzer. Retardations up to 1λ can be measured. A Berek compensator (Fig. 8-14C) allows quantitative measurement of retardations up to 2800 nm($\pm$ 2%) and thus is most commonly used for crystals.

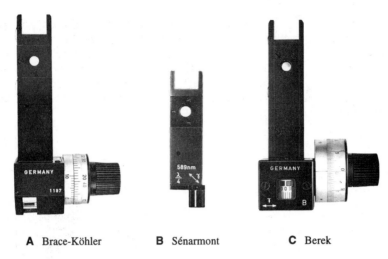

A Brace-Köhler   **B** Sénarmont   **C** Berek

Figure 8-14. Compensators. (Photographs courtesy of Leica, Inc.)

EXTINCTION ANGLES: SIGN OF ELONGATION

The angle between a crystal plate's privileged directions and any linear crystallographic feature present on the plate is called its **extinction angle**. Such linear crystallographic directions may be the lines of intersection of a set of cleavage planes with the crystal plate—these being called cleavage traces (Fig. 8-15)—or it may be the straight boundary of the plate where it is terminated by a crystal face. In either case, the extinction angle can be measured by aligning the observed crystallographic direction with a cross hair (Fig. 8-15A) and recording the angular position of the microscope stage as

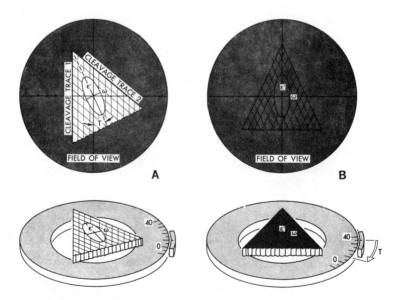

Figure 8-15. Measurement of an extinction angle. (A) Stage rotated until the crystallographic direction, cleavage trace 1 in this case, is parallel to the privileged direction of the polarizer—that is, to the N-S cross hair. (B) Rotation of the stage through angle *T*, the amount of rotation necessary to bring the gain to an extinction position. Angle *T* is the difference between the stage readings for (A) and (B).

indicated at the index mark. The stage should then be rotated until the crystal plate is at extinction (Fig. 8-15B), its privileged directions now being parallel to the cross hairs; the stage's angular reading at the index mark is again noted. The difference between the reading for positions A and B equals T, the extinction angle. The extinction angle between cleavage trace 1 and the second privileged direction (ω) would be $(90 - T)$. This complementary relationship always holds since the two privileged directions are always mutually perpendicular for crystal plates.

Figure 8-16. (A) Intersections between the optic indicatrix and the prismatic faces (m) and pyramidal faces (u) of a tetragonal crystal. (B) View between crossed polarizers of a crushed fragment of the crystal that is resting on one prism face and is bounded laterally by the traces of others. The angle between the trace of m_2 and the grain's ε privileged direction is 0°; for this reason, the grain is said to have *parallel extinction*. (C) View between crossed polarizers of a fragment at extinction that is resting on one pyramidal face and is bounded by the traces of two others. The angle T between its privileged direction and either trace u_2 or u_4 is equal. This grain thus possesses *symmetrical extinction*. For illustrative purposes the extinct crystals in (B) and (C) have been made slightly lighter than the background.

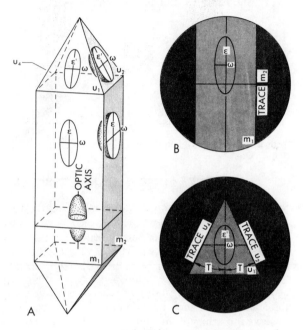

In uniaxial crystals, two special types of extinction are observed: (1) **parallel** and (2) **symmetrical**. The type depends upon whether the crystallographic directions involved are parallel (see m planes in Fig. 8-16A) or at an angle (see u planes in Fig. 8-16A) to the optic axis of the crystal. An elongated crystal lying on one of the m planes and bounded by another of them (Fig. 8-16B) shows parallel extinction, angle T equaling 0°. On the other hand, fragments of a crystal that cleaved parallel to a pyramidal set of faces—that is, parallel to faces labeled u in Figure 8-16A—would likely rest on a u plane and be bounded by other u planes (Fig. 8-16C). The extinction angle between the ε' direction and cleavage trace u_4, would precisely equal the angle between this ε' direction and trace u_2. Thus arose the term "symmetrical extinction."

In thin sections, crystals do not lie on cleavage planes. Instead they will be randomly oriented relative to the plane of the section. In such case, uniaxial crystals may exhibit random extinction angles (whereby the extinction is neither parallel or symmetrical).

If a grain is elongated dimensionally such as that in Figure 8-16B, two possibilities exist with respect to the orientation of the N and n directions to this elongation: (1) The N direction is parallel (or within 45°) to the elongation (as for Fig. 8-16B), in which case the grain is said to be **length slow** or to possess a **positive elongation**; or (2) The n direction is parallel (or within 45°) to the direction of grain elongation, in which case the grain is said to be **length fast** and to possess a **negative elongation**.

ABSORPTION AND PLEOCHROISM

Like isotropic materials (p. 13), uniaxial crystals may exhibit general absorption (to appear gray or opaque in transmitted light) or selective absorption (to appear colored). As with refractive index, absorption may differ according to vibration direction within a uniaxial crystal. Most tourmalines, for example, are generally strongly absorbent for light vibrating parallel to an ω direction whereas for light vibrating parallel to its optic axis, the crystal is highly transparent (Fig. 8-17).

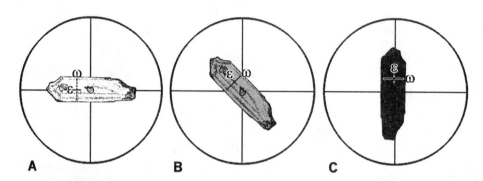

Figure 8-17. Tourmaline, which shows strong general absorption for light vibrating parallel to ω (no analyzer, E-W polarizer only). The crystal changes from colorless for light vibrating parallel to ε (A), to gray (B), to black (C) as the microscope stage is rotated. For orientation (C) the crystal absorbs almost all of the E-W vibrating light that enters it.

For some minerals, either ε or ω, or both, may represent a direction of selective absorption. Moreover, both directions, if absorbent, need not absorb the same portion of the spectrum. In such cases a crystal plate, rotated within a beam of polarized light, is observed to transmit different colors according to whether the ε or ω vibration is parallel to the privileged direction of the polarizer (Fig. 8-18). This change in color with rotation in the polarized beam is called **pleochroism**.

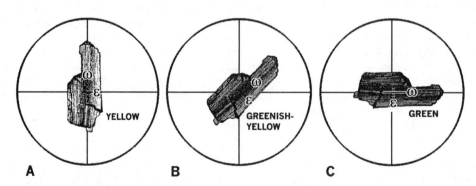

Figure 8-18. Crystal showing the following pleochroism: ε = yellow; ω = green (no analyzer, E-W polarizer only). In position (A) it appears yellow, in position (B) it appears greenish yellow, and in (C) it appears green.

A crystal's absorption coefficients[8] for light vibrating at 90° and 0° to the optic axis—respectively symbolized as k_ω and k_ε—may vary for different wavelengths of light.

---

[8] See p. 14 for the definition of absorbtion coefficient.

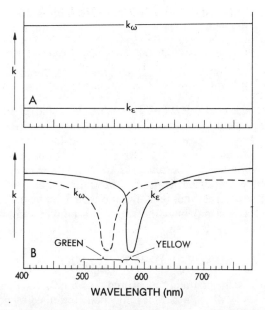

Figure 8-19. Variation for different wavelengths of the absorption coefficients for light vibrating parallel to the optic axis (k_ε) and perpendicular to it (k_ω): (A) For the crystal in Figure 8-17 for which light vibrating perpendicular to the optic axis was almost completely absorbed for all wavelengths whereas light vibrating parallel to the optic axis was almost completely transmitted; (B) For the crystal in Figure 8-18 for which the pleochroism was ε = yellow and ω = green.

Figure 8-19A illustrates this variation for a crystal that exhibits a strong general absorption for light vibrating perpendicular to the optic axis but little absorption for light vibrating parallel to the optic axis. Figure 8-19B similarly illustrates the variation in k_ω and k_ε for a crystal that selectively absorbs all wavelengths but green for light vibrating perpendicular to the optic axis and all wavelengths but yellow for light vibrating parallel to the optic axis. This second crystal thus has the following pleochroic formula: ω = green; ε = yellow. For light of a particular wavelength vibrating within this crystal at an angle theta to the optic axis, the absorption coefficient k_ε varies between k_ε and k_ω for this wavelength, approaching k_ε as the value of theta decreases. For this reason, pleochroic colors may vary according to the orientation of the section within the crystal. For example, a plate cut nearly perpendicular to the optic axis—so that its ε' index differs little from ω—shows the following pleochroic colors if viewed in plane-polarized light: ε' = yellowish green; ω = green. A plate cut exactly perpendicular to the optic axis would appear green for all positions of the stage.

ABNORMAL INTERFERENCE COLORS

An abnormal interference color is one whose hue does not match any of the normal interference colors of the scale (Fig. 8-13). Abnormal colors indicate that the spectral composition of the light being transmitted by the analyzer (after its prior passage through the mineral) differs from that of crystal plates and grains (of comparable retardation values) of the majority of minerals. In uniaxial crystals abnormal interference colors are usually produced as the result of (1) intrinsic body color, that is, strong selective absorption of a particular wavelength during its passage through the crystal; or (2) large variation in the value of ($\varepsilon - \omega$) for different wavelengths of light, ($\varepsilon - \omega$) sometimes decreasing to zero at a particular wavelength. By way of an example of the first possibility, consider a deep green crystal whose retardation is 200 nm. Ordinarily, the spectral transmission by the analyzer for a retardation of 200 nm is like the dashed curve in Figure 7-8. For this crystal, however, as its green color testifies, a large portion of the red wavelengths of light was absorbed during passage through the crystal. Consequently, a different spectral transmission curve results and, instead of the first-order white usually seen for a retardation of 200 nm, a greenish interference color would be seen.

For a few minerals the coefficients of dispersion for ε and ω differ significantly in value and their birefringence ($\varepsilon - \omega$) thus differs appreciably for different colors of light. In metatorbernite (see Fig. 8-11) the birefringence (and therefore the retardation of a given plate) is, for red light, double what it is for blue light. Moreover, wavelengths in the region of 512 nm, for which metatorbernite is isotropic, will be completely extinguished at the analyzer (and therefore absent from the spectral composition of the interference colors) for all plates of metatorbernite, regardless of their thickness. Consequently, plates of metatorbernite yield abnormal interference colors between crossed polarizers, all lacking the wavelengths around 512 nm.

MINERAL IDENTIFICATION

After ε and ω have been accurately measured for an unknown uniaxial mineral, the particular mineral species to which it belongs may be determined by consulting *MinIdent* (see p. 195), a data base of optical properties for minerals.

REVIEW QUESTIONS

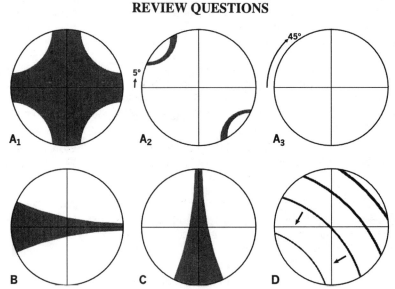

1. Given an E-W polarizer, what refractive index (ω, ε, ε') will be measurable for the uniaxial crystal displaying interference figure A_1 given that A_2 and A_3 represent its interference figures after a slight clockwise rotation? Same question for a N-S polarizer.

2. Given an E-W polarizer, what refractive index (ω, ε, ε') will be measurable for the crystal displaying interference figure B? That displaying interference figure C?

3. What is the optic sign of a uniaxial crystal whose isochromes move, as shown in D, when the quartz wedge is inserted, thin edge first?

9   INTRODUCING THE SPINDLE STAGE

OVERVIEW

A uniaxial crystal—cemented onto the clipped-off eye-end of a needle (which is then inserted into a spindle stage)—can be oriented, within minutes, so that its optic axis lies parallel to the microscope stage. This done, its two principal indices, ω and ε, can be compared to n for the oil. Following these comparisons, the oil mount can be slid out from the spindle stage's dock, without changing the crystal's orientation, and new oil mounts successively slid into place until matches are obtained for ω and ε. After these matches are made, the needle, with grain attached, can be stuck into a cork and inserted into a glass vial. This preserves the crystal as evidence (or for re-study).

The method—rapid, simple, elegant—requires only a single grain as sample.

INTRODUCTION

Anisotropic crystals become amazingly tractable in optical crystallography if they can be rotated about an axis that is parallel to the stage of a polarizing microscope. Although single-axis stages that permitted this were available in the 1860s, they seem to have fallen into disuse until their recent revival by Joel, Hartshorne, Rosenfeld (1950), Saylor, Tocher, and, in particular, by Ray E. Wilcox of the U.S. Geological Survey. Wilcox vigorously espoused single-axis techniques and introduced a very inexpensive version, which he named the **spindle stage**. The term was so apt that it has practically become a synonym for *single-axis stage*.

The spindle stage itself has proved equally apt. With it, undergraduate students can quickly orient a small crystal or crystal fragment so that all of its principal indices can be accurately measured by the immersion method. Wilcox (1959) enumerates the following advantages of the spindle stage for study of individual crystal fragments by the immersion method:

1. *Any* direction in the crystal can be rotated *into the plane* of the microscope stage. Consequently, all principal indices may be determined from the same crystal fragment.

2. No corrections are required for angular rotations.

3. Either orthoscopic or conoscopic illumination may be used (and readily alternated).

4. It is simple and inexpensive.

After the writer introduced his classes to spindle-stage techniques, the response was enthusiastic from all sides. There is little doubt that students in geology, mineralogy, ceramics, forensics, and chemistry should be instructed in these techniques early in their careers.

THE DETENT SPINDLE STAGE

The detent spindle stage devised by F.D. Bloss with help from James F. Light

(Fig. 9-1A) retains the simplicity of the Wilcox spindle stage but offers the following advantages: (1) it is less expensive and commercially available from McCrone Microscopes & Accessories, 850 Pasquinelli Drive, Westmont, Illinois 60559. (2) Its oil cells, on glass slides (Figs. 9-1B and 9-1C), can be slipped into (and out of) its "dock" to greatly facilitate changes of the immersion oil surrounding the grain. (3) Its protractor, which is permanently attached to the baseplate, carries detents that cause the spindle to "click" into place at the 10° settings roughly marked in Figure 9-1A. Relative to the prototype spindle stage, this feature permits greater accuracy and a considerable saving of time. (4) Another improvement is the use of fine, stainless steel tubing to form the spindle. This permits ordinary sewing needles to be inserted into the spindle's tube (Fig. 9-1A)—a No. 8 size, depending upon the brand, may fit well. These serve as removable tips onto which grains may be cemented (Fig. 9-1D) and later compactly stored after conclusion of the study. Advantages 2 and 4 incorporate suggestions by Jones (1969).

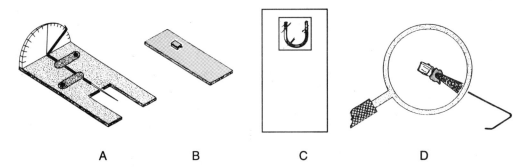

A   B   C   D

Figure 9-1. (A) The spindle stage of Bloss and Light (1973). Its detents (shown along the protractor's edge) cause the spindle, which consists of appropriately bent stainless steel tubing, to "click" into every 10° position (0°, 10° ... 180°) and, not shown, less strongly into 5° positions (5°, 15° ... 175°). A sewing needle—with a crystal cemented to its clipped-off eye-end—should insert deeply (and tightly) into the spindle tube. (B) An oil cell mounted on a 25 × 45 mm glass slide can be inserted into the spindle stage's "dock" until oil surrounds the grain. (C) Top view (enlarged) of an insertable cell that consists of a piece of a jumbo paper clip, cover glass atop, filled with immersion oil. Gunter (1997) provides details as to how to build such cells. For such cells, when the spindle is rotated from 0° to 180°, the grain should touch neither the cover glass above nor the glass slide below. (D) When cementing the grain to needle, avoid coating the sides of the grain. Such undesirable and self-defeating coatings are more easily detected if a dark-colored nail polish is used as the cement. Of course, any cement should be prior-tested to insure that, when dry, it is not soluble in the immersion oil(s) to be used. After the grain's optical properties have been measured, the needle containing it may be stuck into a cork and inserted into a vial for either future study or as evidence.

PRE-ADJUSTMENTS OF THE MICROSCOPE

Spindle-stage techniques yield best results if the microscope's objective, substage assembly, and Bertrand lens are precisely centered.

Centering the objective and the substage assembly

To center the substage assembly, first center the lowest-power objective in the usual way (Fig. 4-7), then gently constrict the substage assembly's iris diaphragm as far as possible. The circle of light now visible in the field of view should be centered on the cross-hairs. If not, adjust the centering screws for the substage assembly until this circle of light (and consequently the substage assembly itself) is centered. Replace the lowest-power objective with the objective to be used during the spindle-stage examination. Generally, a 0.65-N.A. (numerical aperture) objective is preferred because it provides sufficient working distance and yet permits interference figures to be obtained from anisotropic grains. (Frequently, a 0.85-N.A. objective has too short a working distance to permit its use with a spindle stage).

Centering the Bertrand lens

The Bertrand lens must be centered with care so that measurements made from interference figures will be accurate. To do this, *after centering the objective and the substage assembly*, place a slide containing a small opaque grain on the microscope stage. Next, insert the Bertrand lens, withdraw the analyzer, and raise the objective so far above its normal position of focus relative to the stage that a telescopic view of the grain is seen. If the Bertrand lens is centered, a point on the grain at the cross-hair intersection will remain there during rotation of the microscope stage. If not, adjust the Bertrand centering screws to achieve this.

Other adjustments

It is wise to verify that the privileged directions of analyzer and polarizer are parallel to the cross-hairs of the ocular (Fig. 4-8) and precisely perpendicular to each other.

CARTESIAN COORDINATE SYSTEM FOR MICROSCOPES

Microscope manufacturers have defined a Cartesian coordinate system for microscope directions such that, in the plane of the microscope stage, due east is called x and due north is called y (Fig. 9-2). As customary, the observer is always assumed to face due north. The direction that is perpendicular to the microscope stage and that points in the direction of travel of the light is called z. As one looks through a microscope, a direction that is located anticlockwise relative to a given direction—for example, OP relative to the x axis in Figure 9-1—is defined to be at a positive angle to the given direction. Thus, OP is at a positive angle E relative to x in Figure 9-2B. Note that a clockwise rotation of the microscope stage, if equal to E in value, will bring OP into the position x (due east).

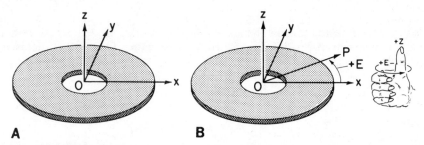

A **B**

Figure 9-2. (A) Cartesian coordinate axes x, y, z as adopted for polarizing microscopes. The $+z$ axis points in the direction light travels along the axis of the microscope. Thus, x and y lie in the plane of the microscope stage, $+y$ due north and $+x$ due east. The observer is by convention assumed to face north. (B) A direction OP will be at a positive angle E relative to x if located counterclockwise relative to $+x$. Thus, a *clockwise* rotation would be needed to cause OP to become due east (= coincide with $+x$).

AXES OF ROTATION

A crystal mounted on a spindle stage can be rotated about two axes: (1) the horizontal axis S provided by the spindle stage and (2) the vertical axis M provided by the microscope stage (Fig. 9-2C). We can thus say "rotate on S" instead of "rotate about the spindle-stage axis" or "rotate on M to extinction" instead of "rotate the microscope stage until the crystal becomes extinct." Positions and rotations relative to axis S are measured

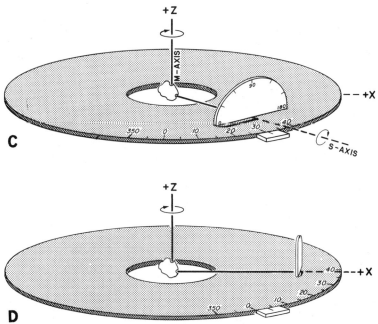

Figure 9-2 (continuation). (C) Spindle stage attached onto the microscope stage so that the crystal may be (1) rotated about a horizontal axis *S* by means of this spindle stage and (2) rotated about *M*, the vertical axis of the microscope, through rotation of the microscope stage. The *M* settings are then read against the index for the microscope stage, which should be equipped with a vernier scale. The *S* settings are read from the protractor scale of the spindle stage. For illustrative purposes in (C) and (D), the oil cell holding the crystal has been omitted. (D) The accepted rest position of a spindle stage: (1) its *S* reading is at 0° and (2) its axis has been made to coincide with *x*, its tip pointing toward -*x*.

on the spindle stage's protractor scale and vary from 0 to 180°. (For more elaborate single-axis stages, a full 360° rotation about axis *S* is possible.) Positions and rotations relative to axis *M* are measured from the graduations at the edge of the microscope stage; these usually increase from 0 to 360° in an clockwise direction. Less recent microscopes may have anticlockwise stages (0 to 360° increases anticlockwise).Whatever the case, these *M* positions need to be read against a vernier scale so that *M* readings can be estimated to tenths of a degree. Most microscope stages have such vernier scales, although some manufacturers may have made the serious error of omitting them from their student microscopes.

A spindle stage is at its *rest position* if its *S* reading is at 0° and its spindle axis coincides with axis *x* of the recently proposed coordinate system (Fig. 9-2D), the spindle's tip pointing due west. The microscope stage reading M_R that precisely orients the spindle axis in this E-W rest position will be called the **reference azimuth**.

The spindle stage should be *securely clamped* onto the microscope stage so that the crystal cemented onto its needle remains centered, or nearly so, as the spindle is rotated from *S* = 0° to *S* = 180°. The steps described in Figure 9-3 will provide a precise value for M_R. Step (1), the "eyeball estimate," guards against gross errors. For example, M_R would be off by 45° if, in Figure 9-3B, *n* rather than *N* had been oriented E-W.

DETERMINING OPTIC SIGN, ε, AND ω

For a uniaxial crystal glued with its optic axis at a random angle θ to the spindle

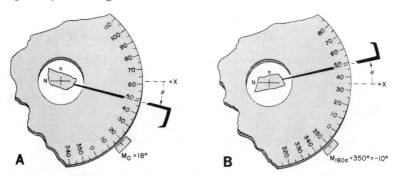

A $M_0 = 18°$

B $M_{180a} = 350° = -10°$

Figure 9-3. Determination of the reference azimuth M_R. For simplicity the protractor scale of the spindle stage is omitted, but the spindle, as indicated by its handle, is set at 0° in (A) and at 180° in (B). For illustrative purposes the crystal has been drawn vastly oversized relative to both the spindle and the microscope stage.

Step 1: Rotate the microscope stage until, as judged by eye, the spindle is E-W and points west. Record the microscope reading as $\sim M_R$ (= approximate reference azimuth). For this example, assume that $\sim M_R = 6°$.

Step 2: As done in (A), set S at 0° and rotate the microscope stage *clockwise* from $\sim M_R$ until the crystal becomes extinct, this microscope stage reading being called M_0 and in this case equaling 18°.

Step 3: Rotate the microscope stage back to $\sim M_R$, set S at 180°, and then rotate the microscope stage *anticlockwise* to extinction as in (B). Call this reading M_{180a}. For this example, $M_{180a} = 350°$ (= -10°). The reference azimuth M_R then equals the reading midway between M_0 and M_{180a}, thus

$$M_R = \frac{M_0 + M_{180a}}{2} = \frac{18° + (-10°)}{2} = 4°$$

Rationale: In both (A) $S = 0°$ and (B) $S = 180°$, the crystal has been brought to extinction with its slow vibration N exactly E-W. The angle between N and the spindle, labeled θ, remains the same for (A) and (B), but in (A) the spindle axis is precisely θ degrees clockwise of $+x$ whereas in (B) it is exactly θ degrees anticlockwise. The mid-setting between (A) and (B) will thus orient the spindle axis exactly E-W.

Caution: In Step 3 be sure to bring the *same* vibration direction to E-W extinction as was done in Step 2. In this example the slow vibration direction N was made E-W in both steps. However, if in Step 3 the fast vibration direction n had been made E-W instead of N, the calculated value for M_R would be off by 45° and equal 49°. The approximate M_R value of 6° will immediately disclose this error—and that M_R actually equals 49° minus 45°.

stage's needle (Fig. 9-4), it is physically impossible, by rotation about S, to orient this optic axis perpendicular to the microscope stage—unless θ just happens to equal 90°. By contrast, rotation about S can *always* orient this optic axis parallel to the microscope stage (to permit measurement of ε). To achieve this orientation, rotate the microscope stage to M_R and then rotate the spindle about S until the crystal becomes extinct between crossed polarizers. For this setting—here called S_v— the optic axis will now lie in an E-W vertical plane (Fig. 9-5A). As a result, the crystal's ω vibration lies N-S and its ε' vibration lies E-W. With this known, rotate the microscope stage 45° anticlockwise to orient ε' to be NE-SW and ω to be NW-SE (Fig. 9-5B). With an accessory determine whether $\varepsilon' > \omega$ (crystal +) or $\varepsilon' < \omega$ (crystal –).

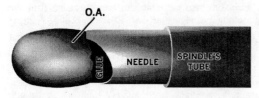

O.A.

GLUE NEEDLE SPINDLE'S TUBE

Figure 9-4. A crystal has been glued onto the needle with its optic axis at a random angle to the S axis. Rotation about S can bring this optic axis parallel to the stage, but never perpendicular to it. However, one can easily orient the optic axis to be in an E-W vertical plane. Simply set the microscope stage to M_R and then rotate the crystal abut the spindle axis S until the crystal becomes extinct. At this point the crystal's optic axis will lie in the E-W vertical plane so that its ω vibration will be N-S and its ε' vibration E-W (see Fig. 9-5A).

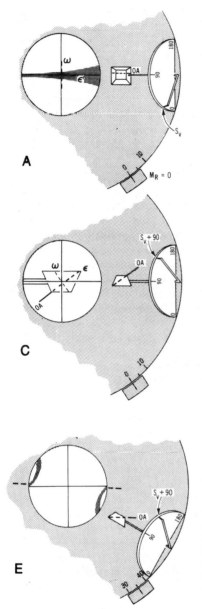

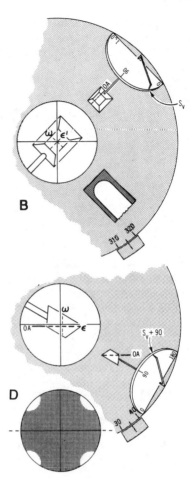

Figure 9-5. Top views of a disproportionately enlarged crystal attached to a schematic (too-short) spindle whose protractor scale is tilted to avoid an edgewise view of it. Microscopic views of the crystal, showing image reversal, are drawn at the stage's center. (A) With $M = M_R$, the spindle is rotated about S until the crystal becomes extinct under orthoscopic view or under conoscopic view, as shown here, until an isogyre is bisected by the E-W cross-hair. The spindle setting that achieves this, symbolized S_V,

orients the optic axis in an E-W vertical plane. Thus, the E-W vibration is ε'. (B) The microscope stage rotated 45° from its position in (A) so as to orient ε' to be NE-SW whereupon, by inserting a quartz wedge or full wave plate during an orthoscopic view of the grain, one can determine whether $\varepsilon' > \omega$ or $\varepsilon' < \omega$, that is, the crystal's optic sign. (C) The microscope stage returned to M_R as in (A) but with S set at $S_V + 90°$ so as to orient the crystal's optic axis parallel to the plane of the microscope stage. (D) With S still set at $S_V + 90°$, the microscope stage is rotated clockwise until the crystal becomes extinct (orthoscopic view) or until a centered flash figure results (conoscopic view). (E) Relative to its position in (D), the microscope stage has been rotated clockwise by a very small angle. Under conoscopic view this small rotation resolves the centered uniaxial flash figure—that is, the broad cross in (D)—into two hyperbolic curves which, as stated in Lommel's rule, speedily leave the field of view within the quadrants (= SE and NW) into which the optic axis is being rotated. These results would indicate that the optic axis in (D) had been oriented E-W rather than N-S.

To compare ε as well as ω to n for the index oil, rotate about S to $S_v \pm 90°$ (Fig. 9-5C). This orients the optic axis horizontal so that, after rotating the crystal to extinction (Fig. 9-5D), ε and ω can be compared to n for the oil. Slip new oil cells into (and out of) the spindle-stage dock until matches are obtained for ε and ω.

A Bonus for Students

In the preceding method, the spindle-stage setting was changed abruptly from S_v to $S_v \pm 90°$. However, it is instructive to institute this change as a series of smaller shifts, all the while viewing the interference figure. One advantage of this stepwise technique is that when $S_v \pm 90°$ is reached, ε is known to be oriented E-W. A second advantage, particularly for students, is the opportunity to see an off-centered uniaxial interference figure develop into a uniaxial flash figure. The step method is initiated by starting with the spindle at S_v (and the microscope stage at M_R) as in Figure 9-6A. A slight shift toward $S_v \pm 90°$ causes the isogyre to move laterally away from the E-W cross-hair (Fig. 9-6B). Next, rotate the microscope stage sufficiently away from position M_R until the isogyre is once more bisected by the E-W cross-hair (Fig. 9-6C). If these two processes are alternated, the isogyre, when brought to bisection by the E-W cross-hair, becomes broader and broader (*cf.* Figs. 9-6A and 9-6C). At $S_v \pm 90°$, the centered uniaxial flash figure (see Fig. 9-6D) results and the crystal's optic axis is now horizontal and E-W. Lommel's rule (Fig. 8-9) should confirm it to be E-W.

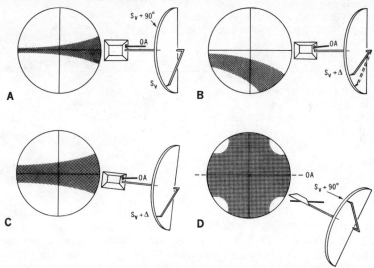

Figure 9-6. (A) As for Figure 9-5A, the microscope stage was set to read M_R and the spindle then rotated about axis S until an isogyre was bisected by the E-W cross-hair. Consequently, $S = S_v$, and the optic axis now lies in a vertical E-W plane. (B) The spindle setting S has been rotated through a small angle Δ toward, in this case, the setting $S_v + 90°$. The settings thus attained, $S = S_v + \Delta$; $M = M_R$, bring the optic axis out of the vertical plane and toward the horizontal plane so that the isogyre has now moved away from the E-W cross-hair and is also broader than it was in (A). (C) The microscope stage has been rotated until the isogyre seen in (B) is once more bisected by the E-W cross-hair. (D) Alternate applications of the operations in (B) and (C) have been repeated until the isogyre in (C) has broadened into a diffuse cross that fills the field of view (= uniaxial flash figure). The optic axis is now horizontal and E-W, being parallel to the dashed line shown.

Special orientations

By chance, a uniaxial crystal may be cemented onto the spindle so that its optic axis is parallel (= OA_{pa}) *or perpendicular* (= OA_{pe}) to the spindle axis. For either special orientation, if M is set at M_R while S is varied from 0 to 180°, the crystal will remain extinct between crossed polarizers, if viewed orthoscopically. Viewed conoscopically, the OA_{pa} orientation yields a flash figure like Figure 9-6D at *all* settings of S. In contrast, the OA_{pe} orientation is distinguished by an isogyre that is bisected by the N-S cross-hair (Fig. 9-7A), but eventually becomes a centered optic axis figure (Fig. 9-7B,C) at a certain value of S (symbolized S_v). At $S_v \pm 90°$, a flash figure results. If the grain is too small for conoscopy, observe it orthoscopically at 45° off extinction ($M = M_R \pm 45°$) to distinguish the two special orientations. At $M_R \pm 45°$, as S is varied from 0 to 180°, the grain's retardation color will decrease to first-order black only for the OA_{pe} orientation, the setting S that causes this (symbol S_v) having then oriented the optic axis perpendicular to the microscope stage.

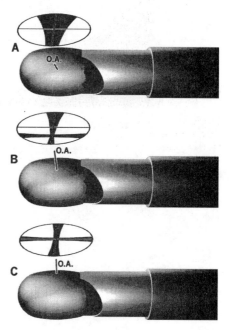

Figure 9-7. Conoscopic figures, as seen if the microscope stage is set at M_R for a uniaxial crystal that happened to be cemented onto the spindle with its optic axis precisely perpendicular to the spindle's axis. In (A) the spindle's S-setting is such that the optic axis is at an oblique angle relative to the microscope stage. Next, the spindle's S-setting is gradually changed to make the optic axis (B) almost perpendicular and then (C) precisely perpendicular to the microscope stage. For (C) the S-setting equals S_v, the value that orients the optic axis perpendicular to the microscope stage. Note that if the S-setting is changed to $S_v \pm 90°$, a centered flash figure (Fig. 9-6D) would result.

After a special orientation has been established to be the OA_{pa} or OA_{pe} orientation, the crystal's optic axis may be oriented to lie parallel to the microscope stage. For the OA_{pa} orientation, the optic axis, being parallel to the spindle, remains so oriented for every setting S. For the OA_{pe} orientation, the optic axis becomes parallel to the stage if S is set at $S_v \pm 90$. Having located the crystal's optic axis so that one knows which of the grain's vibration directions is ε and which is ω, one can readily determine the crystal's optic sign and measure its principal indices, ω and ε, relative to the immersion oil.

WEB SITE SPINDLE STAGES

Instructions for manufacturing a very inexpensive spindle stage (Fig. 9-8), using heavy cardboard, may be obtained at <www.uidaho.edu/~mgunter/opt_min/ss/ss.html> or from Gunter (1997). There is also a video that shows orthoscopic and conoscopic views of uniaxial crystals at this web site. Alternatively, cardboard spindle stages, already assembled, may be ordered from the Mineralogical Society of America (1015 Eighteenth Street, NW, Suite 601, Washington, DC 20036; Web site: <www.minsocam.org>). Measurements made with this spindle stage will be less precise than those made with a detent stage. On the other hand, its inexpensiveness allows every class member to construct or purchase one for personal use.

Figure 9-8. A poster board spindle stage (PBSS) as devised by Dr. Thomas Armbruster of the University of Bern (and made, slightly modified, by Dr. M.E. Gunter of the University of Idaho). Details about its construction and use—as well as a series of spindle stage laboratory exercises—are available from Gunter (1997) or <www.idaho.edu/~mgunter/opt_min/ss/ss.html>. Ready-made poster board spindle stages may be purchased by contacting the Mineralogical Society of America website: <www.minsocam.org>.

10 BIAXIAL CRYSTALS

OVERVIEW

For monochromatic light vibrating along one of the three mutually perpendicular, principal vibration axes (X, Y or Z in Fig. 10-1A), a biaxial crystal will exhibit a principal refractive index (respectively: α, β or γ). Any two principal axes define a principal plane (to which the third is perpendicular). For vibrations not coinciding with X, Y or Z, a biaxial crystal generally exhibits an index α' (by definition a value between α and β) or an index γ' (by definition between β and γ). Considering vibrations varying from X to Z within the XZ plane (Fig. 10-1B), the corresponding refractive indices vary from α to α' to β to γ' to γ. From X to Y in the XY plane, indices vary from α to α' to β and define the dark-shaded ellipse in Figure 10-1B.

For vibrations within any non-principal plane hinged on Z (e.g., planes 1, 2, 3 in Fig. 10-2A), the corresponding indices range from γ (parallel Z) down to α'. Each such plane thus contains one vector of length β. Consequently, within the biaxial indicatrix, there exist *two* circular sections of radius β (ruled, Fig. 10-2A) and, perpendicular to each, an optic axis (dashed, Fig. 10-2B). The **biaxial indicatrix**, so-called because it has *two* optic axes, represents what mathematicians call a triaxial ellipsoid (elongated along Z, flattened along X, and with a Y axis intermediate in length between Z and X). Any random section through it (= not parallel to X, Y, Z) will be an ellipse (minor axis α', major axis γ'). For principal planes, the ellipses will have semiaxes α and β (XY section), β and γ (YZ section), and α and γ (XZ section). The XZ plane, because both optic axes lie in it, is called the **optic plane** and the Y axis—because it is normal (perpendicular) to the optic plane—is called the **optic normal**.

The acute angle between the two optic axes is called $2V$. The bisector of the acute $2V$ is called the **acute bisectrix**, the bisector of the obtuse angle ($180°\text{-}2V$) is called the **obtuse bisectrix**. Biaxial crystals are said to be optically (+), if Z is the AB, but (–), if X is. Alternatively, one can stipulate $2V$ as $2V_x$, if measured across X, or $2V_z$, if measured across Z. Equivalent descriptions of the crystal whose indicatrix is illustrated in Figure 10-2B are: (1) $2V = 70°$, optically (-); (2) $2V_x = 70°$; or (3) $2V_z = 110°$.

The mathematical relationship between $2V$ and indices α, β and γ is

$$cos\,V_z = \frac{\alpha}{\beta}\sqrt{\frac{\left(\gamma^2 - \beta^2\right)}{\left(\gamma^2 - \alpha^2\right)}}$$

(Eqn. 10-3)

The in-air equivalent of $2V$ is $2E$ (Fig. 10-7), where $\sin E = \beta \sin V$ (Eqn. 10-5).

If $2V$ is small enough, two melatopes, one for each optic axis will be visible in AB-centered figures, which are those for which the acute bisectrix crops out at (or near) the cross-hair intersection. Each melatope is the site of blackness ($\Delta = 0$). Outward from each, the retardation increases (Fig. 10-15). For a wave normal traveling along X in Figure 10-15, the retardation, Δ_x, equals $(\gamma - \beta)t$, where t equals thickness. For Figure 10-15A, the 3° (third-order) green indicates $\Delta_x \approx 1300$ nm; for Figure 10-15B the 1° yellow indicates $\Delta_x \approx 300$ nm. If these crystals were in thin sections of rock (= 0.03 mm or 30,000 nm thick), $\Delta_x \div t$

—and thus $(\gamma - \beta)$—would equal 0.043 (Fig. 10-15A) and 0.010 (Fig. 10-15B). Note that greater birefringence, 0.043 vs. 0.010, results in more isochromes.

For any wave normal within a biaxial crystal, its two associable vibration directions—always perpendicular to it and each other—will bisect the angle between the two planes formed by connecting this wave normal to each of the two optic axes (Biot-Fresnel rule, Fig. 10-9A). Consequently, the vibration directions associable with any wave normal that crops out in an interference figure are roughly obtainable by (1) joining its point of outcrop to those for the two optic axes and then (2) bisecting the angle thus formed. Doing this at various points where wave normals emerge in an AB-centered interference figure wherein the optic plane trends NE-SW (Fig. 10-16A), hyperbola-shaped isogyres, black between crossed polarizers (because they consist of N-S and E-W vibrations), become identified. Moreover, where principal planes emerge (dot-dashed lines, Fig. 10-16A), the vibration directions will be parallel (or perpendicular) to their trace. Consequently, if the stage is rotated 45° until the optic plane becomes N-S (Fig. 10-16B), the isogyres become a cross whose bars mark where principal planes emerge in the field. In general the narrower bar always marks the optic plane. The wider bar marks the principal plane parallel both to Y and to the AB [namely, X for (−) crystals; Z for (+) ones].

Whenever a more-or-less straight isogyre lies N-S or E-W, it marks the outcrop of a principal plane. This plane will be perpendicular to the stage, if the isogyre is bisected by the N-S (or E-W) cross-hair (Fig. 10-17A), but tilted at an angle if not (Fig. 10-17B). Figure 10-17A discloses that (1) a principal plane lies N-S and vertical and (2) that the principal axis perpendicular to this plane is E-W and horizontal. Depending upon whether this horizontal axis is X, Y or Z, a principal index α, β or γ can then be compared to n for the oil (E-W polarizing microscope assumed).

If neither bar of a biaxial cross is bisected by a cross-hair (Fig. 10-23A), the crystal is randomly oriented such that no principal direction (X, Y or Z) is parallel or perpendicular to the stage.

Figure 10-28 illustrates the very important point that, *whatever occurs at the cross-hair intersection for an interference figure will occur for the entire crystal when viewed orthoscopically.*

For biaxial crystals, all three principal indices, and thus $2V$, undergo dispersion (Fig. 10-29). If $2V$ for red light is less than that for violet, as true in Figure 10-29, this is summarized as $r < v$. For other minerals $r > v$ or even $r \gg v$ may pertain. Blue or red dispersion fringes along the edges of isogyres in AB-centered figures, if observable, will disclose whether $r < v$ or $r > v$ (see Fig. 10-30).

Biaxial crystals may display abnormal interference colors because of selective absorption of a particular wavelength, dispersion of the birefringence, or dispersion of X, Y or Z and/or the optic axes.

INTRODUCTION

A biaxial crystal belongs to the orthorhombic, monoclinic, or triclinic system and possesses *three* **principal indices of refraction**, commonly symbolized as α, β, and γ. Of these, α and γ represent, respectively, the smallest and largest refractive indices exhibited by the crystal; β is intermediate in value between them. Alternative symbols are $n_\alpha \, n_\beta \, n_\gamma$—$n_p \, n_m \, n_g$—or $n_x \, n_y \, n_z$.

BIAXIAL INDICATRIX

As in uniaxial crystals, the index of refraction for monochromatic light varies with its vibration direction in biaxial crystals. Within such crystals two unique, mutually perpendicular directions may be located for which, and only for which, the crystal respectively exhibits its greatest and least refractive indices, γ and α. For a third direction, at right angles to these two the crystal exhibits the refractive index β. These three directions, commonly symbolized as X, Y, and Z are called the three **principal vibration axes**. The correspondence between these directions and the refractive indices that the crystals exhibit for light vibrating parallel to them is always as illustrated in Figure 10-1A. For any vibration direction not coinciding with X, Y, or Z, the corresponding refractive index will be between α and β or between β and γ in value. The former index is symbolized as α', the latter as γ'. Consequently, the following relationship always holds true : $\alpha < \alpha' < \beta < \gamma' < \gamma$.

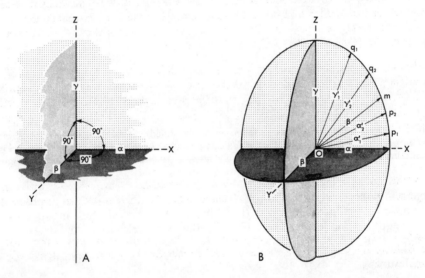

Figure 10-1. (A) The three, mutually perpendicular, principal vibration axes, X, Y, and Z and the common symbols for the indices of refraction of a biaxial mineral for light vibrating parallel to them. (B) Elliptical distribution of the index of refraction (as shown by the vector lengths) for light vibrating parallel to op_1, op_2, om, oq_2, oq_1 within the ZX plane.

Consider now a few of the random vibration directions within the XZ plane (stippled in Fig. 10-1B). The varying lengths of these radii, drawn to represent the crystal's refractive index for that vibration, define an ellipse whose semiminor axis is α and whose semimajor axis is γ. Note that the length om is exactly equal to β. Similarly, the lengths of random vibrations in the lightly shaded YZ plane also define an ellipse (semiminor axis, β; semimajor axis, γ), and those lying in the deeply shaded XY plane, a third ellipse (semiminor axis, α; semimajor axis, β). Figure 10-1B thus illustrates the basic framework of the biaxial indicatrix.

Countless planes hinging on the Z axis (in addition to the XZ and YZ planes of Fig. 10-1B) could be drawn; in Figure 10-2A unshaded planes 1, 2, and 3 are examples. As is demonstrated in detail for plane 2, the crystal's refractive indices vary with change of vibration direction in each such plane. The vectors representing the crystal's indices for light vibrating parallel to them vary in length like radii of an ellipse. The semiaxes of this ellipse for plane 1 are γ and α_1'; for plane 2, γ and α_2'; and for plane 3, γ and α_3'. In each

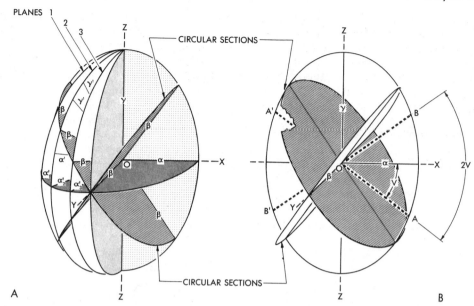

Figure 10-2. (A) Variation of refractive index in a biaxial crystal as shown by ellipses (whose radii are proportional in length to the crystal's refractive index for light vibrating parallel to them). Planes 1, 2, and 3 are typical of the numerous ellipses that could be drawn to hinge on ZZ. All such ellipses contain one radius equal to β in length, these radii lying in the same planes (ruled). These planes, the circular sections, intersect in principal axis Y. (B) The biaxial indicatrix; that is, simply an imaginary three-dimensional ellipsoid whose radii are proportional to the crystal's refractive indices for light vibrating parallel to them. AA' and BB', the normals to the circular sections, are the two optic axes.

case the semiminor axis of the ellipse—that is, α_1', α_2', or α_3'—is also a radius of the deeply shaded $\alpha\beta$ ellipse. Since $\alpha < \beta < \gamma$, in each of these ellipses hinging on Z there exist radii equal to β in length. These β radii define two circles (of radius β), each closely ruled in Figure 10-2A.

Nomenclature

The shape of the biaxial indicatrix has now emerged (Fig. 10-2B). It is a three-dimensional ellipsoid, all central sections of which are ellipses except for two. These two, one unshaded and one closely ruled in Figure 10-2B, are the **circular sections**, the radius of each being β. The two normals to these circular sections, AA' and BB', are called the (primary) **optic axes**, a term often abbreviated as O.A. Since there are two such optic axes (each comparable with the single optic axis of the uniaxial indicatrix), this indicatrix is said to be biaxial.[1] The two optic axes always lie within the XZ ($\alpha\gamma$) plane, which is therefore called the **optic plane**. The principal vibration direction Y, since it is always normal to the optic plane, is called the **optic normal** (abbreviated ON). The acute angle between the two optic axes is called **2V** or simply the **optic axial angle**. The obtuse axial angle—that is, angle BOA'—is always supplementary to $2V$.

The principal vibration axis that bisects the (acute) optic axial angle (that is, X in Fig. 10-2B) is called the **acute bisectrix** (abbreviated AB or *Bxa*). The principal vibration axis which bisects the obtuse axial angle is called the **obtuse bisectrix** (abbreviated OB or *Bxo*). In Figure 10-2A, X (α) is shown to be the acute bisectrix whereas Z (γ) is the

---

[1] In geometrical terminology the biaxial indicatrix is a triaxial ellipsoid in reference not to the optic axes but to its three, mutually perpendicular, principal axes, X, Y, and Z.

obtuse bisectrix. For many minerals this will be reversed; that is, Z will be the acute bisectrix and X will be the obtuse bisectrix. In biaxial minerals the optic sign depends upon this relationship. **Biaxial (+)** crystals are defined to be those for which Z (γ) is the acute bisectrix; **biaxial (–)** crystals are those for which X (α), is the acute bisectrix. For (+) minerals, β is closer in value to α than to γ. For (–) minerals β is generally closer to γ than to α but rare exceptions may occur for minerals in which $2V$ is near 90°. The biaxial indicatrix of a mineral is usually drawn with Z vertical.

Equations for the Biaxial Indicatrix

The equation for the biaxial optical indicatrix is generally given as

$$\frac{X^2}{\alpha^2} = \frac{Y^2}{\beta^2} = \frac{Z^2}{\gamma^2} = 1 \qquad \text{(Eqn. 10-1)}$$

the equation for a triaxial ellipsoid in rectangular coordinates.

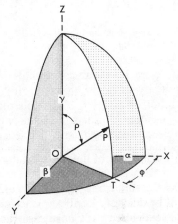

Figure 10-3. Stereographic coordinates, ϕ and ρ, of OP, a randomly directed radius of the biaxial indicatrix whose principal axes X, Y, and Z are as shown. Z is vertical, as preferred for biaxial indicatrices.

From the polar equations for an ellipse, an equation for the biaxial indicatrix may be developed that uses stereographic coordinates and is therefore well suited for the stereographic solution of optical problems. Let OP be a randomly directed radius of a biaxial indicatrix (Fig. 10-3). Define ρ (rho) as its angle with principal axis Z, and ϕ (phi), as the angle between X and the unshaded plane which contains OP and Z. Thus ϕ and ρ represent the stereographic coordinates that serve to orient line OP in the indicatrix; such stereographic coordinates are discussed by Bloss (1994). The length of OP and therefore the crystal's index for light vibrating parallel to OP—namely, γ_{op}' (or α_{op}', if computation discloses it to be less than β)—may be calculated from the following equation

$$\gamma_{op}' \ (or \ \alpha_{op}') = \frac{1}{\sqrt{\dfrac{\sin^2\rho \, \cos^2\phi}{\alpha^2} + \dfrac{\sin^2\rho \, \sin^2\phi}{\beta^2} + \dfrac{\cos^2\rho}{\gamma^2}}} \qquad \text{(Eqn. 10-2)}$$

Variation and Calculation of 2V

The angle between the two optic axes, if denoted as $2V$, is by definition the acute angle between them. An increasingly popular convention, however, uses the symbols $2V_x$ or $2V_z$ to denote the angle between the optic axes according to whether it is measured across the X direction or across the Z direction (Fig. 10-4). The angles so defined may then exceed 90°. The sum of $2V_x$ plus $2V_z$ for a given crystal—for example, either crystal

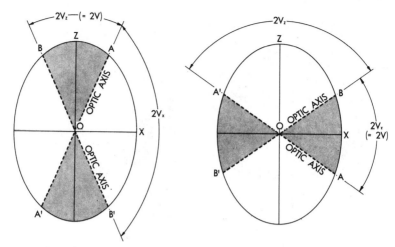

Figure 10-4. Relationship between $2V_x$ and $2V_z$. Note that $2V$ equals $2V_x$ or $2V_z$, whichever is smaller. The dashed lines represent the optic axes.

in Figure 10-4—always equals 180°. Note that the statement that a biaxial crystal is optically negative in sign with $2V = 37°$ may be succinctly restated in this new symbolism as $2V_x = 37°$ or, alternatively, as $2V_z = 143°$. Either of these latter statements implies that X bisects the acute angle between the optic axes and that Z bisects the obtuse angle between them, and that the crystal is optically negative.

The value of the optic axial angle, $2V$, depends upon the extent to which β is closer to α than to γ in value, or vice versa. If, for example, β differs slightly from α but considerably from γ (see Fig. 10-5A), then *Om* (the radius in the $\alpha\gamma$ ellipse equal to β) will be at a very small angle to the unshaded $\alpha\beta$ ellipse. Thus $2V$ is very small, and γ is the acute bisectrix. Consider now a second mineral possessing the same values of α and γ but a larger value of β (Fig. 10-5B). In this case, *Om* is at a larger angle to the $\alpha\beta$ ellipse. Thus V (and consequently $2V$) is larger than for the first mineral.

For a third mineral, again assume the same values of α and γ but this time assume β has a value so close to halfway between α and γ (Fig. 10-5C) that V equals precisely 45° and thus $2V$ equals 90°. As a consequence, neither α nor γ can be properly called the acute bisectrix, because $2V$ now equals a 90-degree angle rather than an acute one. Hence this third mineral is neither (+) nor (–). For a fourth mineral, α and γ are as before, but now β is closer to γ in value (Fig. 10-5D). Consequently, *Om* (the radius in the $\alpha\gamma$ ellipse that is equal to β) is close to the Z axis. As a result, the angle between OX and OA (the optic axis) is now acute, and OX has become the acute bisectrix. This fourth mineral is therefore (–) in sign. Note that if β becomes equal to α in value, the mineral becomes uniaxial positive; if β equals γ, the mineral becomes uniaxial negative.

The angle $2V$ can be readily calculated if the values of α, β, and γ are known. The relationship is

$$\cos V_z = \frac{\alpha}{\beta} \sqrt{\frac{(\gamma^2 - \beta^2)}{(\gamma^2 - \alpha^2)}} \qquad \text{(Eqn. 10-3)}$$

where V_z is the angle between the optic axis and the Z direction. For biaxial negative minerals, V_x may be preferred. In such case, if V_z has been calculated, V_x can be

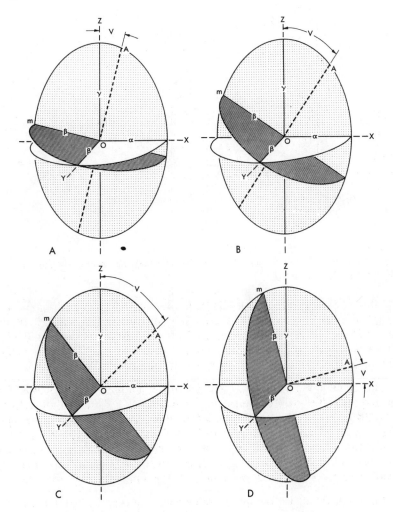

Figure 10-5. The variation of 2V in four crystals all possessing equal values of α and γ but, from (A) to (D), increasing values of β. For simplicity only one circular section (closely ruled) and one optic axis (OA) are drawn. Note the attendant increase in 2V from (A) to (C). With increase in β beyond that in (C), the optic sign becomes negative. Also note that V_Z increases continuously from (A) to (D).

determined readily since

$$V_z + V_x = 90° \qquad \text{(Eqn. 10-4)}$$

If V_z is a value greater than 45°, this indicates that the crystal is actually biaxial negative.

Equation 10-3 indicates that, if given any three of the four variables α, β, γ and V, the fourth may be calculated. To do so, one can use Opt_cal, the computer program devised by Gunter and Schares (1991) or the nomogram (Fig. 10-6A) devised by Mertie (1942). Figure 10-6B illustrates the use of the Mertie chart for determining 2V, if given α, β, and γ. Simply place a transparent straight-edge to indicate the value of α on the left edge of the chart (point 1) and the value of γ on its right edge (point 3). Locate the point on the line joining 1 and 3 for which the refractive index equals β (this is point 2 in Fig. 10-6B). A vertical line through point 2 (marked by an arrow in Fig. 10-6B) indicates

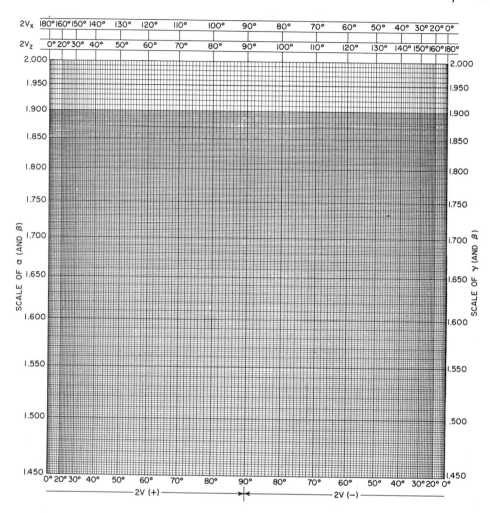

Figure 10-6A. The Mertie Chart.

the value of 2V on Figure 10-6A's upper or lower scale. Thus, in Figure 10-6B, $\alpha =$ 1.550, $\beta = 1.630$, $\gamma = 1.650$, and thereby 2V is determined to be 50°, the mineral's sign being (–). In a similar manner, if 2V, the optic sign, and two of the three indices α, β, and γ are known, points 1, 2, and 3 can be located. (They are always collinear.) Consequently, the value of the third index can be determined from the ordinate value of point 1, 2, or 3 (depending upon whether α, β, or γ represents the unknown value).

The angle 2V represents the angle between the two optic axes *within* the crystal. By contrast, the angle in air between light rays that traveled along the two optic axes while in the crystal is referred to as 2E (Fig. 10-7). As we shall later discuss in detail, the refractive index for rays traveling along the optic axes in biaxial crystals is β. Thus, applying Snell's law, the relationship between E and V is seen to be

$$\beta \sin V = \sin E$$

(Eqn. 10-5)

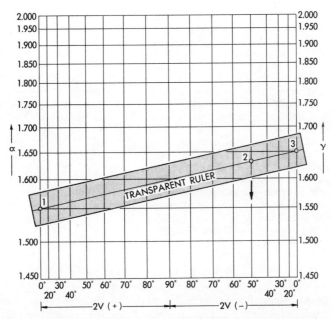

Figure 10-6B. Method of determining $2V$ with the Mertie chart (Fig. 10-6A) from the values of α (point 1), β (point 2), and γ (point 3). The transparent straight edge has a straight line ruled along the center of its bottom surface, this line being used to connect points 1 and 3. Directly below point 2 on this line will be the value for $2V$.

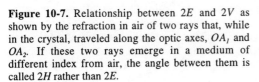

Figure 10-7. Relationship between $2E$ and $2V$ as shown by the refraction in air of two rays that, while in the crystal, traveled along the optic axes, OA_1 and OA_2. If these two rays emerge in a medium of different index from air, the angle between them is called $2H$ rather than $2E$.

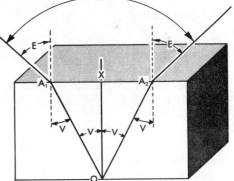

GEOMETRIC RELATIONSHIPS BETWEEN WAVE NORMALS, VIBRATION DIRECTIONS, AND RAY PATHS

Indicatrix Theory

For a random wave normal in a biaxial indicatrix (for example, OW in Fig. 10-8), the associated privileged directions lie, by definition, in a plane perpendicular to the wave normal. When this plane is extended outward from the indicatrix center, it intersects the indicatrix in an ellipse (stippled in Fig. 10-8). The semiminor and semimajor axes of this ellipse (for example, On and ON in Fig. 10-8) represent the only two privileged directions that can be associated with the given wave normal. The crystal's indices for light vibrating parallel to On or to ON are α' or γ', respectively.

Figure 10-8. A given wave normal direction, *OW*, is shown in respect to *ON* and *On*, the only two vibration or privileged directions possibly associable with it; angles *WON* and *WOn* are therefore 90 degree angles. Note that *ON* and *On* are the major and minor axes of the ellipse (stippled) obtained by passing a plane (perpendicular to *OW*) through the indicatrix. Each of these vibration directions, in conjunction with *OW*, defines a plane that also cuts the indicatrix in an ellipse (shaded). Ray paths *OR₁* or *OR₂*, the only two ray paths associable with wave normal *OW*, lie within these ellipses, being radii of the ellipse conjugate to the vibration direction. For illustrative purposes, liberty was taken in drawing ray paths *OR₁* and *OR₂*. Thus, *OR₁*, the conjugate to vibration α′ within the dark ellipse, should have been drawn as the direction tangent to the dark ellipse at point *n*. This true direction, however, would place *OR₁* behind *OW* in the dark ellipse. Similarly, ray path *OR₂* should have been drawn behind *OW* in the gray ellipse.

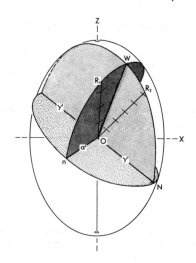

Only one ray path can be linked with a given wave normal and one of its two associated privileged directions; all three (path, normal, and privileged direction) always lie within the same plane. For example, ray path *OR₂* (Fig. 10-8) is the only one that can be associated with wave normal *OW and* privileged direction *ON*. It is readily located since (1) it lies in the same ellipse as do *OW* and *ON*—that is, in the lightly shaded ellipse in Fig. 10-8—and (2) it is the radius conjugate to *ON* in this ellipse. Similarly, ray path *OR₁* is located in the same ellipse as *OW* and *On*—that is, in the more heavily shaded ellipse in Figure 10-8—and is conjugate to *On*.

Biot-Fresnel Rule

Biot (1820), and also Fresnel (1827), formulated a rule that permits determination of the two privileged directions associable with a given wave normal direction. The rule is of great practical use since it is easily adapted to the stereographic solution of optical problems. Given the wave normal direction *OW* and the two optic axes *OA* and *OB* in the crystal (Fig. 10-9A), the vibration directions *WN* and *Wn* associated with wave normal *OW* may be located as follows: Construct a plane containing *OA* and *OW* and another containing *OB* and *OW* (in Fig. 10-9A, each is finely ruled). The vibration directions, *WN* and *Wn,* lie in the unshaded planes that bisect the angle between these finely ruled planes. Since vibration directions *WN* and *Wn* are necessarily perpendicular to *OW* as well, their precise direction in the crystal is known.

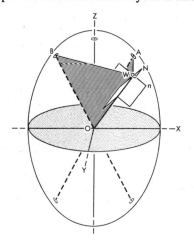

Figure 10-9A. The Biot-Fresnel rule states that the vibration directions (*WN* and *Wn*) associable with a wave normal (*OW*) lie within the planes (unshaded) that bisect the angles between the ruled planes, where each ruled plane is defined to contain *OW* and an optic axis, *OA* or *OB*. In addition, these vibrations, as is always the case, must be perpendicular to their associated wave normal *OW*.

Vibration Directions for Light in Principal Planes

Any plane parallel to two of the three principal vibration axes (X, Y, Z) constitutes a **principal plane**. For light traveling along wave normals lying in principal planes—for example, WN_1 and WN_2 in Figure 10-9B—application of the Biot-Fresnel rule indicates that the vibration directions will be perpendicular to (and/or within) the principal plane. **Axiom**: *As for uniaxial principal planes, light traveling in a biaxial principal plane will vibrate either within or perpendicular to this principal plane.*

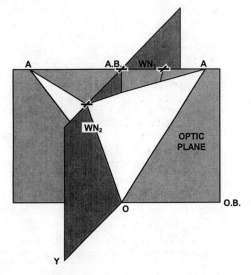

Figure 10-9B. Application of the Biot-Fresnel rule to wave normals that lie in principal planes— for example, OW_1 and OW_2—will disclose that their associated vibrations invariably lie (1) within and/or (2) perpendicular to the principal plane.

Examples for Normal Incidence

As with uniaxial crystals, normal incidence constitutes for biaxial crystals the simplest yet most important type of incidence. For normal incidence, the revised Snell's law indicates that, since the incident wave normal direction is perpendicular to the crystal face or surface, the wave normal of the refracted light must also be (that is, $\angle i = \angle r = 0°$). Thus the two privileged directions associable with the refracted wave normal, since they must always be perpendicular to this wave normal, necessarily lie parallel to the crystal plane upon which normal incidence occurs. More specifically, these two privileged directions represent the major and minor axes of the ellipse formed by the intersection of the crystal plane with the indicatrix, the plane always being assumed to pass through the indicatrix center.

The dimensions of the major and minor axes of the ellipse of intersection depend upon the angular attitude of the plane to the X, Y, and Z principal vibration axes of the indicatrix. Thus, according to whether they are parallel to two, one, or none of these principal vibration axes, crystal planes may be classified (Table 10-1) into three groups: (1) principal planes, (2) semirandom planes, or (3) random planes. An individual plane may be conveniently symbolized by two letters denoting the directions in the indicatrix to which the plane is parallel. The letters X' and Z', for example, represent directions within the indicatrix that are on opposite sides of the circular section. Direction X' is on the same side as X; Z' is on the same side as Z. The symbol YC has been used to indicate a circular section, since a plane parallel to the circular section is always parallel to the Y principal vibration axis as well. Examples of the different types of faces are illustrated in Figure 10-10.

Random Planes. The geometric principles (discussed earlier) govern the location of the refracted ray paths for normal incidence. Figure 10-11A illustrates the general

Table 10-1. Types of planes through the biaxial indicatrix.

Principal axes to which crystal plane is parallel	Convenient optical symbol for plane	Dimensions of ellipse of intersection between plane and indicatrix	
		minor axis	major axis
(1) Principal planes			
X, Y	*X Y*	α	β
X, Z	*X Z*	α	γ
Y, Z	*Y Z*	β	γ
(2) Semirandom planes			
X	*X Z'*	α	γ'
Y	*Y X'*	α'	β
Y	*Y Z'*	β	γ'
Y (plus circular section)	*Y C*	*circle of radius* β	
Z	*Z X'*	α'	γ
(3) Random planes			
None	*X'Z'*	α'	γ'

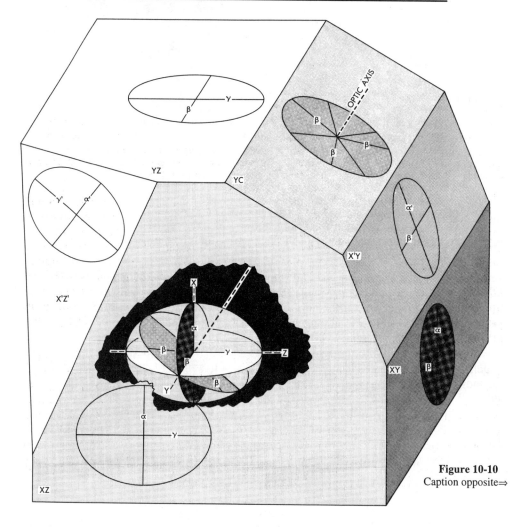

Figure 10-10
Caption opposite⇒

case for normal incidence, that upon a random plane. The refracted wave normal OW is associable with either vibration direction OZ' or OX'. Moreover, OR_1 is the only ray path associable with wave normal OW *and* vibration direction OZ', all three lying within the same plane (heavily shaded in Fig. 10-11A). This plane intersects the indicatrix in an ellipse for which OR_1 and OZ' are conjugate radii. Similarly, ray path OR_2 is the only one associable with wave normal OW *and* vibration direction OX'. Consequently, if unpolarized light is normally incident upon a random section, two rays, OR_1 and OR_2, result. Both act as extraordinary rays, neither coinciding with their common wave normal direction OW. If the incident light is polarized, ray OR_1, ray OR_2, or both OR_1 and OR_2 result, according to whether the direction of light vibration is parallel to OZ', to OX', or to neither.

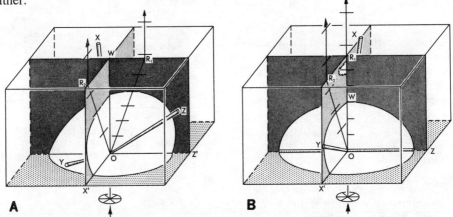

Figure 10-11. (A) The ray paths developed within a biaxial crystal as the result of normal incidence of an unpolarized ray upon a random section $X'Z'$. The ray-containing planes defined by wave normal OW and vibrations OZ' or OX' are shaded dark and light, respectively, each being a random section. Deviations of the ray paths OR_1 and OR_2 from the wave normal OW have been exaggerated for illustrative purposes.
(B) Rays resulting from the normal incidence of an unpolarized ray on a semirandom section $X'Z$. The ray-containing plane defined by wave normal OW and vibration OX' is a principal section XY.

Semirandom Planes. Figure 10-11B illustrates a more special case, normal incidence upon a semirandom section. The situation for ray OR_2 is as before. However, ray OR_1 (the only ray associable with wave normal OW and vibration direction OZ) now coincides with OW in direction (since OW is the radius conjugate to OZ for the ellipse of intersection between heavily shaded plane R_1OZ and the indicatrix). Note that the lightly shaded plane is principal section XY of the indicatrix. It contains principal axes OY and OX and is perpendicular to OZ (and therefore to the stippled, semirandom plane $(X'Z)$ upon which the unpolarized ray is normally incident). Rays OR_2 and OR_1 both lie in principal plane XY and bear the same relationship to it as do the E and O rays to a principal plane of a uniaxial crystal (p. 80, points 8 to 10).

The generalization already discussed again becomes apparent: A ray traveling within a principal plane of a biaxial crystal vibrates either perpendicular to this plane (for example, ray OR_1 in Fig. 10-11B) or within this plane along a direction

Figure 10-10. The biaxial indicatrix in skeletal form is shown at the center of the crystal. Its intersection with different faces of the crystal, if it were moved translationally until its center fell on a crystal face, is shown for several faces. The major and minor axes of these ellipses of intersection represent the privileged directions of the crystal for normal incidence on that face. For face YC, since it intersects the indicatrix in a circle, innumerable privileged directions exist. The crystal's refractive indices for the privileged directions are also shown. See Table 10-1 for details of symbolism used for the faces.

conjugate to its path (for example, OR_2). For the first case, ray path and vibration direction are mutually perpendicular and the ray acts like an ordinary ray. For the second, the ray acts like an extraordinary ray, only its wave normal following Snell's law.

Principal Plane. Light normally incident upon a principal section of a biaxial crystal is the most specialized case of all. Figure 10-11C illustrates that, for unpolarized incident light, two rays are produced, each vibrating parallel to a principal direction of the indicatrix and each coinciding in path with wave normal OW.

Circular Section; Internal Conical Refraction (Optional). A thin pencil of unpolarized light, if normally incident upon a circular section of a biaxial crystal, becomes a hollow cone of light within the crystal and a hollow cylinder of light after emergence (Fig. 10-12A). This phenomenon, known as internal conical refraction, is readily explained by indicatrix theory. As previously discussed, unpolarized light normally incident upon a circular section is

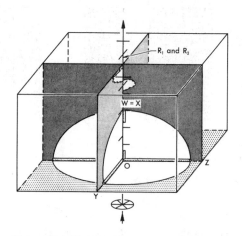

Figure 10-11C. Coincidence of the rays OR_1 and OR_2 produced by normal incidence of an unpolarized ray on a principal plane YZ (stippled). Both ray-containing planes (light and dark shading) are now principal sections.

not constrained to vibrate parallel to any particular direction after entering the crystal. Thus, both before and after entry into the crystal, the unpolarized light vibrates in innumerable directions within the circular section; a few of these possible vibration directions are illustrated in Figure 10-12A as radii labeled "β." After entry into the crystal, all light vibrating parallel to these various radii possesses the common wave normal direction OW (a consequence of normal incidence). Each of these different vibration directions, in conjunction with wave normal OW, gives rise to a different ray path. Thus, light vibrating parallel to OY in Figure 10-12B produces ray 1 (ray 1 is the radius conjugate to β_1 in the lightly shaded ellipse YOW). Similarly, light vibrating parallel to β_2 produces ray 2 (β_2 and ray 2 are conjugate radii lying within the dotted ellipse); light vibrating parallel to β_3 produces ray 3 (β_3 and ray 3 are conjugate radii of heavily shaded ellipse WOX').

If, as for β_3, ray paths were determined for the numerous other vibration directions between β_2 and β_1, the conical distribution of these ray paths (with respect to their common wave normal OW) becomes apparent. Each ray path on the cone is thus the result of a different vibration direction; Figure 10-12C, a slightly enlarged aerial view of the cone of rays, shows the vibration direction for several rays at their points of emergence from the crystal. Note their orientation with respect to the trace of the optic plane. Rays 1 and 2 traveled in this plane, ray 1 acting like a uniaxial O ray, ray 2 like an E ray.

As the crystal plate is made thinner, the radius of the hollow cylinder of light emergent from the crystal decreases, becoming minimal for crystal grains or plates of the thicknesses normally dealt with in optical crystallography. These plates therefore, act much like the circular sections of uniaxial minerals (which are incapable of exhibiting internal conical refraction). Thus an unpolarized ray of normally incident light remains essentially unpolarized during transmission by these plates whereas a polarized ray retains the same plane of vibration even after entry into the crystal.

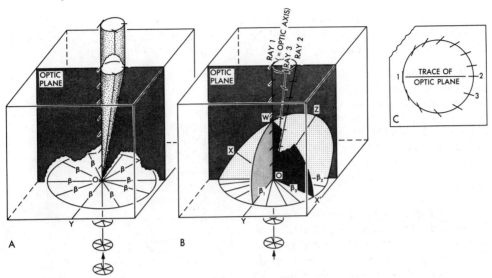

Figure 10-12. (A) Normal incidence of an unpolarized pencil of light on a circular section to produce a cone of rays within the crystal (that is, internal conical refraction) and a hollow cylinder of rays after their exit. (B) Conical distribution of the rays (1, 2, 3, etc.) associated with different vibrations in the circular section (β_1, β_2, β_3, etc.) but with the common wave normal *OW*. (C) Slightly enlarged view of rays emerging on the crystal's upper surface, showing the vibration directions at a few points of emergence.

BIAXIAL INTERFERENCE FIGURES

To be coherent—that is, capable of interfering with each other—two light rays must (1) originate from the same incident beam of polarized light upon its entrance into an anisotropic crystal and (2) travel along the same path after emergence from the crystal. If a biaxial crystal is illuminated by a solid cone of polarized light, closely adjacent rays within the cone may be considered to travel parallel to each other. Let *a* and *b* in Figure 10-13 represent two such rays, the spacing between them being measurable in nanometers but, for purposes of illustration, being greatly exaggerated. Upon entering the

Figure 10-13. Cross-sectional view of two closely adjacent rays *a* and *b* of the cone of illumination, their interspacing greatly exaggerated for illustrative purposes. Rays *a* and *b* respectively break up into rays a_1 and a_2 and b_1 and b_2 after entering an anisotropic crystal. Rays a_2 and b_1 emerge from the same point on the crystal and subsequently travel the same path in air, thus interfering with each other. Crystal thickness is greatly exaggerated.

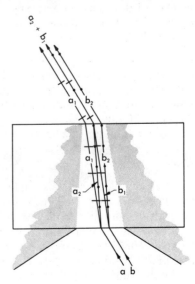

crystal, incident rays *a* and *b* break up into two rays, each vibrating in a different direction and each traveling with different speed; passage through the crystal retards ray a_2 with respect to ray a_1, and ray b_2 with respect to b_1. Rays such as a_2 and b_1, each from a different parent ray, emerge from the same point on the crystal and, since parent rays *a* and *b* were essentially parallel prior to entry into the crystal, a_2 and b_1 travel the same path in air, thus to interfere.

We will purposely make an incorrect assumption in the discussion that follows—namely, that the two rays that mutually interfere after emergence have also traveled the same path while within the crystal. This of course is not true; ray paths a_2 and b_1, for example, do not coincide within the crystal of Figure 10-13. However, within crystals of moderate birefringence the angle between ray paths such as a_2 and b_1 is generally small—that is about 1 to 3°; thus our assumption is not too far from the truth and considerably simplifies the ensuing discussion and illustration.

Acute Bisectrix Figure

Assume that a cone of light is focused with its apex at *O* on the bottom surface of a crystal (Fig. 10-14). Upward from *O*, therefore, numerous rays diverge—some traveling as fast rays, others as slow rays, depending upon their vibration directions in the crystal. Of these multitudinous ray paths, consider *OR*, *OP*, *OQ*, *OX*, *OS*, *OA*, *OT*, and *OU* each to represent the path of a slow and a fast ray—their 1° to 3° angular separation being ignored—that mutually interfere after emerging from the crystal and entering the analyzer. The vibration directions for the slow and the fast ray along each such path are drawn at the point where the path intersects the indicatrix and again, this time orthographically projected, on the crystal's upper surface at the point of the ray's emergence. Since *OX*, *OS*, *OA*, *OT*, and *OU* all lie within the dotted principal plane *ZX*, one ray along each vibrated perpendicular to this plane while in the crystal and therefore is associated with a refractive index β. The second ray traveling along each of these paths

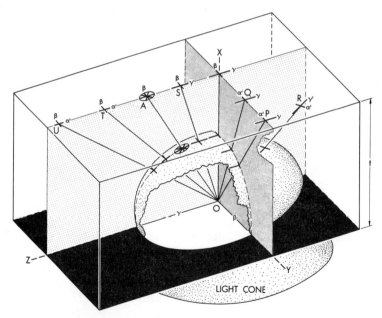

Figure 10-14. Relationship of selected ray paths *OP*, *OQ*, *OR*, *OX*, *OS*, *OA*, *OT*, and *OU* to their associated privileged directions, the latter shown as tangents to the indicatrix (or projected onto the crystal's upper surface at the ray's point of emergence).

vibrates within plane *ZX* but tangent to the indicatrix. Thus the refractive index for the second ray is γ for path *OX*, γ' for path *OS*, but α' for *OT* and a still smaller value of α' for path *OU*. For path *OA*, which coincides with the optic axis, the rays may vibrate parallel to any radius of the circular section; hence the only index associable with the ray along *OA* is β.

Similarly, paths *OQ* and *OP* in Figure 10-14 lie within the lightly shaded *XY* principal plane. Therefore, one of the rays traveling along each must vibrate perpendicular to this plane (and thus parallel to *OZ*); the index of this ray therefore corresponds to γ. The second ray along each vibrates within this plane but tangentially to the indicatrix. The refractive index for this second ray is therefore α' for *OQ* and a still smaller value of α' for *OP*. Path *OR* represents the general case since it does not lie within a principal plane. The fast and the slow ray traveling along it are associable with vibration directions corresponding to indices of α' and γ', respectively.

The retardation between the slow and fast rays when they emerge from the crystal's upper surface in Figure 10-14 depends upon whether they traveled straight through the crystal (as along *OX*) or along a path at an angle θ to *OX*. The retardation between the slow and the fast ray emerging at *OX* equals $(\gamma - \beta)t$ whereas between the two rays assumed to travel along *OS* the retardation approximately equals $(\gamma' - \beta)(t/\cos \theta)$. Note that the retardation decreases to zero for slow-fast ray pairs traveling along paths within the fan between *OX* and *OU* as path *OA* is approached. This is because the index (γ' or α') associated with one ray of the pair approaches the value of the index β associated with the remaining member of the pair, as a path becomes parallel to an optic axis. For paths making increasing angles to *OA*, the rate of increase in retardation is greater for those in the fan between *OA* and *OU* than in the fan between *OA* and *OX*, since path distance increases from *OA* toward *OU* whereas it decreases from *OA* toward *OX*. Retardation increases at the greatest rate in those paths lying outward from *OX* toward *OP*. For such paths the retardation upon emergence approximately equals $(\gamma - \alpha')(t/\cos \theta)$, the value of $(\gamma - \alpha')$, approaching that of $(\gamma - \alpha)$, as θ becomes large. For the numerous random ray paths that do not lie within principal planes—*OR* being an example—the retardation increases as their angle to the closest optic axis increases.

Surfaces of Equal Retardation; Isochromes. The surfaces joining all adjacent rays that emerge from the crystal with equal retardation are known as *surfaces of equal retardation* or as *Bertin's surfaces*. In Figure 10-15A they have been drawn only for retardations of 550, 1100, 1650, 2200, and 2750 nm. The intersection between these surfaces and a horizontal plane parallel to the crystal's upper surface marks the pattern of isochromes visible in a biaxial interference figure in which the rays that traveled along the acute bisectrix emerge at the center of the field of view; this type of interference figure is thus called a centered acute bisectrix figure. If white light is the illuminant, these intersections are marked by first-, second-, third-, fourth-, and fifth-order red isochromes. If monochromatic light of wavelength 550 nm (green) is substituted as the illuminant, black areas, caused by total destructive interference, appear where the red isochromes had been. Approximately midway between these black patterns, bright areas of light of wavelength 550 nm (green), representing constructive interference, will occur.

The number and disposition of the isochromes seen in an acute bisectrix figure depend upon (1) the crystal's thickness, *t*, (2) the difference between its refractive indices for the vibration directions of the slow and fast rays traveling upward along the acute bisectrix—that is, $(\beta - \alpha)$ for positive crystals and $(\gamma - \beta)$ for negative crystals, (3) the value of *2E*, and (4) the numerical aperture of the objective being used. Let Figure 10-15A and B represent equally thick plates of two different minerals that have comparable

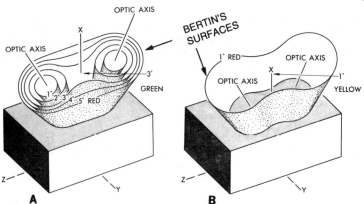

Figure 10-15. (A) Surfaces of equal retardation above a biaxial (–) crystal of moderate to high birefringence. (B) Same for crystal of low birefringence.

values for *2E* but that differ considerably in their value for ($\gamma - \beta$), this value for the crystal in Figure 10-15B being one-quarter what it is for the crystal in Figure 10-15A. Consequently, if the retardation, $t(\gamma - \beta)$, equals 1400 nm (third-order green) for the ray traveling along X in Figure 10-15A, that for the comparable ray in Figure 10-15B equals 350 nm (first-order yellow). These rays emerge at the center of the interference figures. Accordingly, as indicated by the arrows in Figure 10-15, third-order green (3° green) and first-order yellow (1° yellow) respectively appear at the centers of the interference figures. Note that in Figure 10-15B the 1° red isochrome compares in shape and position to the 4° red isochrome in Figure 10-15A. If the crystal in Figure 10-15B were four times as thick, the surfaces of equal retardation for the emergent rays would resemble those in Figure 10-15A. If either crystal had a smaller (or larger) value for *2E*, the spots of 1° black (= melatopes) that mark the points of emergence of rays that had traveled along the optic axis while in the crystal would be closer (or farther) from the center of the field of view. Inevitably, as Figure 10-15 illustrates, retardation colors become of higher order in directions outward from the melatopes.

Isogyres. The orthographic projection of the privileged directions for ray paths emerging in the field of view of an interference figure may be approximately determined by a two-dimensional application of the Biot-Fresnel rule. For example, in Figure 10-16A dashed construction lines may be drawn from point *a* to either melatope; the orthographically projected vibration directions for point *a* are then the bisectors of the angles between the two dashed lines. If this construction is performed for all points of light emergence in Figure 10-16A, there are regions, marked by crosses, where the privileged directions are E-W (solid lines) and N-S (dashed lines). Assuming an E-W vibrating polarizer, only rays vibrating E-W would have emerged at these points; consequently, the N-S privileged directions in Figure 10-16A have been drawn dashed to indicate the absence of a light ray vibrating N-S. Thus, since the interference figure is viewed with the N-S polarizing analyzer inserted, these hyperbolic areas are sites of extinction and appear as hyperbola-shaped black brushes called **isogyres**. The hyperbola's vertices coincide with the melatopes.

If the microscope stage containing the crystal is rotated while the interference figure is being observed, the shape and location of the isogyres change drastically whereas the image of the isochromes merely rotates to the extent that the stage does, their shapes remaining constant. Figure 10-16B illustrates the appearance of the interference figure in Figure 10-16A after the microscope stage was rotated until the crystal's optic plane was

N-S. The Biot-Fresnel rule can again be utilized to locate the points of emergence of rays associated with N-S and E-W privileged directions; one representative construction is shown in the figure. The isogyres are now in the shape of a cross. It differs from the uniaxial cross in that one bar is thinner than the other. This thinner bar coincides with the trace of the optic plane within the interference figure; the thicker bar marks the trace of the principal plane containing the acute bisectrix and the optic normal.

For biaxial interference figures in general, whenever the crystal is rotated so that the trace of a principal plane within the field of view is parallel to a N-S or E-W cross hair, a more or less straight isogyre is developed along the length of this trace.

Crystal with Large 2V. For crystals with large $2V$, $\beta \sin V$ (= $\sin E$) may exceed the objective's numerical aperture (N.A.). If so, the two melatopes for an AB-centered figure will occur outside the field of view. Such would result in Figure 10-16B if a 0.65 N.A. objective were substituted for a N.A. of 0.85. However, even if the melatopes do not appear within the field of view, the trace of the optic plane may be located from (1) the characteristic pattern of the isochromes or (2) the location of the thinner bar of the cross that marks the trace of the optic plane.

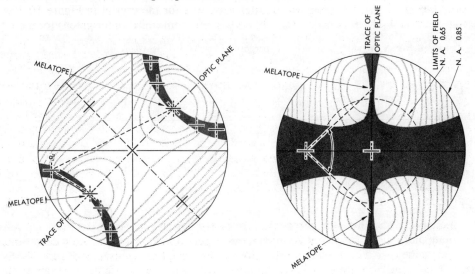

Figure 10-16. (A) Centered, acute bisectrix figure at 45° off extinction position. The two-dimensional analog of the Biot-Fresnel law is applied to point a to determine (approximately) the privileged directions for rays emerging there. At several points in the field of view the privileged directions for the rays emerging there are also shown. (B) Figure 10-16A as seen if the microscope stage is rotated 45° counterclockwise. Extinction occurs in the areas where rays emerge that vibrate parallel to the polarizer. The dashed circle marks the limits of the field of view if an objective of N.A. 0.65 is used instead of one of N.A. 0.85.

RECOGNITION OF INTERFERENCE FIGURES

Key Points

The key to interpreting biaxial (and uniaxial) interference figures is that light traveling in principal planes must vibrate parallel and/or perpendicular to such planes (axiom, p. 145). Thus whenever the trace of a principal plane becomes oriented E-W or N-S in the field of view, this trace will be marked by a more-or-less straight isogyre. Moreover, if this plane, thus oriented, is perpendicular to the microscope stage, the

154   *Chapter 10*

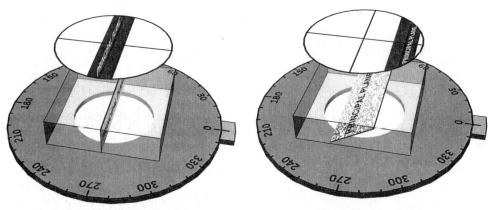

A   PRINCIPAL PLANE, VERTICAL   **B   PRINCIPAL PLANE, TILTED**

Figure 10-17. (A) The trace of a principal plane that lies perpendicular to the microscope stage, if oriented N-S, will, in the interference figure, become the site of a straight isogyre that is longitudinally bisected by the N-S cross-hair. Note that a principal axis, the one perpendicular to this principal plane, will now be E-W and horizontal so that the principal refractive index corresponding to this horizontal axis can be compared to *n* for the immersion oil (E-W polarizing microscope assumed). (B) The trace of a principal plane that lies tilted relative to the microscope stage (but emerges in the field of view) will, if oriented N-S, result in an offset N-S isogyre. [For illustrative purposes, Figures 10-17 to 10-20 are drawn with the viewer looking, not due north, but slightly west of north.]

isogyre will be *bisected* by a cross-hair (Fig. 10-17A); if the plane is tilted, the isogyre marking its trace, though remaining parallel to the cross-hair, will be offset from it (Fig. 10-17B).

Centered Figures

For a crystal oriented with two principal axes parallel to the stage, the third principal axis—and thus two mutually perpendicular principal planes—must lie perpendicular to the stage (Fig. 10-18A). Thus, when the stage is rotated until these perpendicular planes strike N-S and E-W, a **centered biaxial cross** results whose center (at the cross-hair intersection) marks where the perpendicular principal axis emerges in the field. Upon a 45° rotation of the microscope stage, this cross may become a hyperbola whose vertices, which coincide with the sites where the two optic axes emerge, lie inside the field of view (Fig. 10-18B). Alternatively, if 2*V*, the angle between the two optic axes, is large, the hyperbola (and its vertices) may lie outside the field of view.

Depending upon the optical identity of the centered (perpendicular) principal axis, a centered biaxial cross may represent an **acute-bisectrix-centered figure**, an **obtuse-bisectrix-centered figure**, or, if *Y* the optic normal is the centered axis, an **optic-normal-flash figure**. Figure 10-18A clearly represents an **AB-centered figure** because, after the 45° rotation, the melatopes are seen to lie within the field of view (Fig. 10-18B). On the other hand, Figure 10-19A, as drawn, represents an **OB-centered figure** for which, after the 45° rotation, no melatopes appear within the field of view (Fig. 10-19B).

Figure 10-20A represents an **ON-centered figure** that has been rotated into the biaxial-cross position. Its two vertical planes are now oriented N-S and E-W and a broad, poorly defined cross almost completely fills the field of view. Just a small rotation of the microscope stage will cause this diffuse cross to break up into isogyres that abruptly leave the field (Fig. 10-20B). This figure closely resembles the uniaxial flash figure, even to the disposition of any isochromes present. Accordingly, the ON-centered figure is often called the **optic-normal-flash figure**.

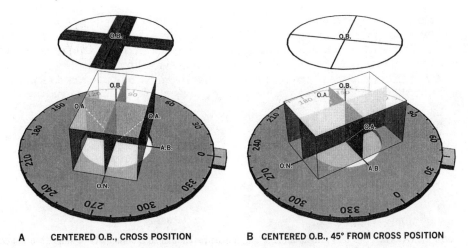

| A | CENTERED O.B., CROSS POSITION | B | CENTERED O.B., 45° FROM CROSS POSITION |

Figure 10-18. (A) A crystal—with its acute bisectrix (AB) *and thus two principal planes* perpendicular to the stage—has been rotated until the two principal planes are N-S and E-W. The interference figure that results consists of a centered biaxial cross whose center, the point of emergence of the AB, coincides with the cross-hair intersection. (B) To verify that the cross's center represents the acute bisectrix (and not the obtuse bisectrix), rotate the stage 45° as has been done here. If the vertices of the hyperbola-shaped isogyres, which mark the locations of the optic axes (OA), remain in the field, the cross' center assuredly coincides with the AB and not the OB. If they leave the field of view, the center of the cross represents either (1) the obtuse bisectrix or (2) the acute bisectrix for a crystal with a very large 2V value.

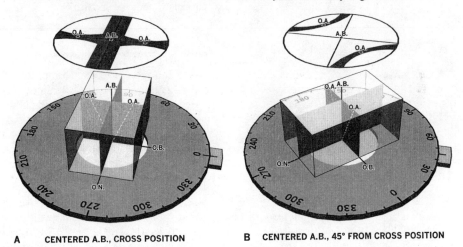

| A | CENTERED A.B., CROSS POSITION | B | CENTERED A.B., 45° FROM CROSS POSITION |

Figure 10-19. (A) A crystal—oriented with its obtuse bisectrix (OB), and thus two principal planes (one shaded, one stippled) perpendicular to the microscope stage—has been rotated until the principal planes are N-S and E-W. In consequence, its interference figure displays a centered biaxial cross. (B) After a 45° rotation from position (A), if no isogyres appear in the field of view (because the two optic axes OA emerge outside the field), the figure represents either (1) an OB-centered figure, as shown here, or (2) an AB-centered figure for a crystal with 2V so large that its two optic axes emerge outside the field of view.

Partly Off-centered (Semi-random) Figures

If only one axis—X, Y or Z—lies parallel to the stage, then only one principal plane, the one perpendicular to this stage-parallel axis, will be perpendicular to the stage. Figure 10-21A shows this stage-parallel axis, Y, to be N-S so that the plane perpendicular to it, the optic plane, is vertical and E-W. The E-W trace of this optic plane is accordingly marked by an isogyre that is longitudinally bisected by the E-W cross-hair. Note that the *YZ* principal plane, though somewhat tilted off perpendicularity, crops out in the field of view as the offset N-S bar of the off-centered cross. A rotation of 45° (Fig. 10-21B) shows that the vertex of the hyperbola (at *A'*) is offset from the cross-hair intersection. In other words, the crystal's optic axis is not quite perpendicular to the microscope's stage.

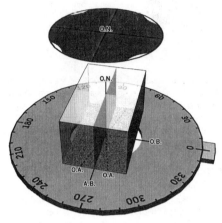

A   O.N. CENTERED FIGURE IN CROSS POSITION

**B   ISOGYRES LEAVE FIELD UPON
       SLIGHT ROTATION OF STAGE**

Figure 10-20. Crystal with optic normal (O.N.) perpendicular to the stage. (A) Crystal rotated until its two principal planes are N-S and E-W. The resultant interference figure is a diffuse black cross that almost completely fills the field of view. (B) In response to a slight rotation of the stage, the isogyres rapidly (and entirely) leave the field of view. This figure so closely resembles the uniaxial flash figure that it is often called the **optic normal flash figure**. Note that, because the optic plane is parallel to the stage, the crystal allows α and γ to be compared to *n* for the immersion oil.

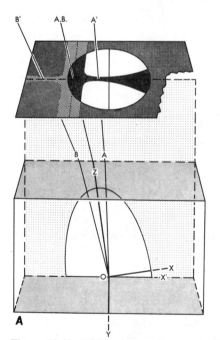

A

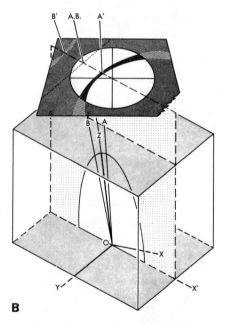

B

Figure 10-21. (A) Interference figure, rotated into the cross-position, for a crystal whose *XZ* plane lies perpendicular to the stage but whose *YZ* plane is tilted. Note that the N-S isogyre, which marks the outcrop of the tilted principal plane, is offset from the N-S cross-hair. The E-W isogyre, marking the outcrop of the perpendicular principal plane, is bisected by the E-W cross-hair. If this crystal is rotated 90° the index β becomes measurable. (B). Appearance of the interference figure after rotating the stage 45° from its position in (A). Note that the melatope, which coincides with the vertex of the hyperbola, is offset from the cross-hair intersection. This discloses that the optic axis is not perpendicular to the stage.

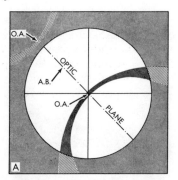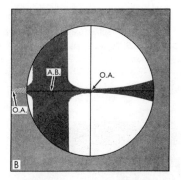

Figure 10-22. Interference figure for a crystal whose optic axis (and therefore its *XZ* or optic plane) is perpendicular to the microscope stage so that the melatope is located at the cross-hair intersection. (A) Appearance if the *XZ* plane is oriented NW-SE. (B) Appearance after the (vertical) *XZ* plane has been oriented E-W. This produces the biaxial cross whose thin bar marks the outcrop of the *XZ* (optic) plane and whose off-set thick bar marks the N-S outcrop of the tilted principal plane containing *Y* and the acute bisectrix.

For *Y* parallel to the stage, a special case exists if an optic axis, as well as the optic plane, lies perpendicular to the stage (Fig. 10-22A). The point of emergence of the optic axis (= the melatope) now coincides with the cross-hair intersection. At all times, isogyres must pass through a melatope. Consequently, during rotation of the stage, the isogyre remains "pinned" to the melatope—and rotates in a direction opposite to the direction of stage rotation. After a 45° rotation the hyperbola becomes an off-centered cross (Fig. 10-22B). For this particular figure, called an **optic-axis-centered figure**, the crystal will exhibit the index β for all positions of the stage (because a circular section will lie parallel to the stage).

Random Orientations

Most crystals will be in random orientations—that is, have no principal axis parallel to the stage. For such orientations, rotation of the stage may produce a biaxial cross both arms of which are offset from the cross-hairs (Fig. 10-23A). This cross's center marks where a principal vibration axis (X or Z) emerges in the field of view. As always, the

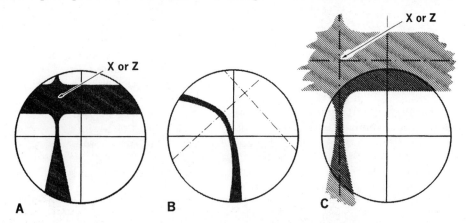

Figure 10-23. Random figure (that is, off-centered acute bisectrix figure). (A) With traces of its principal planes (dash-dotted lines) parallel to the cross hairs. (B) Same figure with stage rotated clockwise until an isogyre passes through the cross-hair intersection. (C) Cross position for an acute bisectrix so off-centered that it falls outside the field of view.

narrower arm of the cross will mark the trace of the optic plane. Rotation of the stage may resolve the cross into a hyperbola (Fig. 10-23B). In many cases, the off-centering may be so extreme that the biaxial cross falls outside the field of view (Fig. 10-23C).

Crystals in random orientations exhibit two non-principal indices—α' and γ'.

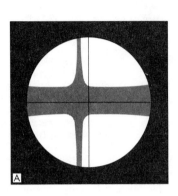 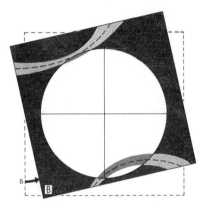

Figure 10-24. (A) A slightly off-centered biaxial interference figure in an extinction position. For this position an isogyre passes through the cross-hair intersection. (B) Appearance of this same figure after the stage has been rotated counterclockwise through δ, an angle just sufficient to cause the center of an isogyre (dashed line) to be tangent to the NW edge of the field of view. See text for further discussion.

Differentiation of Interference Figures

The different interference figures representing different orientations of a biaxial crystal may not always be distinguishable. For example, as previously noted, if 2V is large for the crystal, a centered acute bisectrix figure may be readily mistaken for a centered obtuse bisectrix figure. Such figures may also be mistaken for an optic normal figure. Distinction between them may sometimes be made by determining δ, the angle of rotation of the stage necessary to cause the isogyres to move from an extinction position (Fig. 10-24A) until the center line through the hyperbolic shadow (dashed in Fig. 10-24B) is tangent to the edge of the field of view. Let δ_{NW}, δ_{SW}, δ_{SE}, and δ_{NE} denote the angles of stage rotation necessary to produce such tangency to the edges of the NW, SW, SE, and NE quadrants of the field of view, respectively. For example, to alter the interference figure from Figure 10-24A to 10-24B required a counterclockwise rotation through the angle δ_{NW}. Note that a counterclockwise rotation through an angle slightly larger than δ_{NW} would have caused the central line of the lower hyperbolic isogyre (dashed in Fig. 10-24B) to become tangential to the edge of the SE quadrant; thus δ_{SE} is larger than δ_{NW}. Similarly, clockwise rotations from the extinction position of Figure 10-24A would permit measurement of δ_{SW} and δ_{NE}. These four angles—δ_{SE}, δ_{NW}, δ_{SW}, and δ_{NE}—are equal only for perfectly centered interference figures; that is, those for which a principal axis emerges at the cross-hair intersection. Even for slightly off-centered figures, however, δ—the average of these four angles—permits V to be determined by use of the curves (Fig. 10-25) developed by Kamb (1958), where V represents the angle (within the crystal) between the centered (or nearly centered) principal axis and the optic axis. In order to decide which curve in Figure 10-25 to use, it is necessary to know the approximate value of β for the unknown and to observe the interference figure with an objective of numerical aperture of 0.85. The principal axis that emerges at the center of the field of view is then (1) the acute bisectrix, if V is less than 45°; or (2) the obtuse

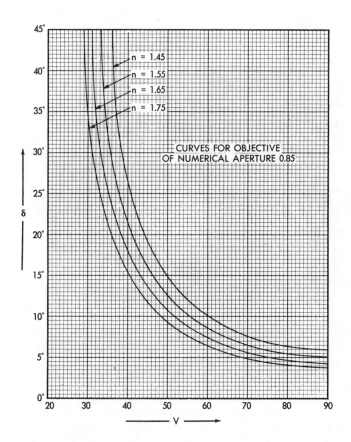

Figure 10-25. Chart for determining V, the angle between the bisectrix emerging at the center of the field of view and an optic axis, provided the value of δ has been measured from a centered interference figure viewed with an objective of numerical aperture 0.85. (After Kamb, 1958.)

bisectrix, if V exceeds 45°; or (3) the optic **normal,** if δ is so small that a horizontal line through its value falls below the curve. The accuracy to which $2V$ can be determined by this method depends in part upon the degree to which the observed interference figure is truly centered—and upon the observer's ability to judge the δ values for which the center of the isogyre becomes "tangent" to the field of view.

Some biaxial interference figures may be mistaken for uniaxial figures, but others may be definitely distinguished. Biaxial figures for which an optic axis occurs within the field of view are generally easy to differentiate from uniaxial figures. Centered acute bisectrix figures of minerals with very small $2V$ (1° to 5°), however, are difficult to differentiate from a uniaxial figure, because the separation of the melatopes that occurs when the optic plane is in the 45 degree position is hard to observe. This separation may be better observed, provided the grain is large enough, by substituting a medium-power objective (10×, N.A. 0.25) for the high-power objective and thus obtaining an enlarged view of the center of the interference figure. [The interference figure may sometimes be sharpened by raising the objective slightly above its orthoscopic position of clear focus.]

When the optic axis does not occur within the field of view, a biaxial crystal with small $2V$ may be indistinguishable from a uniaxial crystal (Fig. 10-26). However, some interference figures, even though no optic axis falls within the field, may be clearly differentiated by rotating the stage until an isogyre passes through a cross-hair intersection. For this position, as previously discussed, an undoubtedly biaxial crystal will be distinguished by an isogyre that does not parallel either cross hair (Fig. 10-27A). In contrast, an isogyre that is bisected along its length by a cross hair (Fig. 10-27B) may indicate either a uniaxial crystal or a biaxial crystal resting on a semirandom section.

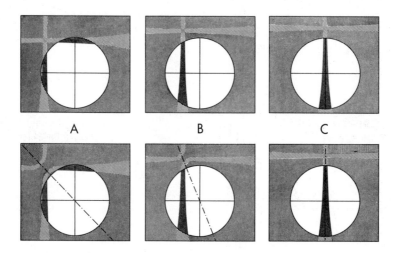

Figure 10-26. Similarity between an off-centered, uniaxial figure (upper diagrams) and a biaxial figure with small 2V (lower diagrams) for the crystal (A) at 45° off extinction, (B) at 22° off extinction, and (C) at extinction.

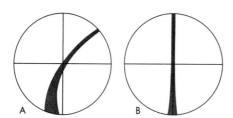

Figure 10-27. Comparison of the shape and alignment of two isogyres after the stage has been rotated until each passes through the cross-hair intersection. (A) An unequivocally biaxial isogyre is characterized by its curved shape and nonparallelism to either cross hair. (B) An isogyre that may represent either a uniaxial crystal or a semirandom section of a biaxial crystal. Note its longitudinal bisection by the N-S cross hair.

Relationship to Orthoscopic Observations

From the interference figure of a crystal plate, the microscopist can deduce several features that the crystal would exhibit if viewed orthoscopically. For such deductions, the key area to observe is at the intersection of the cross hairs—that is, where the central ray of the cone of light that passed through the crystal emerges in the field of view. This central ray essentially passes through the crystal in the same direction as do *all* the rays when the crystal is viewed orthoscopically (Fig. 10-28A). Consequently, the retardation color represented by that isochrome of the interference figure which passes through the cross-hair intersection is also the retardation color of the crystal plate (feathered edges excepted), if viewed orthoscopically (Fig. 10-28B). Similarly, the crystal is at a position of orthoscopic extinction whenever an isogyre passes through the cross-hair intersection (Fig. 10-28C).

Students may demonstrate these relationships to their own satisfaction by observing a crystal both orthoscopically and conoscopically.

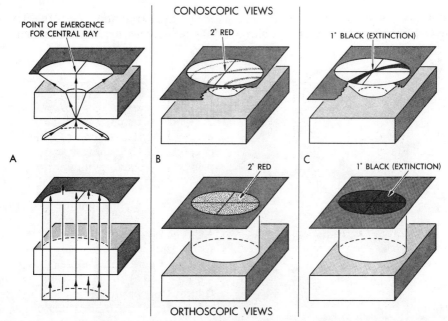

CONOSCOPIC VIEWS

POINT OF EMERGENCE
FOR CENTRAL RAY

2° RED

1° BLACK (EXTINCTION)

A

B

2° RED

C

1° BLACK (EXTINCTION)

ORTHOSCOPIC VIEWS

Figure 10-28. (A) Equivalence of the path of the central ray in conoscopic illumination (upper) with *all* the ray paths in orthoscopic illumination (lower). (B) Identification of the interference color in the isochrome passing through the cross hairs in the interference figure (upper) with the interference color exhibited by the entire plate when viewed orthoscopically (lower). (C) Passage of an isogyre through the cross-hair intersection (upper) signifies that the entire crystal is at extinction when viewed orthoscopically (lower).

DISPERSION AND CRYSTALLOGRAPHIC
ORIENTATION OF *X*, *Y*, AND *Z*

Dispersion of the Optic Axes

Biaxial minerals possess different values of α, β, and γ for different wavelengths of light. Thus for C, D, and F light, the principal refractive indices may be symbolized α_C, α_D, α_F; β_C, β_D, β_F; and γ_C, γ_D, γ_F. In detailed optical measurements, all nine may be determined. If these indices, or indices for additional wavelengths, are plotted on Hartmann dispersion paper, straight lines usually result (Fig. 10-29). For barite, as Figure 10-29 illustrates, β more closely approaches α in value for the longer wavelengths of light. As a consequence, $2V$ for barite decreases for the longer wavelengths. Thus $2V_r$ is less than $2V_v$, where the subscripts r and v respectively denote red and violet light (the opposite ends of the visible spectrum). The foregoing inequality is generally abbreviated to read $r < v$. On the other hand, if β had diverged from α for the longer wavelengths (dashed hypothetical line), $2V$ would have increased for the longer wavelengths; $r > v$ describes such a situation. In biaxial minerals, therefore, the optic axes do not maintain a constant position for all wavelengths of light. The degree of their dispersion is expressed by the slope of the $2V$ curve in Figure 10-29. Depending upon the extent by which r exceeds v (or v exceeds r), the dispersion of the optic axes is classified as weak, moderate, or strong. Of course, if r equals v, there is no dispersion at all. All crystals of barite exhibit weak dispersion, with $r < v$; all crystals of sillimanite exhibit strong dispersion, with $r > v$. The degree of dispersion thus may help to identify a mineral.

Orthorhombic Crystals

In the orthorhombic system the three, mutually perpendicular, crystallographic axes

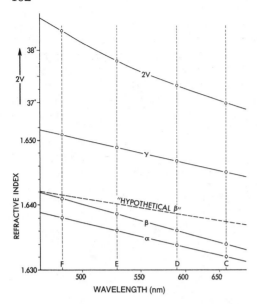

Figure 10-29. Change in value of α, β, γ and therefore of $2V$ for different wavelengths of light in the mineral barite. (Based on data from Winchell, 1931.) If β had changed as indicated by the dashed line labeled "hypothetical β," the slope of the $2V$ curve would have been reversed and the angle $2V_C$ would then exceed $2V_F$.

a, b, and *c* coincide with the three, mutually perpendicular, principal vibration directions *X, Y,* and *Z* (but not necessarily respectively), for all wavelengths of light. For example, in all barite crystals *a = Z, b = Y,* and *c = X* whereas in all olivine crystals *a = Z, b = X,* and *c = Y*. In orthorhombic crystals, therefore, only the dispersion of the optic axes—caused by the dispersion of the principal refractive indices α, β, and γ—can occur.

Normal Orthorhombic Dispersion. This dispersion of the optic axes in orthorhombic crystals is best observed from centered or near-centered acute bisectrix figures in which both optic axes appear in the field of view. In such figures for barite (Fig. 10-30A) and sillimanite (Fig. 10-30B) this dispersion causes the melatopes, A_r and A_v—and thus the isogyres for red and violet light—to be displaced from each other. Sillimanite, since $r \gg v$, shows the greater displacement. The melatopes and isogyres for intermediate wavelengths are located

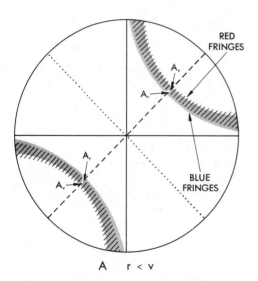
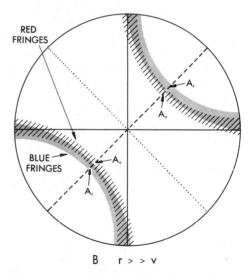

Figure 10-30. Origin of dispersion fringes in acute bisectrix figures (A) for barite and (B) for sillimanite. The isogyre locations for red light are shown as shaded areas; for blue light, as ruled areas. Red light emerging along the red (shaded) isogyre is extinguished at the analyzer whereas blue light is transmitted. Blue light emerging along the blue (ruled) isogyre is extinguished whereas red light is transmitted. Where both isogyres are superimposed, all wavelengths are extinguished; these areas thus appear black. Where they are not superimposed, a blue coloration is developed along the red isogyre and melatope whereas a red coloration is developed along the blue isogyre and melatope. The dotted and the dashed lines represent the traces of principal planes. For the biaxial figure (no gypsum plate) on the back cover, is $v > r$ or $v < r$?

between those for red and violet. Areas of overlap between the red and violet isogyres mark areas that are isogyres for all wavelengths—that is, areas of extinction for light of all wavelengths. For areas where only the isogyre for red light (shaded in Fig. 10-30) occurs, red light is extinguished at the analyzer whereas violet or blue light is transmitted. For areas where only the isogyre for violet light (ruled in Fig. 10-30) occurs, violet or blue light is extinguished at the analyzer whereas red is transmitted. Consequently, within interference figures of crystals exhibiting at least a weak dispersion of the optic axes, the black isogyre is fringed—especially in the region of the melatope—by a reddish tint on one side and a violet (or blue) tint on the other. The red fringe marks the melatope and a portion of the isogyre for violet light; the violet (or blue) fringe marks the melatope and a portion of the isogyre for red light. These color fringes are, however, easily overlooked.

The dispersional color fringes for orthorhombic crystals are always symmetrically disposed with respect to the trace of the optic plane (dashed in Fig. 10-30) *and* the principal plane normal to it (dotted in Fig. 10-30). If sufficiently distinct, this symmetry of the dispersion colors with respect to the traces of *two* principal planes permits the crystal system of a biaxial crystal to be unequivocably established as orthorhombic.

Crossed Axial Plane Dispersion. The orthorhombic mineral brookite displays an extraordinary dispersion of the optic axes, since its refractive index for vibrations parallel to the *c* axis is the lesser index (α) for wavelengths less than 555 nm but the intermediate index (β) for wavelengths longer (Fig. 10-31). Consequently, for the shorter wavelengths, the optic plane (stippled in Fig. 10-32A) is parallel to the *b* and *c* axes—that is, to the (100) crystal plane—whereas for wavelengths that are longer than 555 nm the optic plane (shaded) is parallel to the *a* and *b* axes—that is, to the (001) plane. For the 555 nm wavelength the crystal is uniaxial (+), the *b* axis being the optic axis. Within the stippled (100) plane, the optic angle is smaller for the longer wavelengths of light; thus, $r < v$. Within the (001) plane, the optic angle is larger for the longer wavelengths (*cf.* $\lambda = 650$ nm and $\lambda = 600$ nm); thus $r > v$.

The acute bisectrix figure of brookite (observable if its *b* axis is perpendicular to the plane of stage) consequently shows a type of dispersion known as *crossed axial plane dispersion*. In white light, two mutually perpendicular optic planes (Fig. 10-32B) are developed, one for the wavelengths shorter than 555 nm, the other for the longer wavelengths. The resultant interference figure is complicated and typical of crossed axial plane dispersion. Illuminated with monochromatic light, the interference figures appear normal, being uniaxial (+) if the wavelength is 555 nm but biaxial (+) for longer or shorter wavelengths. The isogyres for only a few wavelengths of light are shown in Figure 10-32B.

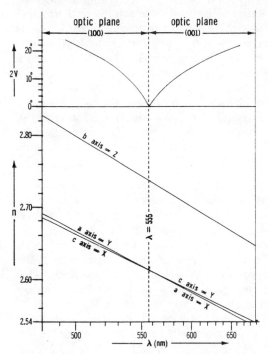

Figure 10-31. Variation of refractive indices with respect to wavelength for light vibrating parallel to the *b* axis, *a* axis, and *c* axis in brookite. Top scale: variation of 2*V* for different wavelengths of light.

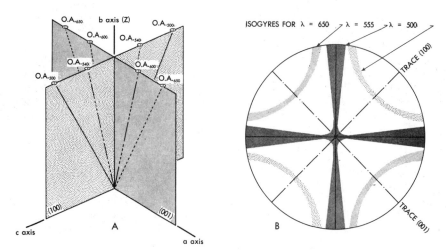

Figure 10-32. Crossed axial plane dispersion in brookite. (A) Location of the optic axes (OA_λ) for four wavelengths (nm). The optic plane for wavelengths shorter than 555 nm is (100); for those longer than 555 nm it is (001). For light of wavelength 555 nm, $2V$ equals $0°$, the single optic axis coinciding with the *b* axis. (B) Location in the acute bisectrix figure of isogyres for 500 nm, 555 nm, and 650 nm only.

Monoclinic Crystals

In monoclinic crystals only one principal axis (*X, Y,* or *Z)* coincides for, *all wavelengths of light*, with the symmetry-dictated *b* axis.[2] The remaining two principal axes always lie within a plane perpendicular to the *b* axis but occupy different locations within this plane for different wavelengths (Fig. 10-33A). They may coincide with the *a* or *c* axis only by chance. The dispersion of these two principal axes (coupled with a dispersion of the optic axes similar to that discussed for orthorhombic crystals) further reduces the symmetry of the distribution of the dispersional fringes in the interference figures of monoclinic crystals. In some cases the distribution of these dispersional fringes is sufficiently distinct to permit not only a differentiation of a monoclinic crystal from an orthorhombic crystal but also, if the crystal is monoclinic, determination of whether the *b* axis coincides with (1) *Y,* the optic normal, (2) the obtuse bisectrix, or (3) the acute bisectrix.

Inclined Dispersion (*b = Y*). If the Y principal axis of the indicatrix coincides with the symmetry-controlled *b* axis, this axis will be the *Y* direction for light of all wavelengths; that is, there is no dispersion of *Y* (Fig. 10-33A). Moreover, *for all wavelengths* the optic plane will be normal to this axis. However, within this plane, the location of the acute and obtuse bisectrices will vary for the different wavelengths of light. In consequence, this dispersion of the bisectrices (added to the dispersion of the optic axes) reduces the symmetry of the disposition of the dispersion fringes below what it was in the orthorhombic case. As shown in Figure 10-33B, the dispersion colors are bilaterally symmetrical with respect to the trace of only one plane (in contrast to orthorhombic crystals, which were symmetrical with respect to two). This trace (dot-dashed in Fig. 10-33B) represents the trace of the optic plane for all wavelengths. This is called inclined dispersion; it is characterized by a common optic plane for all light but different bisectrices and melatope positions for the different wavelengths.

---

[2] By definition, in monoclinic crystals the *b* axis coincides with the single two-fold axis or with the normal to the single plane of symmetry, or with both.

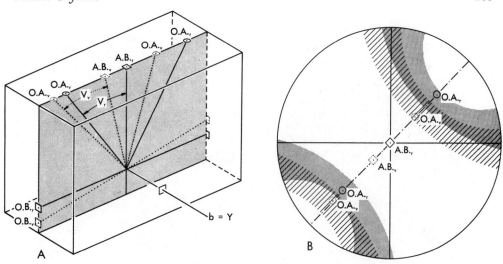

Figure 10-33. Inclined dispersion in a monoclinic crystal for which $b = Y$ and $V_r > V_v$—that is, $r > v$. (A) Dispersion of the optic axes, acute bisectrix, and obtuse bisectrix. Their positions for red light and violet light are indicated by subscripts. (B) Acute-bisectrix-centered interference figure of the crystal, optic plane at 45° to vibration of polarizer. Blue-tinted fringes (shaded) mark the locations of the red isogyres. Red-tinted fringes (ruled) mark the edges of the violet isogyres. (Degree of dispersion is highly exaggerated.)

Parallel or Horizontal Dispersion (b = obtuse bisectrix). If the obtuse bisectrix (O.B.) coincides with the b axis, this axis serves as the obtuse *bisectrix for light of all wavelengths*. On the other hand, the optic normal (Y) and the acute bisectrix occupy different positions within the plane normal to the b axis for the different wavelengths; Figure 10-34A illustrates their positions for violet and red light only. The optic planes for

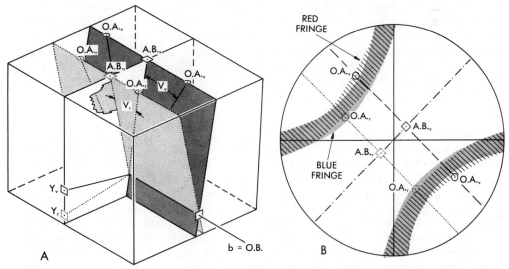

Figure 10-34. Parallel or horizontal dispersion in a monoclinic crystal for which b = O.B. and $r < v$. (A) Crystal oriented to yield an acute-bisectrix-centered figure. The positions of the acute bisectrix (A.B.) and optic normal (Y) are shown for the red and violet light ends of the visible spectrum. The optic plane for red light (lightly shaded) and violet light (heavily shaded) intersect at the b axis, which is the obtuse bisectrix for all wavelengths. (B) Acute-bisectrix-centered figure of this crystal (at 45° off extinction). The blue-tinted fringes (shaded) mark the red melatopes; the red-tinted fringes (ruled) mark the violet melatopes. The trace of the optic plane for red light is shown as a dotted line; that for violet light, as a dashed line.

the different wavelengths (shaded lightly for red light and more heavily for violet or blue light in Fig. 10-34A) intersect at a common hinge, the *b* axis. Within an acute-bisectrix-centered figure of such a crystal (Fig. 10-34B), these optic planes intersect the field of view as a series of parallel traces; hence the term parallel or horizontal dispersion. Within such an interference figure the parallelism of these traces of the optic planes can be deduced from the distribution of the dispersional color fringes; for example, the line (dotted in Fig. 10-34B) joining the blue-tinted fringes (which locate the melatopes for red light), and that (dashed) line joining the red-tinted fringes (which locate the melatopes for violet light) are parallel. Note that the color fringes are bilaterally symmetrical to only one line (dot-dashed in Fig. 10-34B); it represents the trace of the plane perpendicular to the *b* axis.

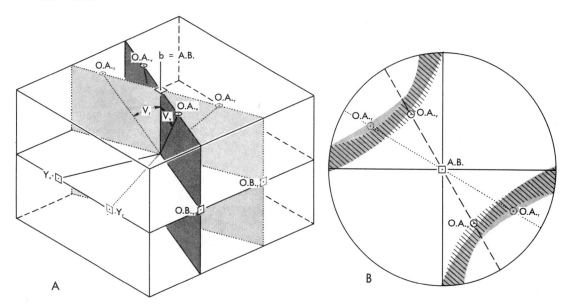

Figure 10-35. Crossed dispersion in a monoclinic crystal for which *b* = A.B. and *r* > *v*. (A) Crystal in orientation so as to yield an acute-bisectrix-centered figure. The locations of the obtuse bisectrix (O.B.) and optic normal (*Y*) are shown for red and violet light, respectively. The optic plane for red light (lightly shaded) and for violet light (heavily shaded) intersect at the *b* axis, which is the acute bisectrix for all wavelengths. (B) The acute-bisectrix-centered figure of this crystal (at 45° off extinction). The blue-tinted fringes (shaded) mark the locations of the red melatopes; the red-tinted fringes (ruled) mark the locations of the violet melatopes. The trace of the optic plane for red light is shown as a dotted line, that for violet light as a dashed line.

Crossed Dispersion (*b* = acute bisectrix). If the acute bisectrix (AB) coincides with the *b* axis, this axis serves as the acute bisectrix for light of all wavelengths; the optic normal and obtuse bisectrix, however, occupy different positions (within the plane normal to this *b* axis) for the different wavelengths. Figure 10-35A illustrates their positions for violet and red light only. For other wavelengths their positions would be intermediate. As may be seen, the optic planes for the different wavelengths intersect in a common axis, this axis representing the acute bisectrix for all wavelengths. Consequently, as viewed in the interference figure (Fig. 10-35B), the traces of the optic planes for the different wavelengths cross each other at the point of emergence of their common acute bisectrix; hence the term crossed dispersion. The disposition of the dispersion fringes in Figure 10-35B reveals no symmetry plane to be normal to the field of view. The normal to the field of view, however, can be regarded as an axis of two-fold symmetry. This normal will coincide with the *b* axis of the crystal.

Differentiation of Crystal Systems

Crystal systems are commonly determined by X-ray or electron diffraction. Under favorable conditions, however, the symmetry of the dispersional color fringes in an acute-bisectrix-centered interference figure may permit the crystal system to be identified as orthorhombic, monoclinic, or triclinic, as the case may be. In general, the color fringes will be symmetrical with respect to *two* mutually perpendicular planes (Fig. 10-36A), if the crystal is orthorhombic. They will be symmetrical to only *one* such plane (Fig. 10-36B) or to a two-fold axis (Fig. 10-36C), if the crystal is monoclinic. Moreover, in monoclinic crystals the *b* axis can be located, since it coincides with the normal to this plane of symmetry or with the two-fold axis, whichever was found; one could therefore deduce from Figures 10-33B, 10-34B, and 10-35B, even if they were unlabeled, that *b* = Y, *b* = OB, and *b* = AB, respectively.

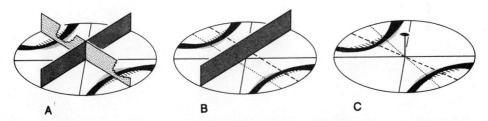

A   B   C

Figure 10-36. Differentiation of orthorhombic and monoclinic crystals from the symmetry of the dispersional color fringes in their acute bisectrix-centered figures. Orthorhombic crystals can always be considered to have two planes of symmetry perpendicular to the interference figure (A). Monoclinic interference figures are symmetrical only with respect to one such plane (B) or to a twofold axis perpendicular to the plane of the interference figure (C). The *b* axis of monoclinic crystals either is the direction perpendicular to this plane (B) or it coincides with the twofold axis (C).

The dispersional color fringes in the acute-bisectrix-centered figures of triclinic crystals, if observable, are asymmetric, lacking either bilateral symmetry or a two-fold axis normal to the plane of the interference figure. In addition to the dispersion of the optic axes, all three principal vibration axes, *X*, *Y*, and *Z*, undergo dispersion. As may be deduced, the three crystallographic axes, *a*, *b*, and *c*, in triclinic crystals do not coincide with the *X*, *Y*, and *Z* axes (except in a chance instance for a particular wavelength of light).

Abnormal Interference Colors

The abnormal interference colors seen in biaxial crystals at 45° off extinction are similar in origin to those previously discussed for uniaxial crystals. However, abnormal interference colors of entirely different origin from these may be seen in biaxial crystals that are within a degree or two of an extinction position. The phenomenon is observed chiefly in biaxial crystals for which the dispersion of the principal vibration axes (*X*, *Y*, and *Z*) or of the optic axes, or of both, is so pronounced that the privileged directions for normal incidence on a given face are not exactly the same for all wavelengths of light. Close to extinction positions, therefore, anomalous interference colors may be observed instead of blackness, the crystal never being simultaneously extinct for all the wavelengths in white light.

OPTICAL EXAMINATION
OF BIAXIAL CRYSTALS

OVERVIEW

Find the largest crystal showing the lowest order interference color in the powder mount. Viewed conoscopically, it will likely display a melatope in the field of view. To determine the optic sign, rotate the stage until the trace of the optic plane is at 90°, or nearly 90°, to the N-direction of an accessory when inserted. For (–) crystals insertion of the accessory will cause subtraction—*1° gray becoming 1° yellow (gypsum plate inserted) or low-order isochromes moving toward higher-order isochromes (quartz wedge being inserted)*—to the convex side(s) of the isogyre(s). For (+) crystals addition—*1° gray becoming 2° blue (plate inserted) or high-order isochromes moving toward lower ones (wedge being inserted)*—will occur along the convex side(s) of the isogyre(s). See Figures 11-2 and 11-3.

Given a centered optic axis figure (Fig. 10-22), the index β can be compared to n_o for the immersion oil for any position of the microscope stage. If it is off-centered (Fig. 10-21), rotate the stage until the trace of the optic plane is bisected by (or only slightly offset from) the N-S cross-hair. Now, assuming an E-W polarizer, orthoscopically compare β to n_o.

To compare α and γ to n_o, find one of the smallest grains that exhibits the highest order interference color. Such grains, viewed conoscopically, should display an optic normal flash figure (Fig. 10-20), or one close thereto. In such case N and n for the grain likely equal γ and α, respectively, so that each may be compared to n_o.

From a grain displaying an A.B.-centered figure (Fig. 11-4A), the refractive index corresponding to the obtuse bisectrix—γ for a (–) crystal but α for a (+) one—can be compared to n_o. So, too, may be β (after the crystal's horizontal Y axis is oriented E-W) even though the O.A. is not centered (Fig. 11-4B).

From the measured values for α, β, and γ, 2V can be calculated (Eqn. 10-3) or estimated graphically from the Mertie chart (Fig. 10-6). Small errors in α, β, and γ, particularly if the birefringence ($\gamma - \alpha$) is small, may propagate large errors in 2V. Alternatively, 2V can be determined from centered A.B. figures by either Mallard's method or Tobi's method (Fig. 11-5B). If the melatopes fall outside the field of view, Kamb's method (Fig. 10-25) may be useful.

For single crystals, the spindle stage method (see Chapter 12) provides the best and most accurate method of all for determining 2V.

Biaxial crystals that exhibit just one set of mutually parallel cleavage traces in thin sections—or which cleave to form needle-shaped fragments—are said to exhibit **parallel extinction** if, between crossed polarizers, the crystal becomes extinct when these cleavage traces are aligned parallel to a cross-hair, in other words, if the extinction angle equals 0°. If not, the crystal exhibits **inclined extinction**. A crystal is said to exhibit **symmetrical extinction** if its privileged direction bisects the angle between two cleavage traces.

A population of needle-shaped particles may result from two cleavages that are parallel to X, Z, or Y (Fig. 11-11). If the needles are parallel to X (Fig. 11-11A), every needle will exhibit **elongation (–)**, which means its n (or fast) privileged direction, actually α, lies parallel to the length of the needle. This is also called **length-fast**. If parallel to Z (Fig. 11-11B), every needle exhibits **elongation** (+). In other words, the N (or slow) direction, actually γ, lies parallel to every needle's length. This is also called **length-slow**. However, if Y is parallel to the needle lengths (Fig. 11-11C), some needles will exhibit elongation (+), but others elongation (–), depending upon which cleavage they lie. Such elongation, called elongation (±), indicates that Y is parallel to the needle lengths.

The monoclinic pyroxenes and amphiboles display a wide range of extinction angles relative to their {110} cleavage, depending upon their orientation in rock thin-sections. Frequently, petrographers assume that the maximum of these extinction angles represents the angle $Z \wedge c$, an important characteristic of these minerals. However, in cases where the crystal's O.B. lies within 45° of its c-axis, extinction angles that significantly exceed $Z \wedge c$ may result. Extinction angles measured from pyroxene or amphibole crystals displaying maximum retardation colors (and thus centered or near-centered flash figures) will yield the most reliable values for $Z \wedge c$.

INTRODUCTION

In all respects sample preparation of biaxial crystals is the same as for uniaxial crystals. The crushed grains, if no dominant cleavage exists, will rest on fracture surfaces that are randomly oriented with respect to principal axes X, Y, and Z and the two optic axes. Whenever such a surface is parallel to a principal axis, this axis will serve as a privileged direction for the grain. Consequently, the grain will exhibit a principal refractive index (α, β, or γ) whenever this principal axis $(X, Y, $ or Z, respectively) is oriented horizontal *and* parallel to the privileged direction of the polarizer. Table 11-1 summarizes the refractive indices and retardations measurable from grains resting on the different types of surfaces previously discussed (see also Table 10-1, p. 46). If, as for the micas, a dominant cleavage causes all grains to rest on optically identical surfaces, ground glass may be liberally added to the oil mount before adding the mineral. Mineral grains propped up by grains of glass will then diversify the optic orientations. Even better, the spindle stage (Chapter 12) solves this problem with dispatch.

Barring a dominant cleavage, the majority of grains in a powder mount are likely to rest on random planes. Measurement of their indices is of little value since the measured values, α' and γ', will differ from one grain to the other. The significant indices α, β, and γ, on the other hand, can only be measured from the small minority of grains resting on principal or semirandom planes (Table 11-1). The microscopist thus faces the task of searching out these grains from among the myriads of random orientations in the mount. Techniques for recognizing the grain types and subtypes will be discussed incidental to the problem of measuring α, β, and γ. First, however, the determination of the optic sign of biaxial minerals will be discussed, since, in practical optical mineralogy, this is usually one of the first optical characteristics to be established.

DETERMINATION OF BIAXIALITY

With polarizers crossed and a low-power objective, search for the largest grain exhibiting a first-order gray (or lesser) retardation color at 45° off extinction. This grain is most likely to rest on a YC plane since Δ_{yc} (Table 11-1) is less than the retardation of any other grain type; thus conversion from orthoscope to conoscope will usually produce a centered or near-centered optic axis interference figure from which the crystal's biaxial nature and optic sign are readily determinable. Grains less well oriented may also permit

Table 11-1. Relationship of the orientation of a grain's plane
of rest to its refractive indices and retardation

Plane of rest	Refractive indices measurable for privileged directions of grain	Retardation for a grain of thickness t
(1) Principal planes		
XY	α and β	$\Delta_{xy} = (\beta - \alpha)t$
XZ	α and γ	$\Delta_{xz} = (\gamma - \alpha)t$
YZ	β and γ	$\Delta_{yz} = (\gamma - \beta)t$
(2) Semirandom planes		
XZ'	α and γ'	$\Delta_{xz'} = (\gamma' - \alpha)t$
YX'	β and α'	$\Delta_{yx'} = (\beta - \alpha')t$
YZ'	β and γ'	$\Delta_{yz'} = (\gamma' - \beta)t$
YC	β only	$\Delta_{yc} = 0$
ZX'	γ and α'	$\Delta_{zx'} = (\gamma - \alpha')t$
(3) Random planes		
$X'Z'$	α' and γ'	$\Delta_{x'z'} = (\gamma' - \alpha')t$

these determinations; in general, however, the presence of an optic axis in the field of view simplifies sign determination and, in addition, permits the biaxial nature of the crystal to be more surely recognized. In this respect, note that a far-off-centered figure of a biaxial crystal of small $2V$ is indistinguishable from that of a far-off-centered uniaxial crystal (see Fig. 10-26). Biaxiality can often be established even if no optic axes appear in the field. To test such figures, rotate the stage until an isogyre passes through the cross-hair intersection. For this position of the stage, if the isogyre is not parallel to a cross hair (as, for example, in Fig. 10-27A), the mineral is definitely biaxial. If the isogyre is parallel (Fig. 10-27B), the crystal may be either biaxial or uniaxial.

DETERMINATION OF OPTIC SIGN

Rotate any given acute-bisectrix-centered interference figure until its optic plane lies perpendicular to the N-direction for the accessory plate (or wedge) in use (Fig. 11-1). Of the two vibration directions perpendicular to the acute bisectrix, one (β) will now be parallel to N whereas the second (a vibration coinciding with the obtuse bisectrix) will lie perpendicular to N. Consequently, where the acute bisectrix emerges at the cross-hair intersection—and indeed for the entire area between the convex sides of the isogyres—subtraction will occur for (−) crystals (Fig. 11-1A) but addition for (+) ones (Fig. 11-1B). Subtraction will be marked by (1) the change of 1° gray to 1° yellow upon insertion of the gypsum plate or (2) movement of lower-order isochromes toward higher-order ones as the wedge is inserted. Addition is marked by (1) the change of 1° gray to 2° blue (plate inserted), or (2) movement of high-order toward lower-order isochromes (wedge inserted). Figures 11-2 and 11-3 provide examples.

For interference figures in which the melatopes (and thus the isogyres when the optic plane is at 90° to N for the accessory) fall far outside the field of view, Kamb's method (see p. 158) frequently permits distinction between an acute bisectrix figure with very large $2V$ and an obtuse bisectrix figure. In the latter case, results will be the opposite from those for optic sign determinations on the acute bisectrix figure of the same mineral.

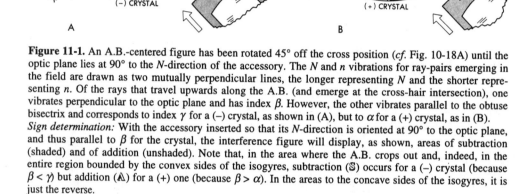

Figure 11-1. An A.B.-centered figure has been rotated 45° off the cross position (*cf.* Fig. 10-18A) until the optic plane lies at 90° to the *N*-direction of the accessory. The *N* and *n* vibrations for ray-pairs emerging in the field are drawn as two mutually perpendicular lines, the longer representing *N* and the shorter representing *n*. Of the rays that travel upwards along the A.B. (and emerge at the cross-hair intersection), one vibrates perpendicular to the optic plane and has index β. However, the other vibrates parallel to the obtuse bisectrix and corresponds to index γ for a (−) crystal, as shown in (A), but to α for a (+) crystal, as in (B).

Sign determination: With the accessory inserted so that its *N*-direction is oriented at 90° to the optic plane, and thus parallel to β for the crystal, the interference figure will display, as shown, areas of subtraction (shaded) and of addition (unshaded). Note that, in the area where the A.B. crops out and, indeed, in the entire region bounded by the convex sides of the isogyres, subtraction (S) occurs for a (−) crystal (because $\beta < \gamma$) but addition (A) for a (+) one (because $\beta > \alpha$). In the areas to the concave sides of the isogyres, it is just the reverse.

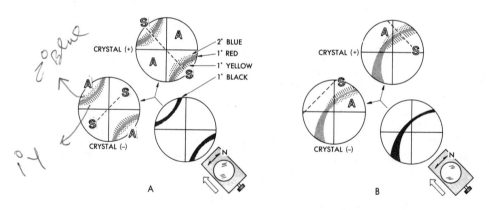

Figure 11-2. (A) Determination of the optic sign of a centered-acute-bisectrix figure by insertion of a first-order red "gypsum" plate. The areas of subtraction (S) and addition (A) can be best recognized near the isogyre's melatope where 1° gray (100 nm) changes to 2° blue (~650 nm ≅ 550 + 100) for addition but to 1° yellow (~450 nm ≅ 550 − 100) for subtraction. Thus, if the optic plane trends perpendicular to the *N* direction of the plate, first-order yellow (ruled areas) develops on the convex side of the isogyre for negative crystals and on the concave side for positive crystals. A dashed line joining the centers of the quadrants in which subtraction occurs has been added to illustrate an alternative convention useful in sign determination. This dashed line will always be parallel to the *N* direction of the accessory plate for negative crystals and perpendicular to it for positive crystals. (B) Determination of the optic sign for off-centered figures. The relationship of these figures to the centered figures in (A) is easily visualized. The reader may improve parts (A) and (B) by coloring ruled areas yellow and stippled areas blue. Also see the back cover.

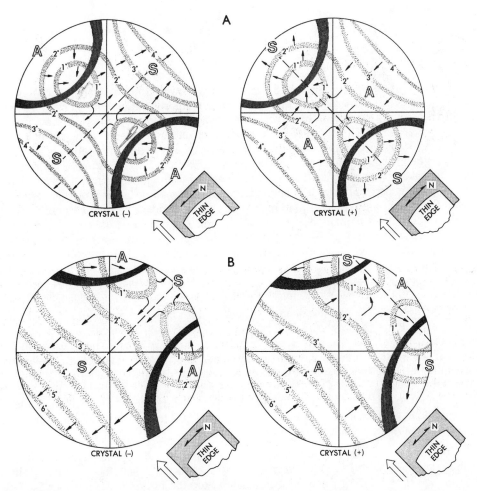

Figure 11-3. (A) Determination of the optic sign of a centered acute bisectrix figure by insertion of a quartz wedge, thin end first. If the optic plane is perpendicular to the *N* direction of the wedge, subtraction (Ⓢ), as evidenced by lower order isochromes moving toward higher order ones, occurs to the A.B. —or convex-side of the isogyres for (−) crystals—but to the O.B. or concave-side of the isogyres for (+) crystals. In the areas of addition (Ⓐ), higher order isochromes displace lower order ones. As in Figure 11-2, a dashed line has been drawn between the centers of the quadrants in which subtraction occurs. (B) Determination of optic sign in off-centered figures is possible if their relationship to the centered figures in (A) can be deduced. In both these off-centered figures it is necessary to determine the direction of the dashed line that joins the centers of the quadrants of subtraction in order to determine the optic sign.

MEASUREMENT OF INDICES

Determination of β

The same large grain with a first-order gray retardation color that was used for the sign determination may also permit measurement of the refractive index β. For example, if the grain rests on a surface broken parallel to a circular (*YC*) section of the indicatrix, a precisely centered optic axis figure (Fig. 10-22) will be observed and the crystal will exhibit the refractive index β for all positions of the microscope stage. If so, convert the microscope from conoscope to orthoscope and compare the refractive index of the grain (that is, β) with the refractive index of the oil (by Becke line, oblique illumination, or dispersion staining). The refractive index β can also be measured from grains oriented with their optic plane—but not necessarily an optic axis—perpendicular to the microscope stage (Fig. 10-21).

Determination of α and γ

With the orthoscope, search the slide (low-power objective suggested) for a relatively small grain displaying a higher retardation color than any other. The privileged directions of such a grain will then likely correspond to α and γ, because this grain would (of all the grains in the mount) show maximum retardation colors by virtue of its birefringence ($\gamma - \alpha$) exceeding that for grains in any other orientation. Correctly oriented grains should, under the conoscope, yield centered optic normal flash figures, since, for this orientation, X and Z should lie parallel to the plane of rest whereas Y, the optic normal, is perpendicular to it and emerges at the center of the interference figure. It is well to test the interference figure by Kamb's method to be sure it represents an optic normal figure rather than an obtuse bisectrix figure. The refractive indices, α and γ, can also be measured from grains other than those yielding optic normal figures. The recognition and correct orientation of such grains by means of their interference figures will be discussed next.

Orientation of Grains by Interference Figures

If a mineral possesses a dominant cleavage, grains resting on principal planes or on a circular section may be rare or absent. Fortunately, α, β, or γ can also be measured from grains for which at least one principal vibration direction (X, Y, or Z) lies parallel to the plane of the stage. Such grains will always have a principal plane of the indicatrix perpendicular to this vibration direction, and therefore to the stage. For example, considering crystals B and C in Figure 11-4, each has a principal vibration direction (Y for B and the O.B. for C) parallel to the stage—and therefore a principal plane perpendicular to it. For crystal A both Y and the O.B. are parallel to the stage and therefore two principal planes are perpendicular to it.

To determine whether a grain rests with a principal plane perpendicular to the plane of the stage (and therefore with X, Y, or Z parallel to the stage), observe the grain's interference figure during rotation of the stage. Stop the rotation whenever an isogyre becomes straight and parallel to a cross hair, because it then marks the trace of a principal plane within the field of view. If this "cross-hair-parallel" isogyre is bisected by the N-S cross-hair, the principal plane whose trace it represents lies N-S and perpendicular to the stage. In such case the grain will be oriented with a principal vibration direction E-W (and parallel to the stage) so that the index for this vibration direction can be measured (if an E-W polarizing microscope is being used).

In summary, *a crystal will be correctly oriented for measurement of a principal refractive index by an E-W polarizing microscope if its interference figure displays an isogyre that is parallel to (and bisected by) the N-S cross-hair.*

With appropriate rotation of the stage (as indicated by the curved arrows), the crystals in Figure 11-4 develop interference figures like those shown at the right. A 45-degree clockwise rotation of crystal A would orient its optic plane N-S and produce

Figure 11-4 (opposite). (A) A crystal—cut so that two principal planes, namely the optic plane (dotted) and the one perpendicular to the obtuse bisectrix (heavily shaded) are perpendicular to the microscope stage—is here shown at 45° off extinction, with its interference figure sketched on its upper surface. This interference figure changes to A_{CW} after a 45° clockwise rotation (to extinction) but to A_{CCW} if the 45° rotation is counterclockwise. For an E-W polarizing microscope, the shift to orthoscope makes β measurable from A_{CW}, whereas the index corresponding to the obtuse bisectrix—which is γ for (−) crystals but α for (+)

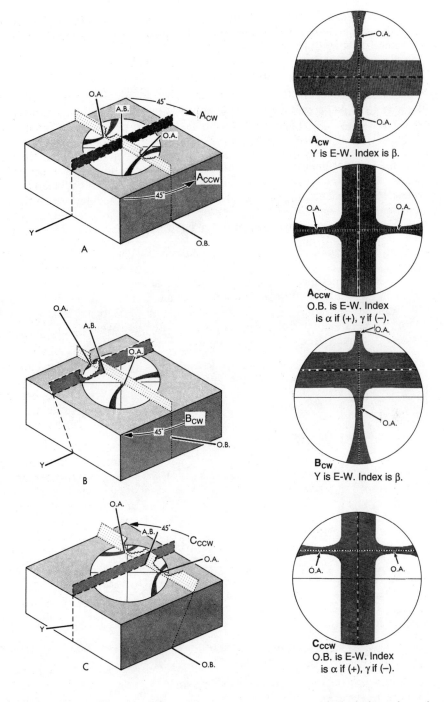

ones—becomes measurable from A$_{CCW}$. (B) A crystal with only one principal plane, the optic plane, perpendicular to the microscope stage. A 45° clockwise rotation changes its interference figure to B$_{CW}$—and thus orients Y to be E-W and makes β measurable. (C) A crystal with its optic plane tilted but with a principal plane—specifically the one containing Y and the A.B.—perpendicular to the stage. A 45° counterclockwise rotation will change its interference figure to C$_{CCW}$. Consequently, the index corresponding to the obtuse bisectrix—in other words, γ for (−) crystals but α for (+) ones—becomes measurable.

interference figure A_{CW}. So oriented, given an E-W polarizer, the index β can now be measured—and, as discussed near this chapter's end, the pleochroic color corresponding to Y can be ascertained. On the other hand, a 45° counterclockwise rotation of crystal A would produce interference figure A_{CCW}. This orients the O.B., which is already horizontal, to be E-W and thus permits measurement of either γ for (–) crystals or α for (+) ones. It also permits ascertainment of the pleochroic color corresponding to either Z or X.

Crystal B, if rotated 45° clockwise, would yield interference figure B_{CW}. As a consequence Y, already horizontal, becomes E-W so that β can be compared to the oil's refractive index —and the pleochroic color associated with Y can be ascertained.

For crystal C, a 45° counterclockwise rotation would yield interference figure C_{CCW}. In such a case the O.B., already horizontal, becomes E-W to allow measurement of α for (+) crystals and γ for (–) ones.

MEASUREMENT OF 2V

The value of $2V$ can be calculated from the measured values of α, β, and γ or, more quickly, by use of the Mertie Chart (Fig. 10-6A). However, for crystals of low birefringence, small experimental errors in the determination of α, β, and γ may produce a large error in the value of $2V$ thus determined. In an approximate manner $2V$ can be estimated from the curvature of the isogyres when the optic plane is at 45° to the vibration directions of the polarizers (Fig. 11-5A). Usually, however, the following, more accurate methods of measuring $2V$ are utilized.

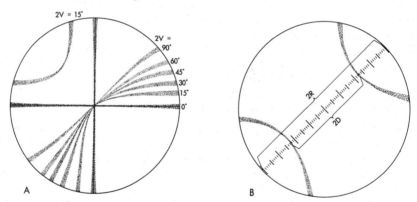

Figure 11-5. (A) Estimation of $2V$ from the curvature of the isogyres when the optic plane is at 45° (NW-SE) to the polarizers. The curvature of the isogyres is illustrated for 15-degree intervals of $2V$ (After Wright, 1907, p. 338.) Both arms of the hyperbola are shown for $2V = 0°$ and $2V = 15°$. (B) Use of the micrometer ocular to measure $2D$ in Mallard's method and $2D/2R$ in Tobi's method.

Mallard's Method

If two melatopes appear within the field of view, Mallard's method of determining $2V$ may be used. The pertinent equation is

$$D = K \sin E = K\beta \sin V$$

where D represents one-half the distance between the melatopes as measured in scale units of a micrometer eyepiece (Fig. 11-5B) and K represents a constant (commonly called Mallard's constant) whose value depends upon the numerical aperture of the objective and the number of micrometer scale divisions corresponding to a diameter of the visible field. For a given microscope, objective, and eyepiece, the value of K can be determined from crystals of known $2E$ (for example, barite, $2E = 63.2°$ $\beta = 1.636$; or aragonite, $2E = 30.87°$, $\beta = 1.681$) that have been cut normal to the acute bisectrix. Assume Figure 11-5B to represent the acute bisectrix figure of a barite plate and that, as illustrated, D equals 22.5 units. Thus, Mallard's constant for this microscope would then be

$$K = \frac{D}{\sin E} = \frac{22.5}{\sin 31.6} = 42.9$$

Henceforward, if the same microscope, objective, and micrometer eyepiece are used to measure D from the centered or near-centered acute bisectrix figure of an unknown, $2E$ or $2V$ can be calculated from the equations applicable to this microscope; that is,

$$\sin E = \frac{D}{K} = \frac{D}{42.9}$$

$$\sin V = \frac{D}{42.9\beta}$$

For very precise work, Mallard's constant should be determined (for the microscope-objective-eyepiece combination to be used) by measurements on two or three different crystals whose known values of $2E$ differ widely.

Tobi's Method

The method of Tobi (1956) eliminates the necessity of determining Mallard's constant, since twice the radius of the field of view (that is, $2R$) is measured in addition to $2D$, the intermelatope distance in Figure 11-5B. If the numerical aperture of the objective used was 0.85, Figure 11-6 permits $2E$ and $2V$ for the mineral to be determined from the ratio $2D/2R$. As inset A indicates, the value of $2D/2R$ locates a point on the vertical axis that also falls on a diagonal; this diagonal, when followed upward, indicates the value of $2E$ for the crystal measured. Similarly, inset B illustrates how the values of $2D/2R$ and of β represent coordinates of a point in the interior of the Tobi chart; this point falls on a diagonal that, if traced upward, indicates the value of $2V$ for this crystal.

Figure 11-6 was constructed for an objective of N.A. 0.85. If an objective of a different numerical aperture (A') is used, the Tobi chart permits determination of $2E$ and $2V$ as before, provided the value $2D/2R$ measured with this objective is first multiplied by the ratio $A'/0.85$. If this objective will be customarily used, the foregoing step may be eliminated by multiplying all $2D/2R$ values in Figure 11-6 by $0.85/A'$. With its vertical scale thus relabeled, Figure 11-6 will be applicable to $2D/2R$ measurements made with this new objective.

Tobi (p. 519) states that the foregoing method may also be applied to off-centered acute bisectrix figures provided the trace of the optic plane passes through or near the center of the field of view. (Fig. 11-4B$_{cw}$, if both melatopes were visible, would illustrate such a figure.) The intermelatope distance, $2D$, could be measured as for centered figures and the ratio $2D/2R$ would yield values of $2V$ with an error of $1°$ or less.

Other Methods

For centered interference figures in which both melatopes lie outside the field of view, $2V$ may be estimated by the Kamb method (see p. 158). For crystals in petrographic thin-sections, $2V$ can be determined to within $1°$ or $2°$ by use of a universal stage (Emmons, 1943; Fairbairn and Podolsky, 1951; Wyllie, 1959). However, as discussed in Chapter 12, the most accurate measurements of $2V$ are obtainable from single crystals mounted on a spindle stage.

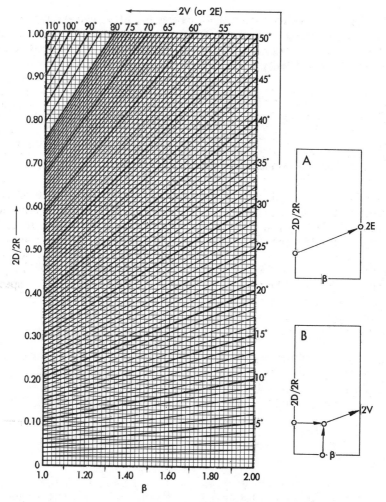

Figure 11-6. Chart for determination of 2V or 2E in interference figures. (After Tobi, 1956.) Inset A shows use of the chart to determine 2E if 2D/2R has been measured; inset B indicates its use to determine 2V from the values of β and of 2D/2R. In each *case the* point located by the measured values (encircled in insets A and B) falls on a diagonal line that indicates the value of the optic angle. Objective's N.A. is 0.85.

MEASUREMENT AND SIGNIFICANCE OF EXTINCTION ANGLES

The angular relations between a crystal's cleavage planes (or the crystal faces typically developed by its habit) and its X, Y, and Z directions determine both the extinction angle and the sign of elongation. In biaxial minerals three types of extinction exist: (1) **parallel** or **straight**, (2) **symmetrical**, and (3) **inclined** or **oblique**. The first two types have already been described for uniaxial crystals and need no further elaboration. The third type, inclined or oblique extinction, occurs if the grain's privileged directions are not parallel to the observed crystallographic features—that is, to its faces (Fig. 11-7A); to its cleavage planes (Fig. 11-7B); or to the traces of its cleavage planes (Fig. 11-7C), if it is in a thin section. Consequently, if such crystals are at extinction, the observed crystallographic features will be at an angle T (the extinction angle) to the cross hairs. For pyroxenes and amphiboles, T is usually measured as the angle between the N privileged direction and the cleavage trace; for feldspars, it is measured as the angle between the *n* privileged direction and the cleavage trace (or twinning plane). As a result, *T* may vary from 0 up to 90° between different members of the pyroxene or amphibole groups, for example. Techniques of measuring *T* for biaxial minerals need no discussion since they are the same as for uniaxials.

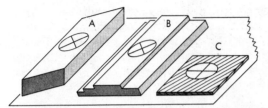

Figure 11-7. Inclined extinction with respect to (A) the planes of an elongated crystal, (B) the cleavage planes in an elongated cleavage fragment, and (C) the traces of the cleavage planes in a thin section of the mineral. In (B) note that the superior (horizontal) cleavage is marked by the development of a larger surface area parallel to it.

In crystallographic terminology a **zone** consists of a set of faces all of which, plus their lines of mutual intersection, are parallel to a given line (that is, the **zone axis**). Faces $(h\bar{k}0)$, (100), *(hk0)*, (110), and (010) in Figure 11-8 belong to the same zone, the *c* axis being the zone axis. If a zone axis coincides with a principal vibration axis—X, *Y*, or Z—all faces in the zone will have a privileged direction (for normal incidence) parallel to this principal vibration axis (for example, the faces parallel to the *c* axis in Fig. 11-8A). Consequently, all faces in the zone will exhibit parallel extinction with respect to their lines of mutual intersection, since the latter are parallel to the zone axis. If the zone axis and principal vibration axis do not coincide, faces in the zone generally do not exhibit parallel extinction (with respect to their intersections). For example, of the planes parallel to the *c* axis in Figure 11-8B, only (100), since it is also parallel to *Y*, shows parallel extinction. The other faces exhibit inclined extinction, the extinction angle T generally increasing to a maximum as these planes approach parallelism to the (010) face. Since the (010) face is parallel to the shaded plane containing axes *Z* and *c*, the angle *T* for this face equals $Z \wedge c$ (read this symbol as "the angle between *Z* and *c*"). The angle *T* for the (010)

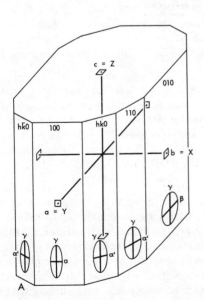

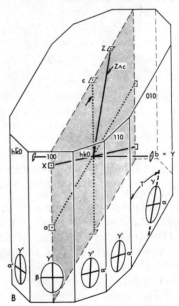

Figure 11-8. Privileged directions for normal incidence
upon the various faces in a zone parallel to the *c* axis. In (A) the zone axis, *c*, coincides with a principal vibration axis (*Z*). In (B) it does not. (A) is the typical case for orthorhombic crystals; (B), the typical case for monoclinic crystals. The ellipses of intersection between the various faces and the crystal's indicatrix (the latter not drawn) are as shown, their major and minor axes being the privileged directions.

face thus has a greater significance than the extinction angles for the other faces in Figure 11-8B since the angle between a principal vibration axis and a crystallographic axis has importance in identifying a monoclinic mineral. Determination of $Z \wedge c$, for example, is helpful in the optical identification of individual varieties of pyroxene and amphibole.

In rock thin-sections, crystals of the monoclinic pyroxenes and amphiboles display a wide range of extinction angles relative to their {110} cleavage, depending upon their orientation. Frequently, petrographers assume that the maximum of these extinction angles represents the angle $Z \wedge c$, an important characteristic of these minerals. However, as noted by Su and Bloss (1984), if the crystal's O.B. lies within 45° of its c-axis, extinction angles that significantly exceed $Z \wedge c$ may result.

For most amphiboles and pyroxenes, the symmetry-dictated b-axis coincides with Y (as in Fig. 11-8B). Consequently in thin sections, wherein their crystals are randomly oriented, the extinction angle T, as measured relative the traces of the {110} cleavage, will approach a true value for $Z \wedge c$ to the extent that the orientation is such that the observer is looking down the b- or Y-axis. *Such desirable orientations can be recognized optically because such crystals will (1) yield a centered optic normal flash figure, and (2) display their highest retardation color—because their birefringence equals their maximum, namely, ($\gamma - \alpha$).*

In biaxial crystals the cleavage or crystal planes commonly observed generally occur in zones parallel to the crystallographic axes a, b, or c. Thus, in the orthorhombic system, since all three of these axes coincide with the principal vibration axes, parallel extinction occurs more frequently than inclined extinction (the latter being observable in orthorhombic crystals only for faces not parallel to a crystallographic axis). In monoclinic minerals, however, only the b axis coincides with one of the principal vibration axes. Thus parallel extinction can occur only for cleavages or crystal faces lying in a zone parallel to the b axis whereas inclined extinction occurs for faces in all other zones. Inclined extinction is therefore more frequent for monoclinic crystals than for orthorhombic. For triclinic crystals, since none of the crystallographic and principal vibration axes coincide, inclined extinction is the rule. By the same token, symmetrical extinction may be observed in orthorhombic crystals and, to a lesser extent, in monoclinic crystals but not in triclinic crystals.

As an example, consider an orthorhombic crystal with a {0l0} cleavage (Fig. 11-9A). Note that, with respect to the cleavage traces on each face, parallel extinction would be observed if the grain were lying on a plane parallel to (001), (101), (110), (1$\bar{1}$0) etc. For an orthorhombic mineral possessing a prismatic {110} cleavage (Fig. 11-9B), the trace of cleavage planes (110) and (1$\bar{1}$0)—on the other faces and on each other—indicates that parallel extinction would be observed on faces (110), (1$\bar{1}$0), and (010) whereas symmetrical extinction would be observed if the crystal were lying on (001) or (101).

For monoclinic crystals, as discussed earlier, only *one* crystallographic axis —the symmetry-dictated b-axis—will coincide with a principal vibration axis (X, Y or Z) for *all wavelengths of light*. Consider, for example, a crystal with {110} cleavage for which b coincides with Y (Fig. 11-10). Resting on most faces—except faces parallel to b such as (001) and (100)—the crystal will exhibit inclined extinction. And if lying on (010), the observed extinction angle will equal $Z \wedge c$, an angle particularly useful for differentiating the various varieties of amphiboles and pyroxenes. This angle will vary slightly with the wavelength of light being used as the illuminant. Indeed, for all random sections through a biaxial crystal exhibiting inclined extinction, the extinction angle will vary slightly with wavelength. This is true because, although the cleavage trace remains constant in position, the crystal's extinction position (= privileged direction) varies slightly with

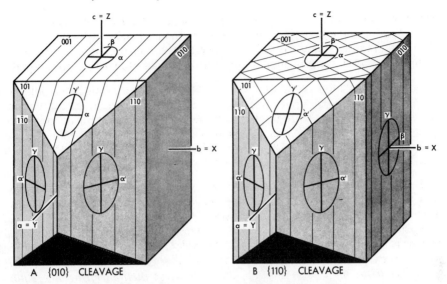

Figure 11-9. Types of extinction for normal incidence of light upon various faces of an orthorhombic crystal if (A) the crystal possesses a cleavage direction that is parallel to (010) or (B) the crystal possesses two cleavage directions, (110) and (1̄10). The traces of the cleavage on the other crystal faces and, in the case of (B), on each other, are drawn as fine lines.

wavelength. Such "dispersion of the extinction position" occurs for biaxial crystals (because their two optic axes shift position with wavelength) but not for uniaxial crystals (because their single optic axis does not).

Chapter 12 illustrates how the computer program EXCALIBR analyzes dispersion of the extinction positions for biaxial crystals and quantitatively determines the dispersion of the five biaxial optic vectors, namely, the two optic axes plus X, Y and Z.

Sign of Elongation

The identity of the principal vibration axis nearest the zone axis to which two or more cleavage or crystal planes are parallel can often be determined by observing the type of elongation for the crystals or fragments. Suppose the crystallographic features are two directions of almost equal ease of cleavage such that needles are developed in crushing the mineral. If the zone axis corresponds to X, the needles, regardless of which plane they are lying on, will exhibit negative elongation (Fig. 11-11A); if it corresponds to Z, the needles will exhibit positive elongation in all orientations (Fig. 11-11B); on the other hand, if the zone axis corresponds to Y, elongation may be positive or negative depending upon which plane the needle rests (Fig. 11-11C). Thus in a powder mount, if all needles exhibit negative elongation, X must be most nearly parallel to the needles' long axes; if all exhibit positive elongation, Z must be most nearly parallel to them; however, if some needles exhibit positive and others negative elongation—that is, the elongation is (±)—Y must be most nearly parallel to their long axes.

For plate-shaped crystals or cleavage fragments, whether the principal vibration axis most nearly perpendicular to the plate is X, Y, or Z can sometimes be determined from edge-on views. In powder mounts, since the grains rest on their flat surfaces, edge-on views are unattainable, but in thin sections cut through randomly oriented plates—for example, flakes of sheet silicates—such views occur. If X is perpendicular to the plates (as it is in the micas, glauconite, chlorites, vermiculite, and so forth), cross sections of the

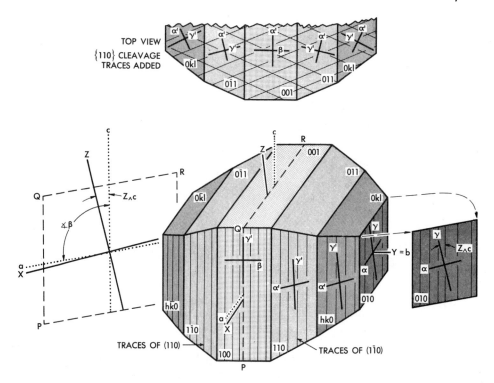

Figure 11-10. Pyroxene and amphibole crystals—generally monoclinic with cleavage parallel to their (110) and ($1\bar{1}0$) faces—display, in thin sections, different types of extinction depending upon which of their faces is most nearly parallel to the plane of the 0.03-mm-thick rock section. Cut along faces parallel to *c*—for example, (100), (110), (*hk*0), and ($0\bar{1}0$)—the crystals will exhibit a single set of cleavage traces, each trace parallel to the *c* axis. And the extinction angle generally varies from 0° (= **parallel extinction**) for face (100), to increasing higher values (**inclined extinction**) from (110) to (*hk*0) to (010). The extinction angle for face (010) actually equals $Z \wedge c$, a value that helps to identify a pyroxene or amphibole.

Faces not parallel to *c* will exhibit *two* intersecting sets of cleavage traces as shown on the top view of the crystal (but, for simplicity, omitted from the lower drawing). Note that for a crystal cut parallel to (001), the α' privileged direction bisects the angle between the cleavage traces (= **symmetrical extinction**). For faces (011), (0*kl*), etc., the privileged direction no longer bisects the angle between the cleavage traces (= **inclined extinction**).

In thin sections a petrographer (1) looks for crystals showing just one set of cleavage traces, this indicating that the plane it lies on is parallel to the *c*-axis; (2) of such crystals looks for the one exhibiting the highest retardation color and a centered, or near-centered, optic-normal-flash figure, and then (3) measures their extinction angle *T*, as a measure of the angle $Z \wedge c$.

plates will always exhibit positive elongation. On the other hand, if *Z* is perpendicular to the plates, cross sections will always exhibit negative elongation. However, if *Y* is perpendicular to the crystal plates, some sections will exhibit elongation (+) and others elongation (−), depending on whether the thin section cuts through the plate more nearly parallel to *Z* than to *X* (Fig. 11-12).

ABSORPTION AND PLEOCHROISM

With the identification of a particular axis (*X*, *Y*, or *Z*) as one of the privileged directions, the crystal is then oriented with this direction parallel to the polarizer in order to measure, as previously described, the principal index (α, β, or γ) associated with this

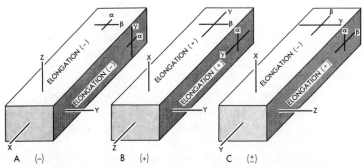

Figure 11-11. Types of elongation in crystals (or cleavage fragments) of biaxial minerals. (A) Crystal is elongated parallel to X; therefore it is length fast (elongation negative) regardless of which face it rests upon. (B) Crystal is elongated parallel to Z; therefore it is length slow (elongation positive) regardless of which elongated face it rests upon. (C) Crystal is elongated parallel to Y and thus appears length fast (elongation negative) if resting on the plane as shown but appears length slow (elongation positive) if resting on the shaded face. Its elongation is thus denoted as (±).

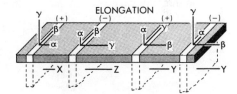

Figure 11-12. Intersection between a rock thin section and crystal plates (unshaded) of varying optic orientations.

to measure, as previously described, the principal index (α, β, or γ) associated with this direction. At the same time, however, the crystal's transmitted color for light vibrating parallel to X, Y, or Z (as the case may be) should also be observed and recorded. One variety of hypersthene, if in crystals about 0.03 mm thick, exhibits pleochroism as follows: X = red, Y = yellow, Z = blue. Obviously, the degree of absorption of the various wavelengths of white light in hypersthene varies according to whether the light is vibrating parallel to the X, Y, or Z principal vibration axes. To express the variations of absorption coefficients k_x, k_y, and k_z with wavelength of light in a manner similar to Figure 8-19 would thus require three individual curves. To express the fact that, on the whole, the absorption of all light wavelengths is greatest for light vibrating, for example, parallel to Y, less if vibrating parallel to X, and least if vibrating parallel to Z, it is customary to write $A_y > A_x > A_z$ or simply $Y > X > Z$.

Vibration directions corresponding to the α' or γ' indices generally are associated with absorptions or transmitted colors intermediate between those for α and β or β and γ, respectively. For the hypersthene crystals cited above, for example, the color transmitted by an α' vibration direction might vary between orangish red and orangish yellow, according to how close the particular value of α' is to α or β, respectively. The transmitted color associated with γ', on the other hand, would vary from greenish blue (if γ' practically equals γ) to greenish yellow (if γ' only slightly exceeds β).

RECORDING DATA

A form for recording data—which also serves as a checklist for the optical properties that can be measured—appears in Appendix III.

REVIEW QUESTIONS

1. What is the optic sign if:
    A. β is much closer to α than to γ?
    B. $(\gamma - \beta) \gg (\beta - \alpha)$?
    C. $2V_z = 118°$?

2. Calculate $(\gamma - \alpha)$, $(\gamma - \beta)$ or $(\beta - \alpha)$—*if there is sufficient data*—for the following biaxial crystals seen in the same thin section (0.03 mm thick):
    A. A (+) crystal displaying a precisely centered A.B. figure with third-order yellow (1500 nm) at the cross hair intersection.
    B. A crystal displaying a precisely centered optic normal flash figure with second-order yellow (900 nm) at the cross-hair intersection.
    C. A (+) O.B.-centered figure, first-order red (550 nm) at cross-hair intersection. Could A and B possibly represent different orientations of the same mineral? Could A and C?

3. For a centered A.B. figure, the isogyres show blue fringes on their convex sides, red on their concave sides. State whether $r > v$ or $r < v$.

4. Does a crystal for which $2V = 90°$ have an optic sign?

12 SPINDLE STAGE STUDY
of BIAXIAL CRYSTALS

OVERVIEW

After a biaxial crystal is mounted onto a spindle stage, rotate the stage by 10° increments from $S = 0°$ to $S = 180°$—or, better, from $S = 0°$ to $S = 360°$ for a 360°-rotating spindle—and at each step rotate the microscope stage to the setting (M_S) that produces crystal extinction. Submit the resultant 18—or 36—S, M_S readings to the computer program EXCALIBR which then calculates $2V$ (to within 1°)—as well as the S, M_S settings that permit the crystal's principal indices (α, β, and γ) to be measured without appreciable error from misorientation. If such extinction data are submitted for two (and up to five) different wavelengths, EXCALIBR makes a statistical analysis of whether significant dispersion has occurred for the two optic axes and X, Y and Z.

By photometrically determining crystal extinctions, the aforementioned studies can be made at wavelengths beyond the visible range. Moreover, a photometric eyepiece will also permit a spindle stage to be fully automated.

The Medenbach spindle stage, which incorporates a heating cell and refractometer, is ideally suited for double variation studies of crystals.

For a more comprehensive in-depth discussion of spindle stage methods, particularly their use in X-ray crystallography, see Bloss (1981). However, the present-day EXCALIBR is superior to the program used then.

INTRODUCTION

Any biaxial crystal, if cemented to the needle of a spindle stage (*cf.* Fig. 9-1), will likely have its principal axes—X, Y and Z—oriented at random angles to the needle (Fig. 12-1). For discussion, let S_X, S_Y, and S_Z denote the settings on the spindle stage's S-axis that will respectively orient X, Y and Z horizontal. And, after each such setting is accomplished, let M_X, M_Y, and M_Z denote the microscope stage settings that will respectively orient X, Y and Z to be E-W (so that principal indices α, β, and γ can be measured with an E-W polarizing microscope). These **strategic settings**, S_X, M_X; S_Y, M_Y; and S_Z, M_Z, may be determined conoscopically, if the crystal is large enough to yield an

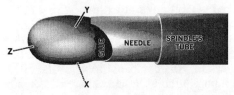

Figure 12-1. A biaxial crystal is here shown cemented in random orientation—that is, neither X, Y, nor Z is parallel (or perpendicular) to the spindle's needle (= the S-axis). Note that, by rotation about the S-axis, principal axes X, Y, and Z, each in turn, can be oriented horizontal (= parallel to the microscope stage). By definition, let S_X, S_Y and S_Z represent the S-settings that achieve this. Similarly, let M_X, M_Y and M_Z denote the microscope stage settings that—after X, Y and Z are oriented horizontal—respectively orient X, Y and Z parallel to the polarizer's privileged direction. These three strategic settings—S_X, M_X; S_Y, M_Y; and S_Z, M_Z—permit α, β and γ to be measured without appreciable error from misorientation and are easily determined by spindle stage techniques. [Note that there are no S-settings that will orient X, Y, or Z *perpendicular* to the stage—unless the crystal happened to be glued onto the needle with X, Y, or Z perpendicular to the needle.]

interference figure (or orthoscopically, if not). The conoscopic method is highly instructive as to the interpretation of biaxial interference figures. However, the orthoscopic method is preferable because it allows use of a computer program (EXCALIBR) that locates the five optic vectors (X, Y, Z and the two optic axes) and calculates $2V$ with unprecedented accuracy.

Either method of study is best begun by sliding a cell containing the 1.57 oil into the spindle stage's dock. Because almost 40% of all biaxial minerals have indices within the range 1.57 $\pm$ 0.04, this increases the likelihood that β for the crystal will be reasonably close to the oil's index. Subsequent oils can be chosen to be even closer to β. Such closeness is particularly desirable if the orthoscopic method is to be applied at two (or more) widely separated wavelengths in order to determine, quantitatively, the dispersion of the five optic vectors.

For either method, an objective whose N.A. equals 0.65 will provide the necessary free-working-distance between the crystal and objective.

THE CONOSCOPIC METHOD

Determining the Extinction Setting (M_S)

A crystal, if observed conoscopically, will be at an extinction position (= M_S) whenever the center of an isogyre passes through the cross-hair intersection (Fig. 12-2).

Figure 12-2. To determine conoscopically the microscope stage setting (M_S) that will produce crystal extinction, simply rotate the microscope stage until, as shown here, the center of an isogyre falls on the cross-hair intersection.

Recognition of Crystal Orientation.

Random Orientation. If, at extinction, the isogyre that passes through the cross-hair intersection is parallel to neither cross-hair, as true for Figure 12-2, the crystal is, without doubt, biaxial and in random orientation.

One Principal Axis Horizontal. If, at extinction, a biaxial crystal's isogyre is longitudinally bisected by a cross-hair (Fig. 12-3), a principal axis (X, Y or Z) will be horizontal and perpendicular to that cross-hair.

Two Principal Axes Horizontal. A centered biaxial cross at extinction (Fig. 12-4) discloses that the crystal has *two* principal axes parallel (and the third perpendicular) to the microscope stage. In such case, the cross's two arms mark where two vertical principal planes emerge in the field of view. Since *two* principal axes are horizontal for such orientations, *two* principal refractive indices may be compared to n for the oil. In Figure 12-4, for example, the indices corresponding to the O.N. and O.B. could thus be measured.

The Conoscopic Scan from $S = 0°$ to $S = 180°$

Figure 12-5 illustrates a detent spindle stage, set at $S = 0°$ (but with its protractor scale omitted), mounted on a counterclockwise microscope stage—so called because its graduations 0°, 10°, 20° ... ascend counterclockwise. For this example, the reference azimuth (M_R) equals 4°. In other words, rotation of the microscope stage until its index reads 4° will orient the spindle axis precisely E-W (with the crystal on its west end).

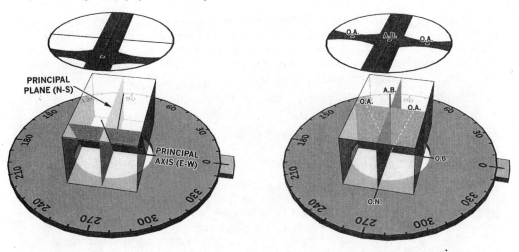

CENTERED A.B., CROSS POSITION

Figure 12-3 (left). Upon rotating the microscope stage until the center of an isogyre coincides with the cross-hair intersection (= extinction), if the isogyre is also longitudinally bisected by a cross-hair as shown here, the isogyre represents the outcrop of a principal plane—for example *XY*, *XZ* or *YZ*—that lies perpendicular to the microscope stage. In such case, the crystal is no longer in random orientation (as for Fig. 12-2) but has a principal axis—for example, *Z*, *Y* or *X*—that is parallel to the microscope stage (and perpendicular to the isogyre-bisecting cross-hair). Note that the crystal's other principal axes (dark lines) lie in the vertical principal plane.

Figure 12-4 (right). If two principal planes lie perpendicular to the microscope stage, then when the crystal is brought to extinction, a biaxial cross results. The two arms of this cross represent the points of emergence of the two principal planes in the field of view. Note that the principal axes perpendicular to these vertical principal planes—labeled O.N. and O.B. in this example—lie parallel to the plane of the stage reads 4° will orient the spindle axis precisely E-W (with the crystal on its west end).

Let v_S and v'_S designate the crystal's two mutually perpendicular vibration directions—v and v'—that become operative (= horizontal) when the spindle is set at the value *S*. In Figure 12-5, assume the spindle to be set at $S = 0°$. In such case v and v' would be more specifically designated as v_0 and v'_0. With *S* set at 0°, rotating the microscope stage clockwise from the reference azimuth (M_R) until the crystal becomes extinct (at $M_0 = 34°$) will orient v_0 to be due east. Moreover, E_0, the angle between v_0 and the spindle axis, becomes known because

$$E_0 = M_0 - M_R \qquad \text{(Eqn. 12-1A)}$$

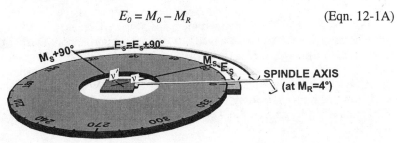

Figure 12-5. A crystal plate, cemented to the tip of a spindle, is shown to exhibit two mutually perpendicular vibration directions, v and v'. Assume that a clockwise rotation of the stage to reference azimuth M_R (= 4°) would orient the spindle axis precisely E-W. Also assume that a clockwise rotation of the stage to $M_S = 34°$ would bring the crystal to extinction. The angle E_S (between v and the spindle axis) thus becomes known since $E_S = M_S - M_R$ (= 34° - 4°). Because v', the crystal's second vibration is at 90° to v, its angle to the spindle axis (E'_S) also becomes known (since $E'_S = E_S + 90°$).

Thus, for this example, E_0 equals 30° (= 34° – 4°). Note that Equation 12-1A may be written in more generalized form as

$$E_S = M_S - M_R \qquad \text{(Eqn. 12-1B)}$$

where S represents the spindle setting when the extinction position M_S was determined and E_S represents the angle between vibration direction v_S and the spindle axis.

For a clockwise stage (so called because its graduations ascend clockwiseand not counterclockwise as they do in Fig. 12-5), Equation 12-1B would become

$$E_S = M_R - M_S \qquad \text{(Eqn. 12-2)}$$

For the time being, we accept v'_0 to be precisely at 90° to v_0 so that it becomes superfluous to determine *its* extinction position (presumably at: $M_S + 90°$) and *its* angle relative to the spindle axis (presumably: $E_S + 90°$).

Let M_S—the extinction position for v determined by rotating the microscope stage *clockwise* from M_R—be denoted as M_0, M_{10}, M_{20} ... according to whether the spindle was set at $S = 0°$, $S = 10°$, $S = 20°$ ... during the clockwise rotation. Thus, as already discussed for Figure 12-5, $M_0 = 34°$. During a conoscopic scan, the values for M_0, M_{10}... M_{180} are conveniently entered under the M_S column of a standard form (Fig. 12-6). While performing this scan, record in the blanks labeled (A), (B) and (C) the S and M_S settings that, at crystal extinction, cause an isogyre to be longitudinally bisected by the N-S cross-hair, such settings being **strategic settings**. [Note: An E-W polarizing microscope is here assumed.] A sketch of each such interference figure in the miniature fields of view provided, as done in Figure 12-7, may prove helpful.

Usually, the crystal will have been cemented to the needle in random orientation (Fig. 12-1). If so, *three* strategic settings—(A), (B) and (C)—will be observed during an $S = 0°$ to 180° scan. If the crystal happens to be cemented with a principal axis perpendicular to the spindle axis, only *two* strategic S settings will be observed. And for one of them, the interference figure at extinction will be a centered biaxial cross (*cf.* Fig. 12-4).

Example of a Randomly Oriented Crystal

R.E. Wilcox, a pioneer in the use of spindle stage methods, determined the extinction positions for a randomly oriented orthopyroxene crystal as S was varied from 0° to 180° (Fig. 12-7). Wherever M_S changed rapidly between successive S settings, as between $S = 70$-100° and $S = 130$-170°, the increments of S were decreased to 5°—or even less when strategic interference figures (A), (B) or (C) were approached. During the scan, Wilcox located three strategic S, M settings—(A) $S = 30°$, $M_{30} = 116°$; (B) $S = 112°$, $M_{112} = 80°$; and (C) $S = 172°$, $M_{172} = 157°$—and, for each, sketched the corresponding interference figure. Each setting oriented a principal axis to be E-W and horizontal. These principal axes, after their corresponding refractive index was measured, were disclosed to be (A) X, (B) Z, and (C) Y.

SOLUTION OF ORTHOSCOPIC DATA: EXCALIBR

Crystal extinction positions may be determined *conoscopically*, as done by Wilcox, or *orthoscopically*, simply by rotating the stage to crystal extinction (= blackness). The orthoscopic method, however, possesses the following distinct advantages: (1) Extinction positions can be measured for crystals too small to yield interference figures. (2) They can be determined for crystals present as small inclusions in grains of an isotropic host

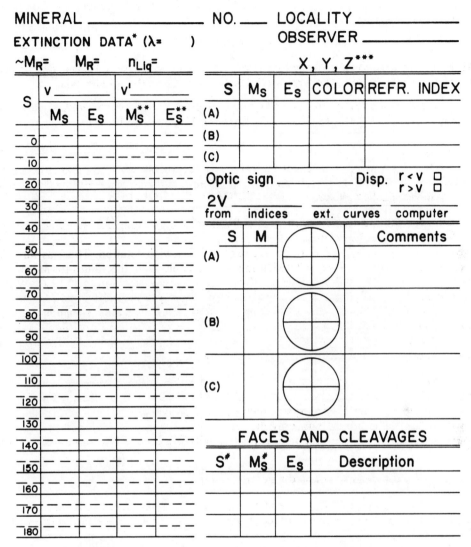

Figure 12-6. A useful form for recording spindle stage data for a crystal. The value $\sim M_R$ represents the microscope stage reading, as judged by eye, that orients the spindle axis E-W with its handle to the east. By contrast M_R represents the precise reference azimuth (determined as described in Fig. 9-3, p. 129).

(fluorite, glass …) cemented to the spindle's needle. (3) They can be determined photometrically—at several different wavelengths within (or beyond) the visible—by substituting a photometer for the human eye and then rotating the microscope stage to a minimum reading (= extinction). Advantage (3) allows extinction measurements to be made beyond the visible and allows the spindle stage to be fully automated.

The extinction data from an S = 0° to 180° scan—or a 0° to 360° scan—can be solved by the program EXCALIBR (Bartelmehs *et al.*, 1992) to determine $2V$ and the S, M_S settings that will orient the A.B., O.B. and O.N. horizontal (and E-W or N-S) so that α, β, and γ can be measured without appreciable error from crystal misorientation. Given such extinction data for up to five different wavelengths, EXCALIBR calculates the dispersion for the A.B., O.B., O.N., and for each optic axis.

MINERAL *Orthopyroxene*   **NO.** *Cr-1-60* **LOCALITY** *Bow Lake, Wash.*

EXTINCTION DATA* (λ=WHITE)   **OBSERVER** *R.E. Wilcox*

~M_R= 0° M_R= 4° n_{Liq}= 1.690   **X, Y, Z*****

S	v ___ M_S	v ___ E_S	v' ___ M_S**	v' ___ E_S**
0	27	23	—	—
10	25	21	—	—
20	23	21	—	—
30	26	22	—	—
40	28	24		
50	31	27	—	—
60	36	32	—	—
70	42	38		
75	47	43		
80	51	47		
85	56	52		
90	60	56		
95	65	61		
100	70	66	—	—
110	76	72		
120	83	79	—	—
130	89	85		
135	93	89		
140	99	95		
145	109	105	—	—
150	121	117		
155	136	132		
160	147	143		
165	152	148	—	—
170	156	152		
180	161	157	—	—

	S	M_S	E_S	COLOR	REFR. INDEX
(A)	29.5	116	112		$\alpha \approx 1.685$-1.687
(B)	113	78	74		$\gamma \approx 1.701$
(C)	170	157	153		$\beta \approx 1.692$-1.694

Optic sign _____ Disp. r<v □ r>v □

2V _____
from   indices   ext. curves   computer

	S	M		Comments
(A)	30	116		X is E-W, horizontal
(B)	112	80		Z is E-W, horizontal
(C)	172	157		Y is E-W, horizontal

FACES AND CLEAVAGES

S#	M_S#	E_S	Description

Figure 12-7. Extinction positions (M_S) determined conoscopically by R.E. Wilcox while varying S from 0° to 180° by increments of 10° (or of 5° where M_S changed markedly from one S setting to the next). For illustrative purposes, Wilcox's data were modified to be consonant with a reference azimuth of 4° rather than of 0°. Thus modified, the crystal vibration directions, v_0, v_{10} . . . v_{180} would exhibit the extinction positions: $M_0 = 27°$, $M_{10} = 25°$ . . . $M_{180} = 161°$. Their actual angles to the spindle axis ($E_S = M_S - M_R$) would thus be: $E_0 = 23°$; $E_{10} = 23°$ . . . $E_{180} = 157°$.
Interference figures (A), (B) and (C) were added by this author; however, the S, M_S settings that produced them are essentially those determined by Wilcox.
The data also illustrate the usefulness of ~M_R, the "eyeball estimate" of the reference azimuth. For example, because $M_0 = 27°$ and $M_{180} = 161°$, Equation 12-1 would yield an M_R value of 94° (whereas M_R actually equals 4°). Bloss (1981, p. 19) discusses the origin of gross errors of 45° or 90° in M_R.

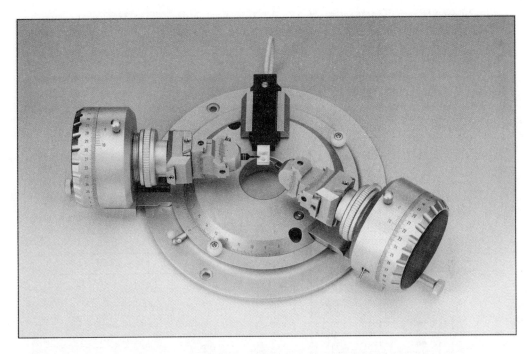

Figure 12-8. The outstandingly versatile spindle stage devised by Dr. Olaf Medenbach (see Fig. 17 from *Kristalle und Licht* by O. Medenbach, Peter Mirwald and Peter Kubath) allows heating and monitoring the temperature of the immersion oil as well as measurement of the oil's refractive index at the moment of grain-oil match. One of its two goniometer heads, each of which functions as a spindle stage having a rotation axis (S) parallel to the microscope stage, contains on its tip a uniaxial (refractometer) crystal whose refractive indices, ω and ε, are known (to the fourth decimal) for wavelengths between 400 and 700 nm in 10 nm steps (Table 1, Medenbach, 1985). The second goniometer head contains the unknown crystal for which the three strategic settings—S_X, M_X; S_Y, M_Y; and S_Z, M_Z—have been determined. With a principal vibration axis aligned horizontal and parallel to the polarizer's privileged direction, the immersion oil's temperature—and the wavelength of the light being supplied by a monochromator (or variable interference filter)—can be varied until the oil's index precisely matches the crystal's principal index. At the time of match, the refractometer crystal can then be rotated about *its* S-axis until its ε' index, which varies systematically with S, precisely matches the oil's for that temperature and wavelength.

An additional advantage of a goniometer-head-accommodating spindle stage is that it permits combined optical and X-ray studies of crystals (Bloss, 1981).

Example 1: Extinctions, $S = 0\text{-}180°$, One Wavelength

Using white light passed through a 433-nm interference filter, Wolfe (1976) visually determined extinction positions for an albite crystal as S was varied from 0° to 180°. His observed data, enclosed in rectangles in Figure 12-9, allowed EXCALIBR to calculate M_R as 180.15, namely (217.9 plus 142.4, divided by 2). This done, EXCALIBR subtracted 180.15 from each observed M_S value to obtain their comparable E_S values. Whenever this subtraction yielded a negative value, EXCALIBR added 180° to the value (to make it positive but not change its direction). EXCALIBR then solved these E_S values, as discussed by Bartelmehs *et al.* (1992), to obtain the Cartesian coordinates (*cf.* p. 127) for the five optic vectors. From these coordinates it calculated the spindle stage coordinates (S, M_S) for each optic vector. In addition, using the Cartesian coordinates of optic axes OA_1 and OA_2, it calculated the angle between them [either $2V$ or $(180° - 2V)$]. The estimated standard errors (*ese*) for these coordinates are enclosed in parentheses.

```
--------------------------------------------------------------------------
EXCALIBR        Bartelmehs, Bloss, Downs, and Birch; Z. Krist (1992)
Detent Spindle Stage Version 4.12.97        (kurtb@mail.utexas.edu)
==========================================================================
```

Tiburon Albite - Wolfe

Experimental Treatment ID number = 433.0
Average Reference Azimuth, Mr (esd) = [180.15](.00)

Biaxial Model
number of iterations (100 max.) =   7
R-squared =   .99956

S	Ms	Es	CALC(Es)	Es-CALC(Es)
.00	217.90	37.75	37.74	.01
10.00	218.50	38.35	38.49	-.14
20.00	219.10	38.95	39.04	-.09
30.00	219.60	39.45	39.31	.14
40.00	219.40	39.25	39.19	.06
50.00	218.60	38.45	38.50	-.05
60.00	217.30	37.15	36.85	.30
70.00	213.60	33.45	33.39	.06
80.00	205.90	25.75	26.01	-.26
90.00	189.90	9.75	10.56	-.81
100.00	171.70	171.55	170.77	.78
110.00	159.20	159.05	158.86	.19
120.00	153.00	152.85	152.93	-.08
130.00	149.80	149.65	149.55	.10
140.00	147.10	146.95	147.31	-.36
150.00	145.80	145.65	145.65	.00
160.00	144.40	144.25	144.31	-.06
170.00	143.50	143.35	143.20	.15
180.00	142.40	142.25	142.26	-.01

Optic Axial Angle, 2V (ese) =   77.567 (.368)

Computed Cartesian Coordinates

	x	(ese)	y	(ese)	z	(ese)
OA1	.9875	(.0006)	-.0205	(.0038)	.1565	(.0040)
OA2	.2304	(.0027)	.9719	(.0007)	.0494	(.0035)
AB	.7811	(.0006)	.6102	(.0008)	.1321	(.0019)
OB	.6044	(.0010)	-.7921	(.0006)	.0855	(.0055)
ON	-.1568	(.0039)	-.0131	(.0043)	.9875	(.0006)

Spindle Stage Coordinates to measure refractive indices.

	S	(ese)	Es	(ese)	Ms	
OA1	97.45	(1.40)	9.08	(.23)		
OA2	2.91	(.21)	76.68	(.16)	(e-w polr.)	(n-s polr.)
AB	12.21	(.17)	38.64	(.06)	218.79	128.79
OB	173.84	(.39)	52.82	(.07)	232.97	142.97
ON	90.76	(.25)	99.02	(.23)	279.17	189.17

Figure 12-9. EXCALIBR's solution of extinction positions (M_S) determined orthoscopically (and visually) by E. Wolfe while varying S from 0° to 180° by 10° increments. All input data have been enclosed in rectangles. From $M_0 = 217.9$ and $M_{180} = 142.4$, EXCALIBR calculated M_R to be 180.15. It also determined $2V$ and its estimated standard error (ese). The cartesian and spindle stage coordinates for the five optic vectors are as shown.

The Skip Signal. After EXCALIBR solves the extinction data to locate the two optic axes, it calculates, using these positions, the expected E_S value for each setting S. Next, it subtracts these calculated values from those observed. In Figure 12-9 the greatest differences between observed and calculated E_S occur at $S = 90°$ and $S = 100°$. This casts doubt on the accuracy of the observed extinction positions M_{90} and M_{100}. If desired, the researcher can re-run the data, but substitute 361.0 for the observed M_S values of 189.9

```
--------------------------------------------------------------------
EXCALIBR       Bartelmehs, Bloss, Downs, and Birch; Z. Krist (1992)
Detent Spindle Stage Version 4.12.97       (kurtb@mail.utexas.edu)
====================================================================


Tiburon Albite - Wolfe

Experimental Treatment ID number = 433.0
User Input Reference Azimuth, Mr =  183.00   (= Wrong Mr)

Biaxial Model
number of iterations(100 max.) =  20
R-squared =   .96063
```

S	Ms	Es	CALC(Es)	Es-CALC(Es)
.00	217.90	34.90	38.10	-3.20
10.00	218.50	35.50	37.96	-2.46
20.00	219.10	36.10	37.57	-1.47
30.00	219.60	36.60	36.87	-.27
40.00	219.40	36.40	35.81	.59
50.00	218.60	35.60	34.22	1.38
60.00	217.30	34.30	31.77	2.53
70.00	213.60	30.60	27.77	2.83
80.00	205.90	22.90	20.68	2.22
90.00	189.90	6.90	7.82	-.92
100.00	171.70	168.70	170.56	-1.86
110.00	159.20	156.20	157.79	-1.59
120.00	153.00	150.00	150.81	-.81
130.00	149.80	146.80	146.96	-.16
140.00	147.10	144.10	144.69	-.59
150.00	145.80	142.80	143.31	-.51
160.00	144.40	141.40	142.48	-1.08
170.00	143.50	140.50	142.04	-1.54
180.00	142.40	139.40	141.90	-2.50

```
Optic Axial Angle, 2V (ese) = 107.783 (4.828)


Computed Cartesian Coordinates
          x      (ese)        y      (ese)        z      (ese)
OA1   -.9991 ( .0020)    -.0363 ( .0493)    .0236 ( .0480)
OA2    .2728 ( .0347)     .9584 ( .0102)    .0833 ( .0420)
AB     .7872 ( .0066)     .6156 ( .0085)    .0370 ( .0203)
OB    -.6162 ( .0086)     .7824 ( .0093)    .0907 ( .0707)
ON     .0269 ( .0493)    -.0942 ( .0546)    .9952 ( .0063)


Spindle Stage Coordinates to measure refractive indices.
          S    (ese)       Es    (ese)            Ms
OA1   147.00 (66.19)    177.52 ( 2.71)
OA2     4.97 ( 2.51)     74.17 ( 2.07)    (e-w polr.)   (n-s polr.)
AB      3.44 ( 1.89)     38.08 (  .61)     221.08        131.08
OB      6.61 ( 5.16)    128.04 (  .63)     311.04        221.04
ON     95.41 ( 3.15)     88.46 ( 2.83)     271.46        181.46
```

Figure 12-10. The Tiburon albite data previously solved (Fig. 12-9) were resubmitted to EXCALIBR but with a (wrong) value of 183.0 supplied for M_R. EXCALIBR now uses this supplied value—rather than the reference azimuth, M_R, it calculated from M_0 and M_{180}. The resultant systematic error in all the E_S values caused EXCALIBR to require 20 iterations before arriving at a solution. Also, compare the $(E_S - CALCULATED\ E_S)$ values to those in Figure 12-9.

and 171.7. In such case EXCALIBR will solve the data with M_{90} and M_{100} omitted. This approach must be used with caution, however, because aberrant values are not necessarily wrong values.

The skip signal finds additional use if, at certain S settings, crystal shape or opacity makes determination of the extinction position M_S either uncertain or impossible.

The Reference Azimuth (M_R). The accuracy of EXCALIBR's solutions strongly depends upon the accuracy to which M_R is known. This holds true because any error in M_R is a systematic error that affects each and every one of the E_S values solved by

EXCALIBR to locate the two optic axes. Consequently, it is advisable to determine M_R (*cf.* Fig. 9-3) several times and use the average of these values.

Best of all is to maintain a spindle stage permanently (and securely) mounted on the stage of a dedicated polarizing microscope. In such case a "tried and true" value for M_R can be supplied to EXCALIBR. If no such value for M_R is supplied, EXCALIBR searches the submitted data for S readings that differ by 180°. Within an $S = 0°$ to 180° scan, there will be only one such pair ($S = 0°$ and $S = 180°$). Thus, for the data summarized in Figure 12-9, EXCALIBR used the M_0 and M_{180} values (217.9 and 142.4) to calculate M_R as 180.15°. For spindle stages capable of making $S = 0°$ to 360° scans, EXCALIBR calculates M_R from each of the eighteen 180°-differing S settings and calculates their average.

Accuracy for M_R is of paramount importance. To illustrate, the data in Figure 12-9 were re-submitted but with a user-stipulated value of 183.0 for M_R. EXCALIBR now causes this user-supplied value to override the more correct value of 180.15. As a result, EXCALIBR required 20 iterations, rather than the previous seven, to achieve a solution (Fig. 12-10—previous page). Moreover, the R-squared value decreased from 0.9996 to 0.9606. Also, it calculated ($180° - 2V$) rather than $2V$. [Note that the printout states that EXCALIBR employed a user-input value for M_R.]

Example 2: Extinctions, S = 0-180°, Four Wavelengths, Dispersion Analysis

Wolfe's extinction data for the Tiburon albite—measured visually for wavelengths 433, 500, 600 and 666 nm—were solved by EXCALIBR (Fig. 12-11, p. 196-197). As the printout states, the M_R used was based upon four pairs of 180°-differing S readings, namely, the $S = 0°$ and $S = 180°$ extinctions for each of the four wavelengths.

Whenever extinction data for two (and up to five) different wavelengths are submitted for a biaxial crystal, EXCALIBR analyzes the crystal's dispersion. In other words, it calculates the changes in position, with wavelength, of the crystal's five optic vectors and statistically assesses their significance (Fig. 12-12, p. 198). Obviously, if extinction data for two very close wavelengths—say, 500 mm and 510 nm—were submitted to EXCALIBR, the angular changes in the five vectors would be so small as to be overwhelmed by experimental errors. Consequently, the most reliable angular changes (Fig. 12-12) will be those involving the two most divergent wavelengths, 433 and 666 nm. For this 433 versus 666 nm dispersion analysis, p values of less than 0.10 indicate that significant dispersion occurred for four of the five optic vectors, but not for the obtuse bisectrix.

Winchell and Winchell (1951) reported albite's dispersion as "$r < v$." Wolfe's results confirmed this. Thus (see Fig. 12-11), $2V$ decreases from 77.6 (433 nm) to 77.4 (500 nm) to 76.9 (600 nm) to 76.0 (666 nm). They also report "Horizontal, very weak" dispersion. In other words, weak dispersion of the A.B. and O.N. occurs but essentially no dispersion of the O.B.—exactly what Wolfe's results reveal.

Example 3: Extinctions, S = 0-360°, Photometrically Determined

For a cordierite from Kragero, Norway, extinction data were photometrically determined, for wavelengths 400, 666 and 900 nm, using a spindle stage capable of 360° rotation. These $S = 0°$ to 360° scans, at three different wavelengths, provided 54 pairs of 180°-differing S readings. All 54 were used to calculate M_R. Results for the 400 nm and the beyond-the-visible 900 nm data (Fig. 12-13, p. 200) differ little in R-squared values.

MEASURING α_D, β_D AND γ_D

After EXCALIBR calculates the S, M_S settings that orient X, Y and Z horizontal (and parallel to the polarizer's privileged direction), a biaxial crystal's principal refractive indices become as easy to measure as n for an isotropic crystal. Accordingly, α_D, β_D, and γ_D can be estimated from Becke line colors, as discussed in Chapter 5, or if dispersion-staining objectives are at hand, by Su's method (p. 55). If even greater precision is desired in measuring these indices, the double variation method (Bloss, 1981; Su *et al.*, 1987; Gunter *et al.*, 1989) can be used. This method changes the refractive index of the oil—until it matches a principal refractive index of the immersed crystal—by varying (1) the temperature of the oil mount *and* (2) the wavelength of light used.

Both methods—Su's and the double variation technique—require knowledge of the immersion liquid's refractive index at various wavelengths and temperatures. To this end, R.P. Cargille Laboratories supplies immersion liquids and, in addition to dn/dt, the Cauchy constants (Appendix I) that permit the refractive indices of each liquid to be calculated for any wavelength within the visible range.

Of the two methods, Su's is simpler and requires only a dispersion-staining objective. By contrast, the double variation method requires (1) the means to heat and monitor the temperature of the liquid and also (2) a monochromator or variable interference filter to alter (and monitor) the wavelength of the light used as the illuminant. As already noted, however, it has the advantage of greater accuracy and precision. The Mendenbach stage (p. 191) offers a promising alternative.

COMPUTER-ASSISTED MINERAL IDENTIFICATION

The computer database *MinIdent* (Smith, 1992) contains, for over 4000 mineral species including many unnamed, such data as chemical composition, refractive indices and $2V_Z$ (and their dispersion), transmitted colors, reflectance (at 470, 546, 589 and 650 nm), and optic orientation. If supplied with some of these data for an unknown, *MinIdent* will invoke a SEARCH/MATCH routine to isolate from its entries those properties that best match those of the unknown. For each possibility thus selected, it calculates a "total matching index"—in essence a measure of "goodness of match"—and ranks the possibilities according to this value. Further information can be obtained from the Internet at www.compusmart.ab.ca/micronex.

POSSIBILITIES

A Fully Automated Spindle Stage

Besançon (1992) achieved partial automation of a spindle stage by mounting it on the stage of a polarizing light microscope (PLM) and using a computer-actuated stepper motor to rotate the PLM's stage until a photometric eyepiece detected the crystal's extinction position, M_S. This was done after the spindle had been successively set, manually, at $S = 0°$, $10°$, $20°$ ... $350°$. Each extinction position thus determined—M_0, M_{10}, M_{20} ... M_{350}—was actually the average of four extinction positions. For example, with S set at $0°$, the four extinction positions determined as the microscope stage is rotated a full $360°$ might be $15.2°$, $104.9°$, $195.1°$, and $285.2°$. In such cases, M_0 would be taken as $15.1°$—that is, the average of 15.2, (104.9 − 90), (195.1 − 180) and (285.2 − 270). This precaution is necessary because, for grains in oils, refraction at oil-grain interfaces may cause the four extinction positions (for a single S setting) not to be $90°$ apart. The total of the four readings, less $540°$ and then divided by four, is then stored as the extinction position M_S for each setting of S. After obtaining the average positions—

Figure 12-11. EXCALIBR's solution of Wolfe's visual extinction data for wavelengths 433, 500, 600 and 666 nm for the Tiburon albite.

EXCALIBR   Bartelmehs, Bloss, Downs, and Birch; Z. Krist (1992)
Detent Spindle Stage Version 4.12.97   (kurt@mail.utexas.edu)

A   Tiburon Albite - Wolfe

Experimental Treatment= ID number = 433
Average Reference Azimuth, Mr (esd) = 180.15 (.00)
based on 4 observations.

Biaxial Model
number of iterations(100 max.) = 7
R-squared = .99956

S	Ms	Es	CALC(Es)	Es-CALC(Es)
.00	217.90	37.75	37.74	.01
10.00	218.50	38.35	38.49	-.14
20.00	219.10	38.95	39.04	-.09
30.00	219.60	39.45	39.31	.14
40.00	219.40	39.25	39.19	.06
50.00	218.60	38.45	38.50	-.05
60.00	217.30	37.15	36.85	.30
70.00	213.60	33.45	33.39	.06
80.00	205.90	25.75	26.01	-.26
90.00	189.90	9.75	10.56	-.81
100.00	171.70	171.55	170.77	.78
110.00	159.20	159.05	158.86	.19
120.00	153.00	152.85	152.93	-.08
130.00	149.80	149.65	149.55	-.10
140.00	147.10	146.95	147.31	-.36
150.00	145.80	145.65	145.65	.00
160.00	144.40	144.25	144.31	-.06
170.00	143.50	143.35	143.20	.15
180.00	142.40	142.25	142.26	-.01

Optic Axial Angle, 2V (ese) = 77.567 (.368)

Computed Cartesian Coordinates

	x	(ese)	y	(ese)	z	(ese)
OA1	.9875	(.0006)	-.0205	(.0038)	.1565	(.0040)
OA2	.2304	(.0027)	.9719	(.0007)	.0494	(.0035)
AB	.7811	(.0006)	.6102	(.0008)	.1321	(.0019)
OB	.6044	(.0010)	-.7921	(.0006)	.0855	(.0055)
ON	-.1568	(.0039)	-.0131	(.0043)	.9875	(.0006)

Spindle Stage Coordinates to measure refractive indices.

	S	(ese)	Es	(ese)	Ms	
OA1	97.45	(1.40)	9.08	(.23)		
OA2	2.91	(.21)	76.68	(.16)	(e-w polr.)	(n-s polr.)
AB	12.21	(.17)	38.64	(.06)	218.79	128.79
OB	173.84	(.33)	52.82	(.07)	232.97	142.97
ON	90.76	(.25)	99.02	(.23)	279.17	189.17

B   Tiburon Albite - Wolfe

Experimental Treatment ID number = 500
Average Reference Azimuth, Mr (esd) = 180.15 (.00)
based on 4 observations.

Biaxial Model
number of iterations(100 max.) = 7
R-squared = .99943

S	Ms	Es	CALC(Es)	Es-CALC(Es)
.00	218.00	37.85	37.77	.08
10.00	218.30	38.15	38.55	-.40
20.00	219.30	39.15	39.11	-.04
30.00	219.70	39.55	39.40	.15
40.00	219.60	39.45	39.29	.16
50.00	218.60	38.45	38.59	-.14
60.00	217.30	37.15	36.92	.23
70.00	213.60	33.45	33.42	.03
80.00	205.90	25.75	25.96	-.21
90.00	189.90	9.75	10.41	-.66
100.00	171.70	171.55	170.74	.81
110.00	159.20	159.05	158.94	.11
120.00	153.00	152.85	153.04	-.19
130.00	149.80	149.65	149.65	-.00
140.00	147.40	147.25	147.39	-.14
150.00	145.70	145.55	145.70	-.15
160.00	144.60	144.25	144.34	.11
170.00	143.40	143.25	143.19	.06
180.00	142.30	142.15	142.23	-.08

Optic Axial Angle, 2V (ese) = 77.410 (.421)

Computed Cartesian Coordinates

	x	(ese)	y	(ese)	z	(ese)
OA1	.9867	(.0007)	-.0184	(.0044)	.1618	(.0045)
OA2	.2313	(.0031)	.9717	(.0008)	-.0471	(.0040)
AB	.7804	(.0007)	.6108	(.0009)	-.1338	(.0022)
OB	.6039	(.0011)	-.7917	(.0007)	.0917	(.0063)
ON	-.1620	(.0044)	-.0093	(.0049)	.9868	(.0007)

Spindle Stage Coordinates to measure refractive indices.

	S	(ese)	Es	(ese)	Ms	
OA1	96.50	(1.55)	9.37	(.26)		
OA2	2.78	(.24)	76.62	(.18)	(e-w polr.)	(n-s polr.)
AB	12.36	(.20)	38.70	(.06)	218.85	128.85
OB	173.39	(.45)	52.85	(.08)	233.00	143.00
ON	90.54	(.29)	99.32	(.26)	279.47	189.47

C   Tiburon Albite - Wolfe

Experimental Treatment ID number = 600.0
Average Reference Azimuth, Mr (esd) = 180.15 (.00)
based on 4 observations.

Biaxial Model
number of iterations(100 max.) = 7
R-squared = .99945

S	Ms	Es	CALC(Es)	Es-CALC(Es)
.00	218.10	37.95	37.75	.20
10.00	218.30	38.15	38.51	-.36
20.00	219.20	39.05	39.06	-.01
30.00	219.50	39.35	39.32	.03
40.00	219.30	39.15	39.19	-.04
50.00	218.90	38.75	38.49	.26
60.00	216.80	36.65	36.84	-.19
70.00	213.80	33.65	33.45	.20
80.00	206.40	26.25	26.33	-.08
90.00	191.30	11.15	11.59	-.44
100.00	172.80	172.65	171.99	.66
110.00	159.50	159.35	159.61	-.26
120.00	153.60	153.45	153.37	.08
130.00	149.70	149.55	149.81	-.26
140.00	147.70	147.55	147.47	.08
150.00	145.90	145.75	145.73	.02
160.00	144.60	144.45	144.35	.10
170.00	143.40	143.25	143.21	.04
180.00	142.20	142.05	142.25	-.20

Optic Axial Angle, 2V (ese) = 76.854 (.424)

Computed Cartesian Coordinates

	x	(ese)	y	(ese)	z	(ese)
OA1	.9876	(.0007)	-.0148	(.0044)	.1563	(.0046)
OA2	.2354	(.0031)	.9701	(.0008)	.0595	(.0041)
AB	.7806	(.0007)	.6097	(.0009)	.1377	(.0022)
OB	.6051	(.0011)	-.7923	(.0006)	.0779	(.0064)
ON	-.1566	(.0045)	-.0225	(.0050)	.9874	(.0006)

Spindle Stage Coordinates to measure refractive indices.

	S	(ese)	Es	(ese)	Ms		
OA1	95.42	(1.61)	9.03	(.26)	(e-w polr.)	(n-s polr.)	
OA2	3.51	(.24)	76.38	(.18)	218.83	128.83	
AB	12.73	(.20)	38.68	(.06)	232.91	142.91	
OB	174.39	(.46)	52.76	(.08)	279.16	189.16	
ON	91.31	(.29)	99.01	(.26)			

D   Tiburon Albite - Wolfe

Experimental Treatment ID number = 666.0
Average Reference Azimuth, Mr (esd) = 180.15 (.00)
based on 4 observations.

Biaxial Model
number of iterations(100 max.) = 7
R-squared = .99941

S	Ms	Es	CALC(Es)	Es-CALC(Es)
.00	218.20	38.05	37.82	.23
10.00	218.60	38.45	38.62	-.17
20.00	219.50	39.35	39.18	.17
30.00	219.30	39.15	39.44	-.29
40.00	219.20	39.05	39.30	-.25
50.00	219.00	38.85	38.56	.29
60.00	216.90	36.75	36.84	-.09
70.00	213.70	33.55	33.34	.21
80.00	206.40	26.25	26.11	.14
90.00	191.60	11.45	11.48	-.03
100.00	172.50	172.35	172.37	-.02
110.00	159.80	159.65	160.09	-.44
120.00	154.00	153.85	153.76	.09
130.00	150.40	150.25	150.10	.15
140.00	147.80	147.65	147.66	-.01
150.00	146.10	145.95	145.84	.11
160.00	144.50	144.35	144.39	-.04
170.00	143.50	143.35	143.18	.17
180.00	142.10	141.95	142.18	-.23

Optic Axial Angle, 2V (ese) = 75.962 (.450)

Computed Cartesian Coordinates

	x	(ese)	y	(ese)	z	(ese)
OA1	.9864	(.0008)	-.0058	(.0047)	.1642	(.0049)
OA2	.2420	(.0033)	.9685	(.0009)	.0581	(.0043)
AB	.7792	(.0007)	.6107	(.0009)	.1410	(.0022)
OB	.6049	(.0013)	-.7917	(.0007)	.0862	(.0069)
ON	-.1642	(.0049)	-.0181	(.0054)	.9863	(.0007)

Spindle Stage Coordinates to measure refractive indices.

	S	(ese)	Es	(ese)	Ms		
OA1	92.04	(1.63)	9.45	(.28)	(e-w polr.)	(n-s polr.)	
OA2	3.43	(.26)	76.00	(.19)	218.96	128.96	
AB	13.00	(.20)	38.81	(.07)	232.93	142.93	
OB	173.79	(.49)	52.78	(.09)	279.60	189.60	
ON	91.05	(.31)	99.45	(.28)			

```
*********************

Tiburon Albite - Wolfe

Dispersion Analysis

    For a given pair of optic vectors:
    1. Angle (ese) in degrees between vectors determined at two treatments.
    2. P-value computed from a t-test assuming the null hypothesis of
       non-dispersion.

Treatment
ID#    ID#       OA1          OA2          AB           OB           ON
433.0  500.0  .327( .347)  .144( .297)  .114( .153)  .356( .479)  .369( .471)
       p-value      .354         .632         .464         .462         .439

ID#    ID#       OA1          OA2          AB           OB           ON
433.0  600.0  .324( .336)  .654( .294)  .325( .166)  .439( .485)  .544( .385)
       p-value      .341         .033         .059         .372         .166

ID#    ID#       OA1          OA2          AB           OB           ON
433.0  666.0  .948( .352)  .852( .275)  .522( .168)  .055( .331)  .522( .178)
       p-value      .011         .004         .004         .870         .006

ID#    ID#       OA1          OA2          AB           OB           ON
500.0  600.0  .380( .366)  .753( .320)  .231( .172)  .795( .516)  .820( .491)
       p-value      .307         .025         .188         .132         .104

ID#    ID#       OA1          OA2          AB           OB           ON
500.0  666.0  .735( .369)  .895( .304)  .415( .180)  .320( .538)  .525( .333)
       p-value      .054         .006         .027         .555         .124

ID#    ID#       OA1          OA2          AB           OB           ON
600.0  666.0  .688( .379)  .392( .268)  .212( .166)  .477( .539)  .510( .518)
       p-value      .078         .153         .209         .382         .331


The p-value represents the probability of observing a t-value greater than
the computed t-value (t=ang/ese). P-values less than 0.10 imply rejection
of the null hypothesis of non-dispersion. In other words, P-values less
than
0.10 imply dispersion.
-----------------------------------------------------------------------
EXCALIBR        Bartelmehs, Bloss, Downs, and Birch; Z. Krist (1992)
Detent Spindle Stage Version 4.12.97        (kurtb@mail.utexas.edu)
=======================================================================
```

Figure 12-12. EXCALIBR's dispersion analysis. After solving the extinction data for wavelengths 433, 500, 600 and 666 nm for the Tiburon albite (Fig. 12-11), EXCALIBR also calculated the angular shifts with wavelength for each of the five optic vectors and (in parentheses) the estimated standard errors (*ese*) for these angles. It also calculated the probabilities (*p*) that these shifts resulted from true dispersion rather than experimental error. For dispersion analyses, shifts between the most widely differing wavelengths—433 and 666 nm in this example—usually yield the most reliable results. Even so, although albite is triclinic, dispersion of the O.B. from 433 to 666 nm, is too small to imply that dispersion of the O.B. occurs. Within the limits of measurement, therefore, the Tiburon albite displays pseudo-monoclinic dispersion—that is, two principal axes display dispersion but the third does not.

$M_0, M_{10}, M_{20} \ldots M_{350}$—the computer closed the file and transferred these data to a second computer for input into EXCALIBR. Besançon's results (Fig. 12-14) demonstrate the precision of the method for determining 2*V*.

Besançon notes that rotation about *S* could also be automated to produce a fully automated spindle. In such event, interference filters with differing peak wavelengths could be successively slid into the light train to produce superb extinction data for several different wavelengths of light. EXCALIBR would then print out results (and dispersion analyses) like those in Figures 12-11, 12-12, and 12-13.

Such minimization of observer time (and subjectivity) should provide new impetus for the optical study of minerals and organic crystals (including drugs), and for their study in forensic mineralogy. [What could be more convincing than to find, in a soil or sand associated with a suspect, biaxial grains with the same 2*V* (*and dispersion*) as those occurring at the site of a crime?]

Figure 12-13 (next page). Results from extinctions determined photometrically for a cordierite from Kragerø, Norway, at 400 nm and the infrared wavelength, 900 nm. The spindle stage used was capable of a 360° rotation. As a result, EXCALIBR used 54 pairs of 180°-differing S readings—18 per wavelength—to calculate M_R.

~~~~~~

An advantage of keeping the spindle stage firmly and securely mounted on the stage of a dedicated PLM is that the reference azimuth M_R is known from past performance. Such knowledge permits EXCALIBR to solve data for as few as four S settings. Such speed could be important if an organic crystal, mounted on the spindle's needle, is dissolving in the immersion oil while its extinction positions are being measured (as was true for the anthracene crystal studied by Julian and Bloss, 1987).

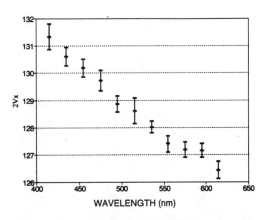

Figure 12-14. Variation with wavelength of $2V_x$ for synthetic enstatite (Besançon, 1992). The error bars represent ±1 *esd* as reported by EXCALIBR. At each (manual) setting of the spindle stage ($S = 0°$, 10°... 350°), a stepper motor rotated the PLM's stage until a photometric eyepiece detected the crystal's extinction position for the wavelength in use. EXCALIBR then solved the extinction data for each wavelength. [Full automation of the spindle stage would result if a stepper motor was used to set S to 0°, 10° ... 350°.]

Relationships between Optical Properties and Atomic Structure

Armbruster and Bermanec (1992) collected spindle stage data of outstanding accuracy from a single crystal of a low albite from Roc Tourné, France, at wavelengths of 480, 540 and 630 nm (using narrow band-pass interference filters), at 589.3 nm (Na-vapor lamp) and at 632 nm (He/Ne laser). For each of 36 S-settings (in steps of 10°), using a Medenbach spindle stage (mounted on a Leitz Ortholux PLM), they determined four extinction positions, each located in a different quadrant of the microscope stage, to avoid errors from refraction of the wave normal. Each of these four positions was measured three times using a Nakamura plate that, as discussed by Bloss (1981), permits highly precise determination of extinction positions. Thus, the extinction position (M_S) determined for each S setting was, in effect, the average of 12 measurements.

This precise optical study disclosed the Roc Tourné albite to possess "weak but highly significant triclinic dispersion..." and that this dispersion resulted from the dispersion of one optic axis (but not the other). What feature in the atomic structure of albite causes the two optic axes to disperse so differently?

Fully automated spindle stages will permit studies like that by Armbruster and Bermanec to be carried out with a great saving in the investigator's time. Moreover, the precision of the results will likely disclose whether a biaxial crystal is orthorhombic (neither X nor Y nor Z undergo significant dispersion), monoclinic (two of them do), or triclinic (all three do).

Inexpensive Equipment

Armbruster and Bermanec investigated whether their results could have been obtained with relatively inexpensive equipment. To this purpose they mounted a detent spindle stage ($S = 0°$ to 180°) onto a student-model PLM. They then repeated the 540-nm extinction measurements "with a normal ocular (without Nakamura half-shade plate) by

EXCALIBR   Bartelmehs, Bloss, Downs, and Birch; Z. Krist (1992)
Detent Spindle Stage Version 4.12.97   (kurtb@mail.utexas.edu)

A KRAGERO CORDERITE

Experimental Treatment ID number = 400.0
Average Reference Azimuth, Mr (esd) = 180.80 (.53)
based on 54 observations.

Biaxial Model
number of iterations(100 max.) = 8
R-squared = .99816

S	Ms	Corr(Ms)	Ms	CALC(Ms)	Ms-CALC(Ms)
.00	125.20	125.20	124.40	124.76	-.36
10.00	128.70	128.70	127.90	127.89	.02
20.00	129.15	129.15	128.35	128.86	-.51
30.00	128.30	128.30	127.50	128.01	-.51
40.00	125.85	125.85	125.05	125.65	-.60
50.00	122.10	122.10	121.30	122.12	-.81
60.00	117.90	117.90	117.10	117.85	-.74
70.00	113.40	113.40	112.60	113.31	-.71
80.00	109.10	109.10	108.30	108.89	-.59
90.00	105.10	105.10	104.30	104.75	-.45
100.00	101.30	101.30	100.50	100.86	-.36
110.00	97.65	97.65	96.85	97.06	-.21
120.00	93.70	93.70	92.90	93.05	-.15
130.00	89.25	89.25	88.45	88.44	.01
140.00	83.65	83.65	82.85	82.80	.05
150.00	76.60	76.60	75.80	75.85	-.04
160.00	68.55	68.55	67.75	68.01	-.26
170.00	60.90	60.90	60.10	60.69	-.58
180.00	55.65	235.65	54.85	55.24	-.38
190.00	52.55	232.55	51.75	52.11	-.36
200.00	51.50	231.50	50.70	51.14	-.43
210.00	52.25	232.25	51.45	51.99	-.53
220.00	54.60	234.60	53.80	54.35	-.55
230.00	57.90	237.90	57.10	57.88	-.78
240.00	62.25	242.25	61.45	62.15	-.70
250.00	66.75	246.75	65.95	66.69	-.74
260.00	71.25	251.25	70.45	71.11	-.66
270.00	75.75	255.75	74.95	75.25	-.30
280.00	79.65	259.65	78.85	79.14	-.28
290.00	83.50	263.50	82.70	82.94	-.24
300.00	87.50	267.50	86.70	86.95	-.25
310.00	92.25	272.25	91.45	91.56	-.11
320.00	97.85	277.85	97.05	97.20	-.15
330.00	104.90	284.90	104.10	104.15	-.05
340.00	112.70	292.70	111.90	111.99	-.08
350.00	119.50	299.50	118.70	119.31	-.61

Optic Axial Angle, 2V (ese) = 103.142 (.801)

Computed Cartesian Coordinates

	x	(ese)	y	(ese)	z	(ese)
OA1	.5091	(.0059)	.2982	(.0069)	.8074	(.0041)
OA2	-.7156	(.0054)	-.5830	(.0063)	.3848	(.0071)
AB	-.7816	(.0019)	.5624	(.0026)	.2697	(.0023)
OB	-.1661	(.0055)	-.2291	(.0100)	.9591	(.0015)
ON	-.6012	(.0033)	.7945	(.0033)	.0857	(.0107)

Spindle Stage Coordinates to measure refractive indices.

	S	(ese)	Ms	(ese)	(e-w polr.)	(n-s polr.)
OA1	69.73	(.48)	59.40	(.40)		
OA2	146.57	(.64)	135.69	(.44)	219.39	129.39
AB	25.62	(.23)	38.59	(.17)	280.36	190.36
OB	103.44	(.58)	99.56	(.32)	307.75	217.75
ON	6.16	(.78)	126.96	(.23)		

B KRAGERO CORDERITE

Experimental Treatment ID number = 900.0
Average Reference Azimuth, Mr (esd) = 180.80 (.53)
based on 54 observations.

Biaxial Model
number of iterations(100 max.) = 7
R-squared = .99907

S	Ms	Corr(Ms)	Ms	CALC(Ms)	Ms-CALC(Ms)
.00	125.70	125.70	124.90	125.00	-.09
10.00	128.60	128.60	127.80	127.94	-.14
20.00	129.38	129.38	128.58	128.74	-.16
30.00	128.20	128.20	127.40	127.76	-.35
40.00	125.75	125.75	124.95	125.31	-.36
50.00	121.65	121.65	120.85	121.76	-.91
60.00	117.93	117.93	117.13	117.55	-.42
70.00	113.50	113.50	112.70	113.12	-.42
80.00	109.23	109.23	108.43	108.82	-.39
90.00	105.23	105.23	104.43	104.79	-.35
100.00	101.63	101.63	100.83	100.98	-.15
110.00	97.78	97.78	97.30	97.22	-.24
120.00	94.10	94.10	93.30	93.21	-.09
130.00	89.48	89.48	88.68	88.55	-.13
140.00	83.33	83.33	82.53	82.79	-.25
150.00	76.33	76.33	75.53	75.65	-.12
160.00	68.50	68.50	67.70	67.66	-.04
170.00	60.95	60.95	60.15	60.33	-.17
180.00	55.63	235.63	54.83	55.00	-.17
190.00	52.73	232.73	51.93	52.06	-.13
200.00	51.78	231.78	50.98	51.26	-.27
210.00	52.70	232.70	51.90	52.24	-.34
220.00	54.98	234.98	54.18	54.69	-.51
230.00	58.40	238.40	57.60	58.24	-.63
240.00	62.75	242.75	61.95	62.45	-.50
250.00	67.28	247.28	66.48	66.88	-.40
260.00	71.53	251.53	70.73	71.18	-.45
270.00	75.70	255.70	74.90	75.21	-.31
280.00	79.90	259.90	78.90	79.02	-.12
290.00	83.45	263.45	82.65	82.78	-.12
300.00	87.50	267.50	86.70	86.79	-.08
310.00	92.15	272.15	91.35	91.45	-.09
320.00	97.88	277.88	97.08	97.21	-.13
330.00	105.10	285.10	104.30	104.35	-.05
340.00	113.10	293.10	112.30	112.34	-.03
350.00	120.33	300.33	119.53	119.67	-.14

Optic Axial Angle, 2V (ese) = 102.860 (.568)

Computed Cartesian Coordinates

	x	(ese)	y	(ese)	z	(ese)
OA1	.5019	(.0042)	.3116	(.0049)	.8068	(.0029)
OA2	-.7230	(.0038)	-.5680	(.0045)	.3933	(.0051)
AB	-.7833	(.0013)	-.5625	(.0019)	.2645	(.0017)
OB	-.1773	(.0039)	-.2056	(.0071)	.9624	(.0009)
ON	-.5958	(.0024)	.8008	(.0022)	.0613	(.0076)

Spindle Stage Coordinates to measure refractive indices.

	S	(ese)	Ms	(ese)	(e-w polr.)	(n-s polr.)
OA1	68.88	(.34)	59.87	(.28)		
OA2	145.30	(.46)	136.30	(.31)	219.23	129.23
AB	25.18	(.17)	38.43	(.12)	281.01	191.01
OB	102.06	(.41)	100.21	(.23)	307.37	217.37
ON	4.38	(.55)	126.57	(.17)		

using the same measurement strategy as for the precise data (three readings of extinction positions for each of the four quadrants of the microscope stage). They note that EXCALIBR's results from the less precise data "had *esd* about twice that as for the precise data." Nevertheless, they concluded that, "this accuracy is still sufficient for a precise dispersion analysis."

APPLICATIONS

McCrone (1992), who has taught the world how to use a PLM to solve many problems —for example, asbestos identification—observes that "few criminalists use this venerable instrument...[but that those who do] have been highly successful as criminalists." In discussing the forensic examination of soils, he notes that soils normally contain a variety of minerals including feldspars and, in lesser amounts, gypsum, amphiboles, pyroxenes and epidotes. For gypsum the composition ($CaSO_4 \cdot 2H_2O$) and $2V$ (= 58°) remain remarkably constant worldwide. Its presence in soil at the crime scene and, say, on the suspect's shoes would thus be only moderately incriminating. Unlike gypsum, however, crystals of feldspars, amphiboles, pyroxenes, and epidotes (Fig. 12-15) display variations in chemical composition—and thus wide variations in $2V$—from one soil to another. Consequently, if a criminalist performs a spindle stage study at four different wavelengths—as for the Tiburon albite (Fig. 12-11)—on crystals of the same mineral, some from the suspect's shoe and some from the crime scene, placement of the suspect at the crime scene would seem iron-clad if EXCALIBR's values of $2V$ for the grains agree to within 1° or 2° for each of the four wavelengths. Moreover, the equipment required would be minimal and inexpensive: (1) a PLM; (2) a spindle stage; (3) four wavelength filters; and (4) access to EXCALIBR.

Gunter (1992) discusses how substitution of one or more chemical elements for another, in a solid solution series, produces wide variations in the optical properties among the minerals that are members of that series. The value of $2V$, so easily and precisely determinable by spindle stage techniques, represents a very sensitive response to such compositional variations. And even if chemical composition is constant as for the K-feldspars, which all have the same composition, $KAlSi_3O_8$, marked changes in $2V$ occur in response to the degree of Al^{3+} and Si^{4+} disordering among the tetrahedral sites in the atomic structures of these minerals (see Su *et al.*, 1984). Note that, for the differentiation of the K-feldspar polymorphs, the lowly PLM and spindle stage will succeed whereas the overwhelmingly more expensive electron microprobe will fail.

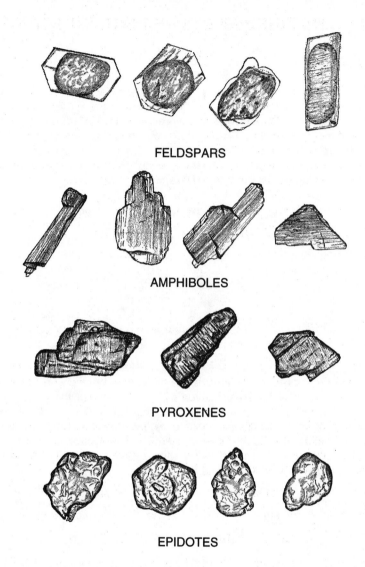

FELDSPARS

AMPHIBOLES

PYROXENES

EPIDOTES

Figure 12-15. Some biaxial minerals, as seen immersed in an oil of index 1.54, that may occur in the 0.149 to 0.105 mm (100 to 150 mesh) size-range in sands or soils. Occasionally, as shown here, feldspars exhibit clear rims (secondary overgrowths) around the primary grains. Usually, a footprint-sized area of soil is considered to supply an adequate sample—and a count of 300 grains per sample is considered sufficient to distinguish between two soils. Even "harder" evidence than mineral counts and the relative proportions of the minerals present would be spindle-stage determinations which show that feldspar, amphibole, pyroxene or epidote crystals associated with a suspect agree in *2V* (to within a degree or two) with those occurring in soils or sands at the crime scene. Grain sketches from W.C. Krumbein and F.J. Pettijohn (1938) *Manual of Sedimentary Petrography*, D. Appleton-Century Co.

13 RAPID OPTICAL DETERMINATION OF ASBESTOS FIBERS BY DISPERSION STAINING [1]

OVERVIEW

Refractive indices are essential for proper optical identification of any asbestiform mineral. During routine examination of asbestos samples, the National Voluntary Laboratory Accreditation Program (NVLAP) requires the γ and α indices of asbestos fibers to be measured (and reported) within ±0.005 to ±0.008 for chrysotile, amosite, anthophyllite, and tremolite-actinolite, or within ±0.010 to ±0.020 for crocidolite. Dispersion staining techniques (described in Chapter 5) are discussed for the listed asbestiform minerals, and determinative tables are provided to facilitate their identification.

STANDARD OPERATING PROCEDURES
FOR ASBESTOS IDENTIFICATION

Sample Preparation

Quite often, asbestos fibers will be coated with a filler or binding material. To insure that a fresh, uncoated surface will be in direct contact with the oil, *a situation that is imperative*, grind or rub the suspect fiber-bundle with a needle or probe to break it up into smaller bundles. Examine these smaller bundles in one of the oils cited in Figure 13-1.

Choice of Immersion Liquids

The desired accuracy in measuring the γ and α indices of asbestiform minerals—that is, within ±0.008 for chrysotile, amosite, anthophyllite, and tremolite-actinolite, or within ±0.020 for crocidolite—can be achieved with a single mount *if* the asbestos is either crocidolite or chrysotile, because their birefringence is small (~0.010; Fig. 13-1). However, the greater birefringences associated with amosite, tremolite, actinolite, and anthophyllite require that, for these minerals, two oils should be used, one to determine γ and a second to determine α. The refractive indices and dispersion coefficients of the six common asbestiform minerals are listed in Table 13-1.

Of course it is most efficient to begin mineral identification by using an oil whose refractive index (R.I.) is as close as possible to the R.I. expected for the fiber.

MEASURING A FIBER'S REFRACTIVE INDICES

Assuming an E-W polarizer, rotate the microscope stage until the fiber lies parallel to the E-W cross hair. Now use central-stop dispersion-staining (CSDS; see pp. 51 ff.) and Table 13-2 to determine $\lambda_{m\parallel}$, the wavelength of match between the oil and the fiber's R.I. for light vibrating along its length. Next orient the fiber perpendicular to the E-W cross hair so as to determine $\lambda_{m\perp}$, the wavelength of match for light vibrating perpendicular to its length. With $\lambda_{m\parallel}$, $\lambda_{m\perp}$ and $T(°C)$ known, γ and α can be calculated (pp. 55-59 and Eqn. 5-8) or *determined without calculation* from the conversion tables for chrysotile (p. 207), crocidolite (p. 208), amosite (p. 209), tremolite (p. 210), actinolite (p. 211) or anthophyllite (p. 212).

---

[1] This chapter is largely written by Dr. Shu-Chun Su, technical expert for the National Voluntary Laboratory Accreditation Program (NVLAP), which is administered by the National Institute of Standards and Technology (NIST).

Liquids for Chrysotile (1.560, 1.550)

If the matching liquids are 1.560 and/or 1.550, the fiber is likely to be chrysotile. In such case, $\lambda_{m\parallel}$ represents the wavelength of match for γ; similarly, $\lambda_{m\perp}$ represents that for α (see Fig. 13-1). Consult Table 13-3 to convert the observed wavelengths and temperature T into the corrected values for γ and α.

Liquids for Riebeckite/Crocidolite (1.700)
and for Grunerite/Amosite (1.700, 1.680)

The fiber is likely to be crocidolite if *two* wavelengths of match— $\lambda_{m\perp}$ and $\lambda_{m\parallel}$—are observed in the 1.700 liquid. In such a case, $\lambda_{m\perp}$ represents the wavelength of match for γ whereas $\lambda_{m\parallel}$ is the match for α (Fig. 13-1). Using the known temperature T, consult Table 13-4 to determine the corrected values for γ and α for crocidolite.

A second possibility is that the fiber is grunerite (sometimes called amosite). If so, only the R.I. for light vibrating along the fiber, namely γ (Fig. 13-1), will closely match 1.700. By contrast with crocidolite, its α index will be significantly lower. If so, the suspected amosite fibers need to be immersed in the 1.680 liquid to determine α (use Table 13-5). Note that, although crocidolite and amosite display essentially the same R.I. (1.700) for light vibrating parallel to the fiber, the fibers are also readily distinguished because the sign of elongation is (–) for crocidolite—that is, its *fast* vibration (α) lies parallel to the fiber's length—but (+) for amosite—that is, its *slow* vibration (γ) lies parallel to the fiber's length.

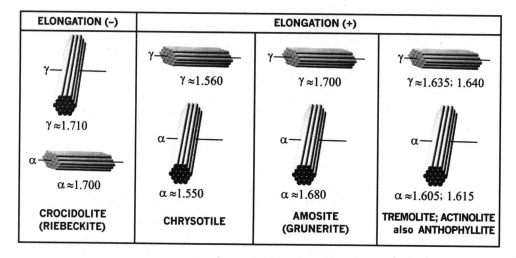

Figure 13-1. Optic orientation and, assuming an E-W-polarizing microscope, the refractive indices of the more common asbestos fibers. As discussed in the text, the preferred liquids for measuring R.I. by CSDS methods are: Cargille liquids 1.550, 1.605, 1.625, 1.635, 1.640 (Series E), and 1.700, 1.680 (Series B).

Liquids for Tremolite (1.635, 1.605)
and for Actinolite and Anthophyllite (1.640, 1.615)

As Figure 13-1 illustrates, measurement of the γ and α indices of tremolite asbestos requires immersion in liquids 1.635 and 1.605 and use of Table 13-6. Similarly, determination of γ and α for actinolite and anthophyllite fibers will require their immersion in liquids 1.640 and 1.615 and use of Tables 13-7 and 13-8, respectively, to convert these λ_m (and T values) to the values for γ and α.

Accuracy

Note that the greater birefringences of anthophyllite, tremolite, actinolite, and amosite necessitate use of at least two oil mounts, one of index close to γ and the other close to α, if these two indices are to be measured to the accuracy required by NVLAP for the test samples they send to asbestos laboratories.

Table 13-1. Refractive indices and dispersion coefficients ($n_F - n_C$) of six common asbestiform minerals (from Su, 1996).

Mineral		n_F	n_D	n_C	$(n_F-n_C)^*$	Reference
Chrysotile	α	1.5563	1.5490	1.5456	0.0107	NIST SRM 1866
	γ	1.5649	1.5560	1.5530	0.0119	
Grunerite (Amosite)	α	1.6931	1.6790	1.6734	0.0197	NIST SRM 1866**
	γ	1.7156	1.7010	1.6951	0.0205	
Riebeckite (Crocidolite)	α	1.7132	1.7015	1.6971	0.0161	McCrone (1987) Figs. 104A and 104B
	γ	1.7206	1.7072	1.7032	0.0174	
Tremolite	α	1.6128	1.6063	1.6036	0.0092	NIST SRM 1867
	β	1.6299	1.6230	1.6201	0.0098	
	γ	1.6423	1.6343	1.6310	0.0113	
Actinolite	α	1.6201	1.6126	1.6095	0.0106	NIST SRM 1867
	β	1.6369	1.6288	1.6254	0.0115	
	γ	1.6485	1.6393	1.6355	0.0130	
Anthophyllite	α	1.6227	1.6148	1.6116	0.0111	NIST SRM 1867
	β	1.6350	1.6273	1.6241	0.0109	
	γ	1.6449	1.6362	1.6326	0.0123	

* $(n_F - n_C)$ is the only parameter used in calculating all the conversion tables (Tables 13-3 to 13-8). Fortunately, for samples in which changes in composition, thermal history, etc. have caused variations in n_F, n_D, and n_C, the dispersion coefficient $(n_F - n_C)$ generally remains relatively unaffected.

** The dispersion coefficient of MIST SRM 1866 grunerite is much higher than that of the grunerite in McCrone (1987; Figs. 104A and 104B). Therefore, some values in Table 13-5, which are based on NIST grunerite, are markedly different than the values for grunerite in McCrone (1989).

Table 13-2. Estimated relationship of λ_m to the edge-colors observed with central-stop and annular-stop illumination. [This is the same as Table 5-1.]

1	2	3	4	5	6	7	8
	Central Stop			**Annular Stop**	**Unilateral Masking**		
	Dark Field						
Matching Wavelength (nm)		*Raising Focus*		*Bright Field*	*Gray Field*		n_D of Grain
	At Focus	Moving In	Moving Out		One Edge	Opposite Edge	
660	bright greenish blue	---	bright greenish blue	red	very dark red	pale greenish azure	Lower than oil
625	sky blue	---	sky blue	orangish-red	dark red	greenish blue	
600	blue	faint dark red	greenish blue	orange	red	light greenish blue	
589	deep violet	weak red	strong blue	orangish-yellow	orangish-red	green	Same as oil
575	purple	red	blue	yellow	reddish-orange	bluish-green	
540	reddish purple	orange-red	bluish-violet	green	orange	blue	
505	orange-red	orange	weak blue violet	bluish green	canary yellow	dark blue	Higher than oil
480	orange	yellow	weak violet	blue	yellow	dark blue-violet	
465	bright gold	bright gold	---	violet	bright yellow	dark violet	

Table 13-3. Determination of chrysotile.

λ_m	α in **1.550** (Cargille Series **E**)					γ in **1.550** (Cargille Series **E**)				
(nm)	*21°C*	*23°C*	*25°C*	*27°C*	*29°C*	*21°C*	*23°C*	*25°C*	*27°C*	*29°C*
400	1.582	1.581	1.580	1.579	1.578	1.580	1.579	1.578	1.577	1.576
420	1.576	1.575	1.574	1.573	1.572	1.574	1.573	1.572	1.571	1.570
440	1.572	1.571	1.570	1.569	1.568	1.570	1.569	1.568	1.567	1.566
460	1.568	1.567	1.566	1.565	1.564	1.566	1.565	1.564	1.564	1.563
480	1.564	1.563	1.562	1.561	1.560	1.563	1.562	1.561	1.560	1.559
500	1.561	1.560	1.559	1.558	1.557	1.561	1.560	1.559	1.558	1.557
520	1.559	1.558	1.557	1.556	1.555	1.558	1.557	1.556	1.555	1.554
540	1.557	1.556	1.555	1.554	1.553	1.556	1.555	1.554	1.553	1.552
560	1.555	1.554	1.553	1.552	1.551	1.554	1.553	1.552	1.551	1.550
580	1.553	1.552	1.551	1.550	1.549	1.553	1.552	1.551	1.550	1.549
589	1.552	1.551	1.550	1.549	1.548	1.552	1.551	1.550	1.549	1.548
600	1.551	1.550	1.549	1.548	1.547	1.551	1.550	1.549	1.548	1.547
620	1.550	1.549	1.548	1.547	1.546	1.550	1.549	1.548	1.547	1.546
640	1.548	1.547	1.546	1.545	1.544	1.549	1.548	1.547	1.546	1.545
660	1.547	1.546	1.545	1.544	1.543	1.547	1.546	1.546	1.545	1.544
680	1.546	1.545	1.544	1.543	1.542	1.546	1.545	1.544	1.544	1.543
700	1.545	1.544	1.543	1.542	1.541	1.546	1.545	1.544	1.543	1.542
750	1.543	1.542	1.541	1.540	1.539	1.543	1.542	1.541	1.540	1.540
800	1.541	1.540	1.539	1.538	1.537	1.542	1.541	1.540	1.539	1.538

Chrysotile

λ_m	α in **1.560** (Cargille Series **E**)					γ in **1.560** (Cargille Series **E**)				
(nm)	*21°C*	*23°C*	*25°C*	*27°C*	*29°C*	*21°C*	*23°C*	*25°C*	*27°C*	*29°C*
400	1.591	1.590	1.589	1.588	1.587	1.589	1.588	1.587	1.586	1.585
420	1.586	1.585	1.584	1.583	1.582	1.584	1.583	1.582	1.581	1.580
440	1.581	1.580	1.579	1.578	1.577	1.580	1.579	1.578	1.577	1.576
460	1.577	1.576	1.575	1.574	1.573	1.576	1.575	1.574	1.573	1.572
480	1.574	1.573	1.572	1.571	1.570	1.573	1.572	1.571	1.570	1.569
500	1.571	1.570	1.569	1.568	1.567	1.570	1.569	1.568	1.567	1.567
520	1.569	1.568	1.567	1.566	1.565	1.568	1.567	1.566	1.565	1.564
540	1.566	1.565	1.564	1.563	1.563	1.566	1.565	1.564	1.563	1.562
560	1.564	1.563	1.562	1.562	1.561	1.564	1.563	1.562	1.561	1.560
580	1.563	1.562	1.561	1.560	1.559	1.563	1.562	1.561	1.560	1.559
589	1.562	1.561	1.560	1.559	1.558	1.562	1.561	1.560	1.559	1.558
600	1.561	1.560	1.559	1.558	1.557	1.561	1.560	1.559	1.558	1.557
620	1.560	1.559	1.558	1.557	1.556	1.560	1.559	1.558	1.557	1.556
640	1.558	1.557	1.556	1.555	1.555	1.559	1.558	1.557	1.556	1.555
660	1.557	1.556	1.555	1.554	1.553	1.558	1.557	1.556	1.555	1.554
680	1.556	1.555	1.554	1.553	1.552	1.557	1.556	1.555	1.554	1.553
700	1.555	1.554	1.553	1.552	1.551	1.556	1.555	1.554	1.553	1.552
750	1.553	1.552	1.551	1.550	1.549	1.554	1.553	1.552	1.551	1.550
800	1.551	1.550	1.549	1.548	1.547	1.552	1.551	1.550	1.549	1.548

Table 13-4. Determination of riebeckite (crocidolite).

λ_m (nm)	α in **1.680** (Cargille Series **B**)					γ in **1.680** (Cargille Series **B**)				
	21°C	*23°C*	*25°C*	*27°C*	*29°C*	*21°C*	*23°C*	*25°C*	*27°C*	*29°C*
400	1.717	1.716	1.715	1.714	1.713	1.714	1.713	1.712	1.711	1.711
420	1.710	1.709	1.708	1.707	1.706	1.708	1.707	1.706	1.705	1.704
440	1.705	1.704	1.703	1.702	1.701	1.703	1.702	1.701	1.700	1.699
460	1.700	1.699	1.698	1.697	1.696	1.699	1.698	1.697	1.696	1.695
480	1.696	1.695	1.694	1.693	1.692	1.695	1.694	1.693	1.692	1.691
500	1.693	1.692	1.691	1.690	1.689	1.692	1.691	1.690	1.689	1.688
520	1.690	1.689	1.688	1.687	1.686	1.689	1.688	1.687	1.686	1.685
540	1.687	1.686	1.685	1.684	1.683	1.687	1.686	1.685	1.684	1.683
560	1.685	1.684	1.683	1.682	1.681	1.685	1.684	1.683	1.682	1.681
580	1.683	1.682	1.681	1.680	1.679	1.683	1.682	1.681	1.680	1.679
589	1.682	1.681	1.680	1.679	1.678	1.682	1.681	1.680	1.679	1.678
600	1.681	1.680	1.679	1.678	1.677	1.681	1.680	1.679	1.678	1.677
620	1.679	1.678	1.677	1.676	1.675	1.679	1.678	1.677	1.677	1.676
640	1.678	1.677	1.676	1.675	1.674	1.678	1.677	1.676	1.675	1.674
660	1.676	1.675	1.674	1.673	1.672	1.677	1.676	1.675	1.674	1.673
680	1.675	1.674	1.673	1.672	1.671	1.675	1.674	1.674	1.673	1.672
700	1.674	1.673	1.672	1.671	1.670	1.674	1.673	1.672	1.671	1.670
750	1.671	1.670	1.669	1.668	1.667	1.672	1.671	1.670	1.669	1.668
800	1.669	1.668	1.667	1.666	1.665	1.670	1.669	1.668	1.667	1.666

λ_m (nm)	α in **1.700** (Cargille Series **B**)					γ in **1.700** (Cargille Series **B**)				
	21°C	*23°C*	*25°C*	*27°C*	*29°C*	*21°C*	*23°C*	*25°C*	*27°C*	*29°C*
400	1.741	1.740	1.739	1.738	1.737	1.738	1.737	1.737	1.736	1.735
420	1.734	1.733	1.732	1.731	1.730	1.732	1.731	1.730	1.729	1.728
440	1.728	1.727	1.726	1.725	1.724	1.726	1.725	1.724	1.723	1.722
460	1.722	1.721	1.720	1.720	1.719	1.721	1.720	1.719	1.718	1.717
480	1.718	1.717	1.716	1.715	1.714	1.717	1.716	1.715	1.714	1.713
500	1.714	1.713	1.712	1.711	1.710	1.713	1.712	1.711	1.711	1.710
520	1.711	1.710	1.709	1.708	1.707	1.710	1.709	1.708	1.707	1.706
540	1.708	1.707	1.706	1.705	1.704	1.708	1.707	1.706	1.705	1.704
560	1.705	1.704	1.703	1.702	1.701	1.705	1.704	1.703	1.702	1.701
580	1.703	1.702	1.701	1.700	1.699	1.703	1.702	1.701	1.700	1.699
589	1.702	1.701	1.700	1.699	1.698	1.702	1.701	1.700	1.699	1.698
600	1.701	1.700	1.699	1.698	1.697	1.701	1.700	1.699	1.698	1.697
620	1.699	1.698	1.697	1.696	1.695	1.699	1.698	1.697	1.696	1.695
640	1.697	1.696	1.695	1.694	1.693	1.697	1.697	1.696	1.695	1.694
660	1.696	1.695	1.694	1.693	1.692	1.696	1.695	1.694	1.693	1.692
680	1.694	1.693	1.692	1.691	1.690	1.695	1.694	1.693	1.692	1.691
700	1.693	1.692	1.691	1.690	1.689	1.693	1.692	1.691	1.690	1.690
750	1.690	1.689	1.688	1.687	1.686	1.691	1.690	1.689	1.688	1.687
800	1.687	1.686	1.686	1.685	1.684	1.688	1.687	1.686	1.685	1.685

Riebeckite (Crocidolite)

Table 13-5. Determination of grunerite (amosite).

λ_m	α in **1.680** (Cargille Series **B**)					γ in **1.680** (Cargille Series **B**)				
(nm)	*21°C*	*23°C*	*25°C*	*27°C*	*29°C*	*21°C*	*23°C*	*25°C*	*27°C*	*29°C*
400	1.710	1.709	1.708	1.707	1.706	1.709	1.708	1.707	1.706	1.705
420	1.705	1.704	1.703	1.702	1.701	1.704	1.703	1.702	1.701	1.700
440	1.700	1.699	1.698	1.698	1.697	1.699	1.698	1.698	1.697	1.696
460	1.697	1.696	1.695	1.694	1.693	1.696	1.695	1.694	1.693	1.692
480	1.694	1.693	1.692	1.691	1.690	1.693	1.692	1.691	1.690	1.689
500	1.691	1.690	1.689	1.688	1.687	1.690	1.689	1.688	1.687	1.686
520	1.688	1.687	1.686	1.685	1.685	1.688	1.687	1.686	1.685	1.684
540	1.686	1.685	1.684	1.683	1.682	1.686	1.685	1.684	1.683	1.682
560	1.684	1.683	1.682	1.681	1.680	1.684	1.683	1.682	1.681	1.680
580	1.683	1.682	1.681	1.680	1.679	1.683	1.682	1.681	1.680	1.679
589	1.682	1.681	1.680	1.679	1.678	1.682	1.681	1.680	1.679	1.678
600	1.681	1.680	1.679	1.678	1.677	1.681	1.680	1.679	1.678	1.677
620	1.680	1.679	1.678	1.677	1.676	1.680	1.679	1.678	1.677	1.676
640	1.678	1.678	1.677	1.676	1.675	1.679	1.678	1.677	1.676	1.675
660	1.677	1.676	1.675	1.674	1.674	1.678	1.677	1.676	1.675	1.674
680	1.676	1.675	1.674	1.673	1.672	1.677	1.676	1.675	1.674	1.673
700	1.675	1.674	1.673	1.672	1.671	1.676	1.675	1.674	1.673	1.672
750	1.673	1.672	1.671	1.670	1.669	1.674	1.673	1.672	1.671	1.670
800	1.671	1.671	1.670	1.669	1.668	1.672	1.671	1.670	1.669	1.668

Grunerite (Amosite)

λ_m	α in **1.700** (Cargille Series **B**)					γ in **1.700** (Cargille Series **B**)				
(nm)	*21°C*	*23°C*	*25°C*	*27°C*	*29°C*	*21°C*	*23°C*	*25°C*	*27°C*	*29°C*
400	1.734	1.733	1.732	1.731	1.730	1.733	1.732	1.731	1.730	1.729
420	1.728	1.727	1.726	1.725	1.724	1.727	1.726	1.725	1.724	1.723
440	1.723	1.722	1.721	1.720	1.719	1.722	1.721	1.720	1.719	1.718
460	1.719	1.718	1.717	1.716	1.715	1.718	1.717	1.716	1.715	1.714
480	1.715	1.714	1.713	1.712	1.711	1.715	1.714	1.713	1.712	1.711
500	1.712	1.711	1.710	1.709	1.708	1.712	1.711	1.710	1.709	1.708
520	1.709	1.708	1.707	1.706	1.705	1.709	1.708	1.707	1.706	1.705
540	1.707	1.706	1.705	1.704	1.703	1.707	1.706	1.705	1.704	1.703
560	1.705	1.704	1.703	1.702	1.701	1.705	1.704	1.703	1.702	1.701
580	1.703	1.702	1.701	1.700	1.699	1.703	1.702	1.701	1.700	1.699
589	1.702	1.701	1.700	1.699	1.698	1.702	1.701	1.700	1.699	1.698
600	1.701	1.700	1.699	1.698	1.697	1.701	1.700	1.699	1.698	1.697
620	1.699	1.698	1.698	1.697	1.696	1.700	1.699	1.698	1.697	1.696
640	1.698	1.697	1.696	1.695	1.694	1.698	1.697	1.696	1.695	1.694
660	1.697	1.696	1.695	1.694	1.693	1.697	1.696	1.695	1.694	1.693
680	1.695	1.695	1.694	1.693	1.692	1.696	1.695	1.694	1.693	1.692
700	1.694	1.693	1.692	1.691	1.691	1.695	1.694	1.693	1.692	1.691
750	1.692	1.691	1.690	1.689	1.688	1.692	1.691	1.690	1.690	1.689
800	1.690	1.689	1.688	1.687	1.686	1.691	1.690	1.689	1.688	1.687

Table 13-6. Determination of tremolite.

λ_m (nm)	α in **1.605** (Cargille Series **E**)					α in **1.615** (Cargille Series **E**)				
	21°C	*23°C*	*25°C*	*27°C*	*29°C*	*21°C*	*23°C*	*25°C*	*27°C*	*29°C*
400	1.635	1.634	1.633	1.632	1.631	1.648	1.647	1.646	1.645	1.644
420	1.630	1.629	1.628	1.627	1.626	1.642	1.641	1.640	1.639	1.638
440	1.625	1.624	1.623	1.622	1.622	1.637	1.636	1.635	1.634	1.634
460	1.621	1.621	1.620	1.619	1.618	1.633	1.632	1.631	1.630	1.629
480	1.618	1.617	1.617	1.616	1.615	1.630	1.629	1.628	1.627	1.626
500	1.616	1.615	1.614	1.613	1.612	1.627	1.626	1.625	1.624	1.623
520	1.613	1.612	1.611	1.611	1.610	1.624	1.623	1.622	1.621	1.620
540	1.611	1.610	1.609	1.608	1.608	1.622	1.621	1.620	1.619	1.618
560	1.609	1.608	1.607	1.607	1.606	1.619	1.619	1.618	1.617	1.616
580	1.607	1.607	1.606	1.605	1.604	1.618	1.617	1.616	1.615	1.614
589	1.607	1.606	1.605	1.604	1.603	1.617	1.616	1.615	1.614	1.613
600	1.606	1.605	1.604	1.603	1.602	1.616	1.615	1.614	1.613	1.612
620	1.605	1.604	1.603	1.602	1.601	1.614	1.614	1.613	1.612	1.611
640	1.603	1.602	1.602	1.601	1.600	1.613	1.612	1.611	1.610	1.609
660	1.602	1.601	1.600	1.600	1.599	1.612	1.611	1.610	1.609	1.608
680	1.601	1.600	1.599	1.599	1.598	1.611	1.610	1.609	1.608	1.607
700	1.600	1.599	1.598	1.598	1.597	1.610	1.609	1.608	1.607	1.606
750	1.598	1.597	1.596	1.595	1.595	1.607	1.606	1.605	1.605	1.604
800	1.596	1.596	1.595	1.594	1.593	1.605	1.604	1.604	1.603	1.602

Tremolite

λ_m (nm)	γ in **1.635** (Cargille Series **E**)					γ in **1.640** (Cargille Series **E**)				
	21°C	*23°C*	*25°C*	*27°C*	*29°C*	*21°C*	*23°C*	*25°C*	*27°C*	*29°C*
400	1.669	1.669	1.668	1.667	1.666	1.676	1.675	1.674	1.673	1.672
420	1.663	1.662	1.662	1.661	1.660	1.670	1.669	1.668	1.667	1.666
440	1.658	1.657	1.656	1.656	1.655	1.664	1.663	1.662	1.661	1.661
460	1.654	1.653	1.652	1.651	1.650	1.660	1.659	1.658	1.657	1.656
480	1.650	1.649	1.648	1.648	1.647	1.656	1.655	1.654	1.653	1.652
500	1.647	1.646	1.645	1.644	1.643	1.653	1.652	1.651	1.650	1.649
520	1.644	1.643	1.642	1.642	1.641	1.650	1.649	1.648	1.647	1.646
540	1.642	1.641	1.640	1.639	1.638	1.645	1.644	1.643	1.642	1.641
560	1.640	1.639	1.638	1.637	1.636	1.643	1.642	1.641	1.640	1.639
580	1.638	1.637	1.636	1.635	1.634	1.643	1.642	1.641	1.640	1.639
589	1.637	1.636	1.635	1.634	1.633	1.642	1.641	1.640	1.639	1.638
600	1.636	1.635	1.634	1.633	1.632	1.641	1.640	1.639	1.638	1.637
620	1.634	1.633	1.632	1.632	1.631	1.639	1.638	1.637	1.636	1.636
640	1.633	1.632	1.631	1.630	1.629	1.638	1.637	1.636	1.635	1.634
660	1.632	1.631	1.630	1.629	1.628	1.636	1.635	1.634	1.634	1.633
680	1.630	1.629	1.628	1.628	1.627	1.635	1.634	1.633	1.632	1.631
700	1.629	1.628	1.627	1.626	1.626	1.634	1.633	1.632	1.631	1.630
750	1.627	1.626	1.625	1.624	1.623	1.631	1.630	1.629	1.629	1.628
800	1.625	1.624	1.623	1.622	1.621	1.629	1.628	1.627	1.626	1.625

Table 13-7. Determination of actinolite.

λ_m (nm)	α in **1.605** (Cargille Series **E**)					α in **1.615** (Cargille Series **E**)				
Actinolite	*21°C*	*23°C*	*25°C*	*27°C*	*29°C*	*21°C*	*23°C*	*25°C*	*27°C*	*29°C*
400	1.632	1.631	1.630	1.629	1.629	1.645	1.644	1.643	1.642	1.642
420	1.627	1.626	1.626	1.625	1.624	1.640	1.639	1.638	1.637	1.636
440	1.623	1.623	1.622	1.621	1.620	1.635	1.635	1.634	1.633	1.632
460	1.620	1.619	1.618	1.617	1.617	1.632	1.631	1.630	1.629	1.628
480	1.617	1.616	1.615	1.615	1.614	1.628	1.628	1.627	1.626	1.625
500	1.615	1.614	1.613	1.612	1.611	1.626	1.625	1.624	1.623	1.622
520	1.613	1.612	1.611	1.610	1.609	1.623	1.622	1.621	1.621	1.620
540	1.611	1.610	1.609	1.608	1.607	1.621	1.620	1.619	1.618	1.618
560	1.609	1.608	1.607	1.606	1.605	1.619	1.618	1.617	1.617	1.616
580	1.607	1.607	1.606	1.605	1.604	1.618	1.617	1.616	1.615	1.614
589	1.607	1.606	1.605	1.604	1.603	1.617	1.616	1.615	1.614	1.613
600	1.606	1.605	1.604	1.603	1.603	1.616	1.615	1.614	1.613	1.612
620	1.605	1.604	1.603	1.602	1.601	1.615	1.614	1.613	1.612	1.611
640	1.604	1.603	1.602	1.601	1.600	1.613	1.612	1.612	1.611	1.610
660	1.603	1.602	1.601	1.600	1.599	1.612	1.611	1.610	1.609	1.609
680	1.602	1.601	1.600	1.599	1.598	1.611	1.610	1.609	1.608	1.608
700	1.601	1.600	1.599	1.598	1.597	1.610	1.609	1.608	1.607	1.607
750	1.599	1.598	1.597	1.596	1.595	1.608	1.607	1.606	1.605	1.604
800	1.597	1.596	1.596	1.595	1.594	1.606	1.605	1.604	1.604	1.603

λ_m (nm)	γ in **1.635** (Cargille Series **E**)					γ in **1.640** (Cargille Series **E**)				
Actinolite	*21°C*	*23°C*	*25°C*	*27°C*	*29°C*	*21°C*	*23°C*	*25°C*	*27°C*	*29°C*
400	1.666	1.665	1.664	1.664	1.663	1.673	1.672	1.671	1.670	1.669
420	1.661	1.660	1.659	1.658	1.657	1.667	1.666	1.665	1.664	1.663
440	1.656	1.655	1.654	1.653	1.653	1.662	1.661	1.660	1.659	1.658
460	1.652	1.651	1.650	1.650	1.649	1.658	1.657	1.656	1.655	1.654
480	1.649	1.648	1.647	1.646	1.645	1.655	1.654	1.653	1.652	1.651
500	1.646	1.645	1.644	1.643	1.642	1.652	1.651	1.650	1.649	1.648
520	1.644	1.643	1.642	1.641	1.640	1.649	1.648	1.647	1.646	1.645
540	1.641	1.640	1.640	1.639	1.638	1.647	1.646	1.645	1.644	1.643
560	1.639	1.638	1.638	1.637	1.636	1.644	1.644	1.643	1.642	1.641
580	1.638	1.637	1.636	1.635	1.634	1.643	1.642	1.641	1.640	1.639
589	1.637	1.636	1.635	1.634	1.633	1.642	1.641	1.640	1.639	1.638
600	1.636	1.635	1.634	1.633	1.632	1.641	1.640	1.639	1.638	1.637
620	1.635	1.634	1.633	1.632	1.631	1.639	1.639	1.638	1.637	1.636
640	1.633	1.632	1.631	1.630	1.630	1.638	1.637	1.636	1.635	1.634
660	1.632	1.631	1.630	1.629	1.628	1.637	1.636	1.635	1.634	1.633
680	1.631	1.630	1.629	1.628	1.627	1.636	1.635	1.634	1.633	1.632
700	1.630	1.629	1.628	1.627	1.626	1.635	1.634	1.633	1.632	1.631
750	1.628	1.627	1.626	1.625	1.624	1.632	1.631	1.630	1.630	1.629
800	1.626	1.625	1.624	1.623	1.622	1.630	1.629	1.629	1.628	1.627

Table 13-8. Determination of anthophyllite.

Anthophyllite										
λ_m	α in **1.605** (Cargille Series **E**)					α in **1.615** (Cargille Series **E**)				
(nm)	*21°C*	*23°C*	*25°C*	*27°C*	*29°C*	*21°C*	*23°C*	*25°C*	*27°C*	*29°C*
400	1.631	1.630	1.629	1.629	1.628	1.644	1.643	1.642	1.642	1.641
420	1.627	1.626	1.625	1.624	1.623	1.639	1.638	1.637	1.636	1.635
440	1.623	1.622	1.621	1.620	1.619	1.635	1.634	1.633	1.632	1.631
460	1.620	1.619	1.618	1.617	1.616	1.631	1.630	1.629	1.628	1.628
480	1.617	1.616	1.615	1.614	1.613	1.628	1.627	1.626	1.625	1.625
500	1.614	1.614	1.613	1.612	1.611	1.625	1.625	1.624	1.623	1.622
520	1.612	1.611	1.611	1.610	1.609	1.623	1.622	1.621	1.620	1.619
540	1.610	1.610	1.609	1.608	1.607	1.621	1.620	1.619	1.618	1.617
560	1.609	1.608	1.607	1.606	1.605	1.619	1.618	1.617	1.616	1.616
580	1.607	1.607	1.606	1.605	1.604	1.618	1.617	1.616	1.615	1.614
589	1.607	1.606	1.605	1.604	1.603	1.617	1.616	1.615	1.614	1.613
600	1.606	1.605	1.604	1.603	1.603	1.616	1.615	1.614	1.613	1.612
620	1.605	1.604	1.603	1.602	1.601	1.615	1.614	1.613	1.612	1.611
640	1.604	1.603	1.602	1.601	1.600	1.613	1.613	1.612	1.611	1.610
660	1.603	1.602	1.601	1.600	1.599	1.612	1.611	1.611	1.610	1.609
680	1.602	1.601	1.600	1.599	1.598	1.611	1.610	1.610	1.609	1.608
700	1.601	1.600	1.599	1.598	1.598	1.610	1.609	1.609	1.608	1.607
750	1.599	1.598	1.597	1.597	1.596	1.608	1.607	1.607	1.606	1.605
800	1.598	1.597	1.596	1.595	1.594	1.607	1.606	1.605	1.604	1.603

Anthophyllite										
λ_m	γ in **1.635** (Cargille Series **E**)					γ in **1.640** (Cargille Series **E**)				
(nm)	*21°C*	*23°C*	*25°C*	*27°C*	*29°C*	*21°C*	*23°C*	*25°C*	*27°C*	*29°C*
400	1.668	1.667	1.666	1.665	1.664	1.674	1.673	1.672	1.671	1.670
420	1.662	1.661	1.660	1.659	1.658	1.668	1.667	1.666	1.665	1.664
440	1.657	1.656	1.655	1.654	1.653	1.663	1.662	1.661	1.660	1.659
460	1.653	1.652	1.651	1.650	1.649	1.659	1.658	1.657	1.656	1.655
480	1.650	1.649	1.648	1.647	1.646	1.655	1.654	1.653	1.652	1.651
500	1.647	1.646	1.645	1.644	1.643	1.652	1.651	1.650	1.649	1.648
520	1.644	1.643	1.642	1.641	1.640	1.649	1.648	1.647	1.646	1.646
540	1.642	1.641	1.640	1.639	1.638	1.647	1.646	1.645	1.644	1.643
560	1.639	1.639	1.638	1.637	1.636	1.645	1.644	1.643	1.642	1.641
580	1.638	1.637	1.636	1.635	1.634	1.643	1.642	1.641	1.640	1.639
589	1.637	1.636	1.635	1.634	1.633	1.642	1.641	1.640	1.639	1.638
600	1.636	1.635	1.634	1.633	1.632	1.641	1.640	1.639	1.638	1.637
620	1.634	1.634	1.633	1.632	1.631	1.639	1.638	1.638	1.637	1.636
640	1.633	1.632	1.631	1.630	1.629	1.638	1.637	1.636	1.635	1.634
660	1.632	1.631	1.630	1.629	1.628	1.637	1.636	1.635	1.634	1.633
680	1.631	1.630	1.629	1.628	1.627	1.635	1.634	1.634	1.633	1.632
700	1.630	1.629	1.628	1.627	1.626	1.634	1.633	1.632	1.632	1.631
750	1.627	1.626	1.625	1.625	1.624	1.632	1.631	1.630	1.629	1.628
800	1.625	1.625	1.624	1.623	1.622	1.630	1.629	1.628	1.627	1.626

PRECAUTIONS

PLM Alignment

Be certain that the polarizer's privileged direction is parallel to the E-W cross hair and the analyzer's to the N-S cross hair. In addition, center the dispersion-staining objective (its central stop) as well as the microscope's substage, and, if possible, use Köhler illumination.

Re-calibration of Immersion Media

Use of the immersion method for determining the refractive indices of unknown solids requires a periodic re-calibration of the oils in use. This insures that significant changes in the R.I. of the oils, through deterioration or contamination, will not go undetected. Such recalibration, required by NVLAP of all asbestos laboratories, may best be achieved using an Abbé refractometer (see p. 40).

Much less conveniently, re-calibration of the oils most commonly used in asbestos determinations—namely, Cargille liquids 1.550, 1.605, 1.615, 1.635, 1.640, 1.680, and 1.700—may also be achieved by use of grains of glass standards whose refractive indices are precisely and accurately known. The necessary materials include:

(1) Standard glasses, which may be purchased from Cargille Laboratories.

(2) A polarizing microscope equipped with a CSDS objective.

(3) A thermometer reading to 1°C.

The procedure involves immersing, in the oil to be re-calibrated, a few grains of that glass standard whose n_D value most closely matches that of the oil. Next, use central-stop dispersion-staining to determine λ_m, the wavelength of match between grain and oil. [Caution: *Sometimes glass shards may display false dispersion-staining colors along flat, smooth, nearly vertical edges, e.g., orange for 1.55 glass fragments in a 1.550 liquid. If this false CSDS color appears, observe the colors on the interiors of the grains, where the grain-oil boundaries will be less vertical.*] Consult Table 13-2 to convert the observed CSDS color to λ_m, and then use Table 13-9 to convert λ_m to k_D, a coefficient previously discussed (pp. 58-59).

When the CSDS color is observed, one should also determine T, the temperature of the oil mount, by placing the thermometer in contact with the cover glass of the oil mount. Unless the substage light source is generating significant heat, T will likely be the room temperature. If this is true, the room's temperature can henceforward be accepted as that of the oil.

The following quantities are now known:

$n_{D,GS}$ – the R.I. of the glass standard for D-light (given in the table of optical constants supplied with the glass standards).

Δ_{GS} – the dispersion coefficient $(n_F - n_C)$ for the glass standard (also in the table).

Δ_{LIQ} – the dispersion coefficient $(n_F - n_C)$ for the liquid (printed on the bottle label).

k_D – the coefficient to which λ_m was converted

These quantities may be inserted in the following re-cast version of Equation 5-6 in which $n_{D,LIQ}$ represents the recalibrated R.I. of the oil:

$$n_{D,LIQ} = n_{D,GS} - (\Delta_{LIQ} - \Delta_{GS})\,k_D \qquad \text{(Eqn. 13-1)}$$

Table 13-9. Conversion of λ_m to k_D and k_i at selected wavelengths
For the single liquid method. (After Su, 1998.)

Matching Wavelength λ_m (nm)	Hartmann Scale	Wavelengths of Selected Fraunhöfer Lines and Lasers (nm)							
		F 486.1	E 508.6	e 546.1	D 589.3	HeNe 632.8	C 656.3	Ruby 694.3	GaAs 840.0
300	10.00	4.99	5.18	5.45	*5.70*	5.90	5.99	6.12	6.47
320	8.33	3.71	3.91	4.17	*4.42*	4.62	4.71	4.84	5.19
340	7.14	2.80	2.99	3.26	*3.51*	3.71	3.80	3.93	4.28
360	6.25	2.11	2.31	2.58	*2.82*	3.02	3.11	3.24	3.59
380	5.56	1.58	1.78	2.04	*2.29*	2.49	2.58	2.71	3.06
400	5.00	1.15	1.35	1.62	*1.86*	2.06	2.15	2.28	2.64
420	4.55	0.81	1.00	1.27	*1.52*	1.71	1.81	1.93	2.29
440	4.17	0.51	0.71	0.98	*1.23*	1.42	1.51	1.64	2.00
460	3.85	0.27	0.46	0.73	*0.98*	1.18	1.27	1.40	1.75
480	3.57	0.06	0.25	0.52	*0.77*	0.97	1.06	1.19	1.54
500	3.33	-0.12	0.07	0.34	*0.59*	0.78	0.88	1.00	1.36
520	3.13	-0.28	-0.09	0.18	*0.43*	0.62	0.72	0.85	1.20
540	2.94	-0.42	-0.23	0.04	*0.29*	0.48	0.57	0.70	1.06
560	2.78	-0.55	-0.35	-0.09	*0.16*	0.36	0.45	0.58	0.93
580	2.63	-0.66	-0.47	-0.20	*0.05*	0.25	0.34	0.47	0.82
600	2.50	-0.76	-0.57	-0.30	*-0.05*	0.15	0.24	0.37	0.72
620	2.38	-0.85	-0.66	-0.39	*-0.14*	0.05	0.15	0.27	0.63
640	2.27	-0.94	-0.74	-0.47	*-0.23*	-0.03	0.06	0.19	0.54
660	2.17	-1.01	-0.82	-0.55	*-0.30*	-0.10	-0.01	0.12	0.47
680	2.08	-1.08	-0.89	-0.62	*-0.37*	-0.17	-0.08	0.05	0.40
700	2.00	-1.15	-0.95	-0.68	*-0.44*	-0.24	-0.15	-0.02	0.34
720	1.92	-1.21	-1.01	-0.74	*-0.50*	-0.30	-0.21	-0.08	0.28
740	1.85	-1.26	-1.06	-0.80	*-0.55*	-0.35	-0.26	-0.13	0.22
760	1.79	-1.31	-1.12	-0.85	*-0.60*	-0.40	-0.31	-0.18	0.17
780	1.72	-1.36	-1.16	-0.89	*-0.65*	-0.45	-0.36	-0.23	0.12
800	1.67	-1.40	-1.21	-0.94	*-0.69*	-0.49	-0.40	-0.27	0.08

If the measured temperature T differs from 25°C, use Equation 5-8 to correct the refractive index to 25°C. Thus,

$$n_{D,LIQ,\ CORR} = n_{D,LIQ} + (25 - T)\ dn/dt \qquad \text{(Eqn. 13-2)}$$

where dn/dt is the temperature coefficient of the liquid as printed on the bottle's label. It is always negative, that is, a liquid's R.I. always decreases as its temperature increases.

When calibrating a Cargille liquid by use of a Cargille glass, the calculations (Eqns. 13-1 and 13-2) necessary to obtain $n_{D,LIQ,\ CORR}$ may be avoided through use of Table 13-10. Thus the observed values for λ_m and T (°C) indicate, within the body of the table, the value for $n_{D,LIQ,\ CORR}$. So long as this indicated value falls within a dotted rectangle in Table 13-10, the liquid can continue in use.

At the bottom of each table comprising Table 13-10 are listed the optical constants inserted into Equations 13-1 and 13-2 when calculating n_D at 25°C for the liquid.

As an example of these tables in use, assume that grains of Cargille Glass 1.55 display a bluish purple CSDS color when immersed in the Cargille (Series E) Liquid 1.550 at 21°C. From Table 13-2 (or a McCrone color chart), this bluish purple color indicates that λ_m, the wavelength of glass-oil match, approximately equals 580 nm. Now look under the 21°C column in Table 13-10. At the level for a λ_m value of 580 nm, a value of 1.548 is indicated. This value equals n_D of the oil corrected to 25°C and indicates that n_D for liquid 1.550 has become 1.548, which is 0.002 below its label value. In general, if this difference is 0.004 or less, the liquid may continue to be used for bulk sample analysis. However, if the difference exceeds 0.004, the liquid should be replaced.

Table 13-10. Calibration of liquids 1.550, 1.605, 1.615, 1.635, 1.640, 1.680 and 1.700.

NOTE: If the observed λ_m and T values indicate a $n_{D,LIQ,CORR}$ value that falls within the dotted rectangle, the liquid does not need to be replaced.

λ_m (nm)	1.550 (Cargille Series E) Cargille Glass 1.55 (Lot B or C)					1.640 (Cargille Series E) Cargille Glass 1.64 (Lot B)				
	21°C	*23°C*	*25°C*	*27°C*	*29°C*	*21°C*	*23°C*	*25°C*	*27°C*	*29°C*
480	1.537	1.538	1.539	1.540	1.541	1.628	1.629	1.630	1.631	1.632
500	1.540	1.541	1.542	1.543	1.544	1.631	1.632	1.633	1.634	1.635
520	1.543	1.544	1.545	1.546	1.546	1.634	1.635	1.636	1.637	1.637
540	1.545	1.546	1.547	1.548	1.549	1.636	1.637	1.638	1.639	1.640
560	1.547	1.548	1.549	1.550	1.551	1.638	1.639	1.640	1.641	1.642
580	1.548	1.549	1.550	1.551	1.552	1.640	1.641	1.642	1.643	1.644
589	1.549	1.550	1.551	1.552	1.553	1.641	1.642	1.643	1.643	1.644
600	1.550	1.551	1.552	1.553	1.554	1.642	1.642	1.643	1.644	1.645
620	1.551	1.552	1.553	1.554	1.555	1.643	1.644	1.645	1.646	1.647
640	1.553	1.554	1.555	1.556	1.557	1.644	1.645	1.646	1.647	1.648
660	1.554	1.555	1.556	1.557	1.558	1.646	1.647	1.647	1.648	1.649
680	1.555	1.556	1.557	1.558	1.559	1.647	1.648	1.649	1.649	1.650
700	1.556	1.557	1.558	1.559	1.560	1.648	1.649	1.650	1.651	1.651

Oil	Δ_{LIQ} 0.0267			−dn/dt 0.0005		Δ_{LIQ} 0.0296			−dn/dt 0.0005	
Glass	Δ_{GS} 0.0111			$n_{D,GS}$ 1.5512		Δ_{GS} 0.0134			$n_{D,GS}$ 1.6425	

λ_m (nm)	1.615 (Cargille Series E) Cargille Glass 1.62 (Lot C)					1.700 (Cargille Series B) Cargille Glass 1.70 (Lot B or D)				
	21°C	*23°C*	*25°C*	*27°C*	*29°C*	*21°C*	*23°C*	*25°C*	*27°C*	*29°C*
400	1.602	1.603	1.604	1.605	1.606	1.663	1.664	1.665	1.666	1.667
420	1.605	1.606	1.607	1.608	1.609	1.670	1.671	1.672	1.673	1.674
440	1.607	1.608	1.609	1.610	1.611	1.676	1.677	1.678	1.679	1.680
460	1.610	1.611	1.611	1.612	1.613	1.681	1.682	1.682	1.683	1.684
480	1.611	1.612	1.613	1.614	1.615	1.685	1.686	1.687	1.688	1.689
500	1.613	1.614	1.615	1.616	1.617	1.688	1.689	1.690	1.691	1.692
520	1.614	1.615	1.616	1.617	1.618	1.692	1.693	1.694	1.694	1.695
540	1.616	1.617	1.617	1.618	1.619	1.694	1.695	1.696	1.697	1.698
560	1.617	1.618	1.619	1.619	1.620	1.697	1.698	1.699	1.700	1.701
580	1.618	1.619	1.620	1.620	1.621	1.699	1.700	1.701	1.702	1.703
589	1.618	1.619	1.620	1.621	1.622	1.700	1.701	1.702	1.703	1.704
600	1.619	1.620	1.620	1.621	1.622	1.701	1.702	1.703	1.704	1.705
620	1.619	1.620	1.621	1.622	1.623	1.703	1.704	1.705	1.706	1.707
640	1.620	1.621	1.622	1.623	1.624	1.705	1.706	1.706	1.707	1.708
660	1.621	1.622	1.623	1.624	1.624	1.706	1.707	1.708	1.709	1.710

Oil	Δ_{LIQ} 0.0258			−dn/dt 0.0005		Δ_{LIQ} 0.0370			−dn/dt 0.0005	
Glass	Δ_{GS} 0.0171			$n_{D,GS}$ 1.6200		Δ_{GS} 0.0171			$n_{D,GS}$ 1.7019	

Table 13-10, continued.

	1.605 (Cargille Series E)					1.635 (Cargille Series E)				
λ_m (nm)	Cargille Glass 1.61 (Lot D)					Cargille Glass 1.64 (Lot B)				
	21°C	23°C	25°C	27°C	29°C	21°C	23°C	25°C	27°C	29°C
440	1.592	1.593	1.594	1.595	1.596	1.622	1.623	1.624	1.625	1.626
460	1.596	1.597	1.597	1.598	1.599	1.626	1.627	1.627	1.628	1.629
480	1.599	1.599	1.600	1.601	1.602	1.629	1.630	1.631	1.632	1.633
500	1.601	1.602	1.603	1.604	1.605	1.632	1.633	1.634	1.634	1.635
520	1.603	1.604	1.605	1.606	1.607	1.634	1.635	1.636	1.637	1.638
540	1.605	1.606	1.607	1.608	1.609	1.636	1.637	1.638	1.639	1.640
560	1.607	1.608	1.608	1.609	1.610	1.638	1.639	1.640	1.641	1.642
580	1.608	1.609	1.610	1.611	1.612	1.640	1.641	1.642	1.643	1.644
589	1.609	1.610	1.611	1.612	1.612	1.641	1.642	1.643	1.643	1.644
600	1.610	1.610	1.611	1.612	1.613	1.642	1.642	1.643	1.644	1.645
620	1.611	1.612	1.613	1.613	1.614	1.643	1.644	1.645	1.646	1.647
Oil	Δ_{LIQ} 0.0243		−dn/dt 0.0004			Δ_{LIQ} 0.0288		−dn/dt 0.0005		
Glass	Δ_{GS} 0.0108		$n_{D,GS}$ 1.6106			Δ_{GS} 0.0134		$n_{D,GS}$ 1.6425		

	1.680 (Cargille Series B)									
λ_m (nm)	Cargille Glass 1.68 (Lot A)					Cargille Glass 1.68 (Lot B or C)				
	21°C	23°C	25°C	27°C	29°C	21°C	23°C	25°C	27°C	29°C
520	1.666	1.667	1.668	1.669	1.670	1.667	1.668	1.668	1.669	1.670
540	1.669	1.670	1.671	1.672	1.673	1.670	1.671	1.672	1.673	1.674
560	1.672	1.673	1.674	1.675	1.676	1.673	1.673	1.674	1.675	1.676
580	1.674	1.675	1.676	1.677	1.678	1.675	1.676	1.677	1.678	1.679
589	1.675	1.676	1.677	1.678	1.679	1.676	1.677	1.678	1.679	1.680
600	1.677	1.677	1.678	1.679	1.680	1.677	1.678	1.679	1.680	1.681
620	1.679	1.680	1.680	1.681	1.682	1.679	1.680	1.681	1.682	1.683
640	1.680	1.681	1.682	1.683	1.684	1.681	1.682	1.683	1.684	1.685
660	1.682	1.683	1.684	1.685	1.686	1.683	1.684	1.685	1.686	1.687
680	1.684	1.685	1.686	1.687	1.688	1.685	1.685	1.686	1.687	1.688
700	1.685	1.686	1.687	1.688	1.689	1.686	1.687	1.688	1.689	1.690
750	1.688	1.689	1.690	1.691	1.692	1.689	1.690	1.691	1.692	1.693
Oil	Δ_{LIQ} 0.0348		−dn/dt 0.0005			Δ_{LIQ} 0.0348		−dn/dt 0.0005		
Glass	Δ_{GS} 0.0123		$n_{D,GS}$ 1.6773			Δ_{GS} 0.0123		$n_{D,GS}$ 1.6781		

RECOMMENDED READINGS

McCRONE, W.C. (1987) *Asbestos Identification.* Chicago: McCrone Research Institute.

McCRONE, W.C. (1989) Calculation of Refractive Indices from Dispersion Staining Data. *The Microscope* 37:49-53.

PERKINS, R.L. and HARVEY, B.W, (1993) Test Method for the Determination of Asbestos in Bulk Building Materials. EPA/600/R-93/116, July 1993, Washington, D.C.: Environmental Protection Agency

STOIBER, R.E. and MORSE, S.A. (1994) *Crystal Identification with the Polarized Light Microscope.* New York & London: Chapman & Hall.

SU, Shu-Chun (1992) Calibration of Refractive Index Liquids by Using Optical Glass Standards with Dispersion Staining. *The Microscope 40:*95-108.

SU, Shu-Chun (1993) Determination of Refractive Index of Solids by Dispersion Staining Method—An Analytical Approach. Rieder, C.L., Editor, *Proceedings of 51st Annual Meeting of the Microscopy Society of America,* 456-457.

SU, Shu-Chun (1996) *Rapidly and Accurately Determining Refractive Indices of Asbestos Fibers Using the Dispersion Staining Method.* Wilmington, Delaware: Hercules Incorporated.

THE ISOGYRE

The homodromes and antidromes
Did swing and switch across the sphere.
Askew were all the skiodromes,
No bisectrix was near.

"Beware the Isogyre, my son!
The curves that light, the bars that lash!
Beware the Isotaque, and shun
the Optic Normal Flash!"

He took his petro-mike in hand,
Long time the Melatope he sought.
So wrested he with X, Y, Z
and sat a while in thought.

And, as in optic thought he sat,
The Isogyre, with bars of flame,
Came swinging through the lattice net,
Converging as it came!

One, two! One, two! And through and through
The polar beam went nicol-knack!
The light dispersed, colors reversed,
He had it in the sack!

"And hast thou tamed the Isogyre?
Come to my arms, my brilliant boy!
Oh, exam day! Hurrah!! An 'A'!"
He chortled in his joy.

The antidromes and homodromes
Did swing and switch across the sphere.
Askew were all the skiodromes,
No bisectrix was near.

JEA 1934*

*JEA, identity unknown, had evidently completed a course in optical crystallography by 1934. At that time most professors, following Johannsen (1918), used skiodromes and isotaques to explain the shapes of isogyres. And in 1934 polarizers of the microscope consisted of calcite (nicol) prisms and not polaroid.

APPENDIX I : DATA FOR CARGILLE LIQUIDS

The following tables summarize the constants kindly supplied by R.P. Cargille Laboratories for their Series AA liquids (1.4000-1.4580), Series A liquids (1.4600-1.6400), Series B liquids (1.6420-1.7000), Series M liquids (1.7050-1.8000), and for their Series E high dispersion liquids (1.5000-1.6400). These constants, substituted along with λ (in nm) into the Cauchy equation

$$n = c_1 + c_2/\lambda^2 + c_3/\lambda^4$$

yield the liquid's refractive index for that value of λ. The writer has retained the seven significant figures to which Cargille supplied c_1, c_2 and c_3 but has shifted their decimal points so that the value of λ can now be supplied in nanometers (rather than Ångströms).

The accuracy to which n can be calculated from the above equation should be adequate if λ_m, the wavelength of match, is being estimated from dispersion-staining colors as done when using Su's method. However, if highly precise refractive indices are desired, as when applying the double variation method and the programs of Gunter et al. (1989), it may be advisable to contact Cargille [telephone: (201) 239-6633] for Cauchy constants more current than the dates of measurement indicated in these tables.

A simple check as to whether the Cauchy constants in the following tables still pertain for a particular liquid will be to use them to calculate n_C, n_D and n_F for that liquid. The resultant values should agree with those printed on the liquid's label.

Cauchy constants and temperature coefficients for Cargille liquids

n_D	c_1	c_2	c_3	dn_D/dt
Series AA Liquids (25-Sep-97)				
1.4000	1.387868	4341.806	-44746850	-0.000412
1.4020	1.389882	4329.281	-41780210	-0.000411
1.4040	1.391891	4316.756	-39308010	-0.000410
1.4060	1.393901	4306.441	-36588580	-0.000409
1.4080	1.395912	4294.653	-33869160	-0.000408
1.4100	1.397926	4283.601	-31396960	-0.000408
1.4120	1.399937	4270.339	-27688660	-0.000407
1.4140	1.401949	4259.288	-25710900	-0.000406
1.4160	1.403958	4249.710	-22744260	-0.000405
1.4180	1.405970	4235.711	-20272050	-0.000404
1.4200	1.407981	4224.659	-17799850	-0.000404
1.4220	1.409992	4212.871	-15080430	-0.000403
1.4240	1.412004	4199.609	-11619350	-0.000402
1.4260	1.414014	4189.294	-8652705	-0.000401
1.4280	1.416028	4174.559	-6674944	-0.000400
1.4300	1.418037	4165.717	-3708302	-0.000400
1.4320	1.420049	4153.929	-1236101	-0.000399
1.4340	1.422058	4142.140	1483321	-0.000398
1.4360	1.424070	4129.615	4449963	-0.000397
1.4380	1.426082	4120.037	7169385	-0.000396
1.4400	1.428093	4105.302	9641586	-0.000396
1.4420	1.430105	4095.724	12361010	-0.000395
1.4440	1.432116	4083.935	15080430	-0.000394
1.4460	1.434128	4069.937	18047070	-0.000393
1.4480	1.436140	4058.148	20766490	-0.000392

n_D	c_1	c_2	c_3	dn_D/dt
1.4500	1.438149	4047.834	23485920	-0.000392
1.4520	1.440161	4036.045	25958120	-0.000391
1.4540	1.442173	4024.257	28677540	-0.000390
1.4560	1.444184	4011.732	31891400	-0.000389
1.4580	1.446195	4001.417	34363600	-0.000388

Series A Liquids (25-Sep-97)

n_D	c_1	c_2	c_3	dn_D/dt
1.4600	1.447924	4074.357	41532990	-0.000389
1.4620	1.449697	4139.930	46230170	-0.000389
1.4640	1.451466	4206.240	51174570	-0.000390
1.4660	1.453239	4269.602	56118980	-0.000391
1.4680	1.455010	4335.912	60816160	-0.000391
1.4700	1.456781	4401.485	65018900	-0.000392
1.4720	1.458555	4465.584	70457740	-0.000392
1.4740	1.460322	4533.367	74907710	-0.000393
1.4760	1.462094	4599.677	79604890	-0.000393
1.4780	1.463866	4664.513	84549290	-0.000394
1.4800	1.465634	4733.033	88999260	-0.000395
1.4820	1.467407	4798.606	94190880	-0.000395
1.4840	1.469178	4861.968	98888060	-0.000396
1.4860	1.470951	4929.752	103585200	-0.000396
1.4880	1.472723	4992.377	108282400	-0.000397
1.4900	1.474492	5059.424	113226800	-0.000398
1.4920	1.476265	5126.470	117676800	-0.000398
1.4940	1.478035	5191.306	122621200	-0.000399
1.4960	1.479808	5258.353	127318400	-0.000399
1.4980	1.481575	5325.399	132262800	-0.000400
1.5000	1.483347	5387.288	136960000	-0.000401
1.5020	1.485118	5454.334	140915500	-0.000401
1.5040	1.486889	5519.170	146354300	-0.000402
1.5060	1.488659	5586.953	150804300	-0.000402
1.5060	1.490433	5651.790	155995900	-0.000403
1.5100	1.492205	5717.362	160445900	-0.000404
1.5120	1.493976	5782.198	165390300	-0.000404
1.5140	1.495745	5849.981	170087500	-0.000405
1.5160	1.497516	5914.818	175279100	-0.000405
1.5180	1.499288	5980.390	179976300	-0.000406
1.5200	1.501059	6046.700	184426200	-0.000407
1.5220	1.502832	6110.800	189370600	-0.000407
1.5240	1.504600	6180.056	194067800	-0.000408
1.5260	1.506372	6244.892	199012200	-0.000408
1.5280	1.508142	6309.728	203709400	-0.000409
1.5300	1.509916	6376.038	208159400	-0.000409
1.5320	1.511686	6442.348	213351000	-0.000410
1.5340	1.513456	6507.183	218048200	-0.000411
1.5360	1.515231	6571.283	222745400	-0.000411
1.5380	1.517000	6637.592	226948100	-0.000412

n_D	c_1	c_2	c_3	dn_D/dt
1.5400	1.518769	6703.165	232139700	-0.000412
1.5420	1.520540	6770.948	236589700	-0.000413
1.5440	1.522312	6837.258	241534100	-0.000414
1.5460	1.524080	6902.831	245489600	-0.000414
1.5480	1.525856	6968.404	250928500	-0.000415
1.5500	1.527626	7032.503	256120100	-0.000415
1.5520	1.529397	7099.550	260817300	-0.000416
1.5540	1.531168	7164.385	266008900	-0.000417
1.5560	1.532941	7229.958	270211700	-0.000417
1.5580	1.534712	7296.268	275156100	-0.000418
1.5600	1.536480	7363.314	279606000	-0.000418
1.5620	1.538251	7429.624	284056000	-0.000419
1.5640	1.540023	7493.723	289000400	-0.000420
1.5660	1.541794	7560.033	293697600	-0.000420
1.5680	1.543566	7625.606	298642000	-0.000421
1.5700	1.545338	7691.915	303091900	-0.000421
1.5720	1.546669	7854.005	327072300	-0.000423
1.5740	1.548351	7922.525	341163800	-0.000424
1.5760	1.550034	7995.466	355008200	-0.000426
1.5780	1.551717	8062.512	369594100	-0.000427
1.5800	1.553395	8134.716	383191300	-0.000428
1.5820	1.555081	8205.446	397035600	-0.000429
1.5840	1.556763	8274.703	411374300	-0.000430
1.5860	1.558443	8343.223	425713100	-0.000431
1.5880	1.560123	8415.426	440051900	-0.000432
1.5900	1.561807	8483.210	454143400	-0.000433
1.5920	1.563488	8553.940	468235000	-0.000434
1.5940	1.565175	8622.460	481832100	-0.000435
1.5960	1.566852	8694.664	496170900	-0.000436
1.5980	1.568536	8764.657	510262400	-0.000437
1.6000	1.570218	8833.914	523859500	-0.000438
1.6020	1.571900	8902.434	538198300	-0.000439
1.6040	1.573582	8973.901	552537100	-0.000440
1.6060	1.575262	9042.421	566134200	-0.000441
1.6080	1.576944	9112.414	580225700	-0.000442
1.6100	1.578628	9183.144	594811700	-0.000444
1.6120	1.580308	9252.401	608408800	-0.000445
1.6140	1.581992	9322.395	622994800	-0.000446
1.6160	1.583672	9393.125	636344700	-0.000447
1.6180	1.585352	9462.382	650930700	-0.000448
1.6200	1.587038	9530.902	665022200	-0.000449
1.6220	1.588717	9603.842	679113800	-0.000450
1.6240	1.590402	9671.626	692958100	-0.000451
1.6260	1.592081	9740.882	707049700	-0.000452
1.6280	1.593764	9813.086	721141200	-0.000453
1.6300	1.595445	9882.342	735480000	-0.000454

n_D	c_1	c_2	c_3	dn_D/dt
1.6320	1.597127	9951.599	749324300	-0.000455
1.6340	1.598809	10023.800	763663100	-0.000456
1.6360	1.600493	10090.850	777507400	-0.000457
1.6380	1.602174	10160.840	791846200	-0.000458
1.6400	1.603857	10233.050	805443300	-0.000459

Series B Liquids (8-Sep-97)

n_D	c_1	c_2	c_3	dn_D/dt
1.6420	1.605535	10303.04	819287600	-0.000461
1.6440	1.607222	10370.09	834120800	-0.000462
1.6460	1.608903	10438.61	848212400	-0.000463
1.6480	1.610586	10509.34	861562200	-0.000464
1.6500	1.612267	10581.54	875901000	-0.000465
1.6520	1.613949	10650.80	890487000	-0.000466
1.6540	1.615630	10720.05	904084100	-0.000467
1.6560	1.617315	10790.78	918175600	-0.000468
1.6580	1.617298	11926.15	765888100	-0.000470
1.6600	1.619131	11939.41	782451800	-0.000470
1.6620	1.620960	11954.15	799015600	-0.000471
1.6640	1.622794	11962.25	815332100	-0.000471
1.6660	1.624623	11974.04	831648600	-0.000472
1.6680	1.626456	11986.57	847965100	-0.000472
1.6700	1.628283	11999.83	863540000	-0.000473
1.6720	1.630115	12011.62	879856600	-0.000473
1.6740	1.631944	12023.41	896914700	-0.000474
1.6760	1.633776	12032.98	912984000	-0.000474
1.6780	1.635606	12045.51	928806100	-0.000475
1.6800	1.637437	12059.51	944875400	-0.000475
1.6820	1.639267	12071.30	961439100	-0.000476
1.6840	1.641097	12083.82	978497400	-0.000476
1.6860	1.642928	12095.61	994566700	-0.000477
1.6880	1.644759	12105.19	1010883000	-0.000477
1.6900	1.646585	12120.66	1026211000	-0.000478
1.6920	1.648420	12129.50	1043516000	-0.000478
1.6940	1.650249	12141.29	1059338000	-0.000479
1.6960	1.652081	12155.29	1076149000	-0.000479
1.6980	1.653913	12167.08	1091477000	-0.000479
1.7000	1.655743	12178.13	1108288000	-0.000480

Series M Liquids (26-Sep-97)

n_D	c_1	c_2	c_3	dn_D/dt
1.7050	1.665713	10655.22	1037583000	-0.000647
1.7100	1.670181	10762.05	1064777000	-0.000656
1.7150	1.674653	10868.88	1091477000	-0.000664
1.7200	1.679121	10974.98	1118177000	-0.000672
1.7250	1.683590	11083.28	1144629000	-0.000681
1.7300	1.688062	11188.64	1171576000	-0.000689
1.7350	1.692531	11295.47	1198523000	-0.000697
1.7400	1.696797	11540.82	1201984000	-0.000701
1.7450	1.700856	11929.10	1181465000	-0.000699
1.7500	1.704910	12315.91	1160451000	-0.000697

n_D	c_1	c_2	c_3	dn_D/dt
1.7550	1.708963	12707.13	1138943000	-0.000696
1.7600	1.713019	13095.41	1118424000	-0.000694
1.7650	1.717079	13480.01	1097657000	-0.000692
1.7700	1.721132	13869.76	1076891000	-0.000690
1.7750	1.725188	14259.51	1055136000	-0.000689
1.7800	1.729244	14647.79	1034616000	-0.000687
1.7850	1.727551	17770.98	756988100	-0.000685
1.7900	1.725704	20967.84	473179400	-0.000684
1.7950	1.723851	24166.17	187887300	-0.000682
1.8000	1.722002	27365.24	-96415800	-0.000681

Series E (High Dispersion) Liquids (8-Sep-97)

n_D	c_1	c_2	c_3	dn_D/dt
1.5000	1.47826	5754.201	623489200	-0.000463
1.5050	1.482607	5835.246	673674900	-0.000465
1.5100	1.486951	5920.712	723613400	-0.000468
1.5150	1.491295	6004.704	774046300	-0.000471
1.5200	1.495639	6086.486	824232000	-0.000474
1.5250	1.499986	6171.215	874417700	-0.000477
1.5300	1.504328	6252.996	924356100	-0.000479
1.5350	1.508673	6336.989	974541800	-0.000482
1.5400	1.513020	6419.508	1024233000	-0.000485
1.5450	1.517363	6503.500	1073924000	-0.000488
1.5500	1.521711	6586.018	1124357000	-0.000491
1.5550	1.526055	6667.800	1175037000	-0.000493
1.5600	1.531458	6900.620	1046236000	-0.000482
1.5650	1.538248	7325.002	681833200	-0.000452
1.5700	1.545039	7750.857	317925100	-0.000423
1.5750	1.549192	7960.838	348580400	-0.000425
1.5800	1.553395	8134.716	383191300	-0.000428
1.5850	1.557602	8308.595	418296500	-0.000430
1.5900	1.561807	8483.210	454143400	-0.000433
1.5950	1.566011	8657.825	489248700	-0.000436
1.6000	1.570218	8833.914	523859500	-0.000438
1.6050	1.574422	9008.529	559459200	-0.000441
1.6100	1.578628	9183.144	594811700	-0.000444
1.6150	1.582834	9358.497	629917000	-0.000446
1.6200	1.587038	9530.902	665022200	-0.000449
1.6250	1.591241	9705.517	700127500	-0.000452
1.6300	1.595445	9882.342	735480000	-0.000454
1.6350	1.599651	10056.22	770585300	-0.000457
1.6400	1.603857	10231.57	805937700	-0.000459

APPENDIX II : PROPERTIES OF ELLIPSES

As shown in Figure II-1 an ellipse possesses a major axis, AA', and perpendicular to it a minor axis, BB'; these are respectively its longest and shortest diameters. One half these distances, labeled a and b, are called the semimajor and semiminor axes. The two foci, F_1 and F_2, are always on the major axis and may be located by swinging an arc of radius a (centered on B, the end of the minor axis) so that it intersects the major axis. The focal distances, OF_1 or OF_2 in Figure II-2, may also be calculated from the Pythagorean formula

$$OF_1 = OF_2 = \sqrt{a^2 - b^2}$$

Radii extending outward from O, the ellipse center, are called simply radii; those extending outward from one of the focal points are called focal radii. A radius OP' (Fig. II-2) is said to be conjugate to a given radius OP if OP' is parallel to the tangent to the ellipse at P. The direction of this tangent $(DP$ in Fig. II-2) may be determined by (1) extending one of the focal radii (F_2P) through point P to a distant point such as R and then (2) bisecting the angle F_1PR. Then OP', the radius conjugate to OP, is the direction through O parallel to DP, the bisector of angle F_1PR.

The construction of an ellipse is sometimes necessary in the graphical solution of optical problems. A convenient method for constructing an ellipse of major and minor axes $2a$ and $2b$, respectively, is the rectangular method wherein two concentric circles of radius a and b are drawn on finely lined graph paper (Fig. II-3). The major and minor axes are then drawn outward from O, the common center of the two circles, each axis being parallel to the rulings of the graph paper. A series of random lines—OR, OR', and so on—are also drawn outward from O. At each line's intersection with the major circle, a dashed construction line parallel to the minor axis is drawn; at its intersection with the minor circle, a dashed construction line parallel to the major axis is drawn. These two dashed lines intersect at a point on the ellipse. Generally, in optical problems, only a small portion of the ellipse need be constructed.

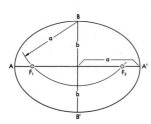

Figure II-1. Location of the two foci, F_1 and F_2, in an ellipse whose semi-axes are a and b. An arc of length a is swung with B as its center. Its points of intersection with major axis AA' locate F_1 and F_2.

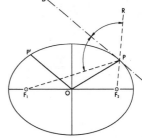

Figure II-2. Construction of OP', the radius of the ellipse conjugate to OP. Dashed construction lines were drawn from foci F_1 and F_2 through P. Line DP, which bisects the angle between these dashed construction lines, corresponds in direction to OP'.

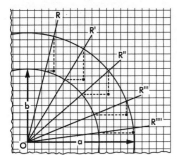

Figure II-3. Rectangular method of constructing an ellipse beginning with circles whose radii correspond to the ellipse's semiaxes, a and b. More closely spaced points along the ellipse can be obtained by drawing more numerous construction radii $(OR, OR', ...)$. Only a quadrant of the ellipse is shown.

APPENDIX III : RECORDING DATA

The form below is a convenient method for recording the measured optical data and serves as a checklist on the observations to be made. Data for a particular mineral are recorded in only one of the three blocks heavily outlined, depending upon whether the mineral is isotropic, uniaxial, or biaxial. By way of example, macroscopic and microscopic data obtainable from crushed diopside (variety salite) have been entered as shown.

MACROSCOPIC RECORDS

Reflected colors:
  a) of crystal:
  b) of streak or powder:
Specific gravity:
Hardness: Cleavage:

Sketches of oil mounts on slides:

(1) (2) (3) (4) (5)   (6) (7) (8) (9)

MICROSCOPIC RECORDS

No. in sketch	Index on label (25°)	Sp. Gr. of oil	Temp. of mount	Isotropic n	Uniaxial: +, — ω	ϵ	Biaxial: +, — α	β	γ
(1)	1.550		23°				all much greater (>>) than oil		
(2)	1.650		23°				>>	>>	>>
(3)	1.700		23°				<	<	>
(4)	1.695		23°				<	>	>
(5)	1.695+1.700		22°				<	Match	>
(6)	1.690		21°				Match		
(7)	1.730	3.20	22°						<
(8)	1.715	(grain	23°						>
(9)	1.720	sinks)	23°						Match
Index of matching oil, uncorrected:							1.690	1.698	1.720
Index, temperature-corrected:							1.692	1.699	1.721
Transmitted color:							Pale green	Brown	Green
Relative light absorption:							Least	Most	Moderate

Angles $2V$ and $2E$ as determined with Mertie nomogram from temperature-corrected, measured values of α, β, and γ: $2V = 58°$ $2E = 111°$

Angles $2V$ and $2E$ as measured from interference figures using Kamb, Mallard, or Tobi method (state which): $2V =$ $2E =$

Observed twinning: none

Inclusions (orientation and type):

Cleavage or fracture: Prismatic

Sign of elongation of crystals or fragments: +

Type of extinction a) Parallel: b) Symmetrical: c) Oblique (max. angle): $Z \wedge c = 40°$

Dispersion: $r < v$ Symmetry of dispersional fringes along isogyres in interference figures:
        $r > v$

a) Two planes (orthorhombic) ☐
b) Inclined (monocl., 2-fold = Y) ☐
   Crossed (monocl., 2-fold = A.B.) ☐
   Parallel (monocl., 2-fold = O.B.) ☐
c) No planes (triclinic) ☐

Mineral identity: #319, Salite

REFERENCES CITED

ARMBRUSTER, Thomas and BERMANEC, Vladimir (1992) Dispersion in low albite: high accuracy spindle stage measurements between 480 and 632 nm. *The Microscope 40:*21-30.

BAMBAUER, H.U., TABORSZKY, F.K. and TROCHIM, H.D. (1979) *Optical Determination of Rock-Forming Minerals. Part I: Determinative Tables* (English edition of the 4th German edition of W.E. Troger's original work). Stuttgart: E. Schweizerbart'sche Verlagbuchhandlung, 188 pp.

BARTELMEHS, K.L., BLOSS, F.D., DOWNS, R.T. and BIRCH, J.B. (1992) EXCALIBR II. *Zeitschrift für Kristallographie 199:*185-196.

BESANÇON, James (1992) An automated spindle stage for polarized light microscopes. *The Microscope 40:*13-19.

BIOT, J.B. (1820) Mémoire sur les lois générales. *Mém. Acad. France, Année 1818,* III:177-384.

BLOSS, F.D. (1961) *An Introduction to the Methods of Optical Crystallography.* New York: Holt, Rinehart and Winston, 294 pp.

BLOSS, F.D. (1981) *The Spindle Stage: Principles and Practice.* Cambridge, UK: Cambridge University Press, 340 pp.

BLOSS, F.D. (1994) *Crystallography and Crystal Chemistry.* Washington, DC: Mineralogical Society of America, 545 pp.

BOUMA, B.J. (1947) *Physical Aspects of Colour.* Eindhoven, Netherlands: N.V. Philips, 312 pp.

CHERKASOV, Yu. A. (1960) Application of "focal screening" to measurement of indices of refraction by the immersion method. (Translated by Ivan Mittin.) *International Geology Review I:*218-235.

CROSSMON, G.C. (1949) The dispersion staining method for the selective coloration of tissue. *Stain Technology 24:*61.

DELLY, J.G. and SROVATKA, J. (1988) A dedicated central-stop dispersion staining objective. *The Microscope 36:*205 et seq.

DITCHBURN, R.W. (1952) *Light.* London: Blackie and Son, 680 pp.

EMMONS, R.C. (1943) The universal stage. *Geological Society of America Memoir 8,* 205 pp.

EMMONS, R.C. and GATES, R.M. (1948) The use of Becke line colors in refractive index determination. *American Mineralogist 33:*612-618.

FAIRBAIRN, H.W. and PODOLSKY, T. (1951) Notes on precision and accuracy of optic angle determination with the universal stage. *American Mineralogist 36:*823-832.

FISHER, D.J. (1958) Refractometer perils. *American Mineralogist 43:*777-780.

FLETCHER, L. (1891) The optical indicatrix and transmission of light in crystals. *Mineralogical Magazine 9:* 278.

FRESNEL, A. (1827) Mémoire sur la double réfraction. *Mém. Acad. France, Année VII:*45-176.

GUNTER, M.E., BLOSS, F.D. and SU, S.C. (1989) Computer programs for the spindle stage and double variation method. *The Microscope 37:*167-171.

GUNTER, M.E. and SCHARES, S.M. (1992) Computerized optical mineralogy calculations, *Journal of Geological Education. 39:*289-290.

GUNTER, M.E. (1992) Variation in optical class and optical orientation: the rule, not the exception, *The Microscope. 40:*81-93.

GUNTER, M.E. (1997) Laboratory exercises and demonstrations with the spindle stage. In *Teaching Mineralogy,* Editors: J.B. Brady, D.W. Mogk, and D. Perkins III, Washington, DC: Mineralogical Society of America, pp. 309-318.

HARDY, A.C. and PERRIN, F.H. (1932) *The Principles of Optics.* New York: McGraw-Hill, 632 pp.

JOHANNSEN, Albert (1918) *Manual of Petrographic Methods.* New York: McGraw-Hill, 649 pp.

JONES, FRANCIS T. (1968) Spindle stage with easily changed liquid and improved crystal holder. *American Mineralogist 53:*1399-1403.

JULIAN, MAUREEN and BLOSS, F.D. (1982) Optical measurements of anthracene, *Acta Crystallo-graphica A38*:167-169

KAMB, W.B. (1958) Isogyres in interference figures. *American Mineralogist 43:*1029-1067.

LONGHURST, R.S. (1973) *Geometrical and physical optics.* London: Longmans.

McCRONE, W.C. (1987) *Asbestos Identification.* Chicago: McCrone Research Institute.

McCRONE, W.C. (1989) Calculation of Refractive Indices from Dispersion Staining Data. *The Microscope* 37:49-53.

MEDENBACH, Olaf (1985) A new microrefractometer spindle-stage and its application. *Fortschritte der Mineralogie 63:*111-133.

MERTIE, J.B., Jr. (1942) Nomograms of optic angle formulae. *American Mineralogist 27:*538-551.

PERKINS, R.L. and HARVEY, B.W, (1993) Test Method for the Determination of Asbestos in Bulk Building Materials. EPA/600/R-93/116, July 1993, Washington, D.C.: Environmental Protection Agency

PHILLIPS, W.R. and GRIFFEN, D.T. (1981) *Optical Mineralogy: The Nonopaque Minerals.* San Francisco: W.H. Freeman and Company, 677 pp.

RINNE, F. and BEREK, Max (1953) *Anleitung zu optischen Untersuchungen mit dem Polarisations-mikroskop.* Stuttgart: E. Schweizerbart'sche Verlagbuchhandlung, 366 pp.

ROSENFELD, J.L. (1950) Determination of a difficultly oriented mineral. *American Mineralogist 35:*902-905.

SAYLOR, C.P. (1935) Accuracy of microscopical methods for determining refractive index by immersion., *Journal of Research, National Bureau of Standards 15:*277-294.

SMITH, D.G.W. (1992) Computer-assisted mineral identification using conventional optical observations. *The Microscope 40:*39-58.

STOIBER, R.E. and MORSE, S.A. (1994) *Crystal Identification with the Polarizing Microscope.* New York & London: Chapman & Hall.

STRENS, R.G.J. and FREER, R. (1978) The physical basis of mineral optics I. Classical Theory. *Mineralogical Magazine 42:19*-30.

SU, Shu-Chun (1992) Calibration of Refractive Index Liquids by Using Optical Glass Standards with Dispersion Staining. *The Microscope 40:*95-108.

SU, Shu-Chun (1993) Determination of Refractive Index of Solids by Dispersion Staining Method— An Analytical Approach. Rieder, C.L., Editor, *Proceedings of 51st Annual Meeting of the Microscopy Society of America,* 456-457.

SU, Shu-Chun (1996) *Rapidly and Accurately Determining Refractive Indices of Asbestos Fibers Using the Dispersion Staining Method.* Wilmington, Delaware: Hercules Incorporated.

SU, Shu-Chun (1998) Dispersion staining: principles, analytical relationships and practical applications to the determination of refractive index. *The Microscope 46-3:*123-146.

SU, Shu-Chun, and BLOSS, F.D. (1984) Extinction angles for monoclinic amphiboles and pyroxenes; a cautionary note. *American Mineralogist 69:*399-403.

SU, Shu-Chun, BLOSS, F.D., RIBBE, P.H. and STEWART, D.B. (1984) Optic axial angle, a precise measure of Al, Si ordering in the T_1 tetrahedral sites of K-rich alkali feldspars. *American Mineralogist 69:*440-448.

SU, Shu-Chun, BLOSS, F.D. and GUNTER, M.E. (1987) Procedures and computer programs to refine the double variation method. *American Mineralogist 72:*1011-1013.

TOBI, A.C. (1956) A chart for measurement of optic axial angles. *American Mineralogist 41:*516-519.

WILCOX, R.E. (1959) Use of the spindle stage for determination of principal indices of refraction. *American Mineralogist 44:*1272-1293.

WILCOX, R.E. (1983) Refractive index determination using the central focal masking technique with dispersion colors. *American Mineralogist 68:*1226-1236.

WINCHELL, A.N. and WINCHELL, Horace (1951) *Elements of Optical Mineralogy.* New York: John Wiley & Sons, 551 pp.

WOLFE, H.E. (1976) *Optical and X-ray Study of the Low Plagioclases.* M.S. thesis, Blacksburg, VA: Virginia Polytechnic Institute and State University

WRIGHT, F.E. (1913) The index ellipsoid (optical indicatrix) in petro-graphic microscope work. *American Journal of Science 185:*133-138.

WRIGHT, F.E. (1923) Interference figures, *Journal of the Optical Society of America 7:*779-817.

WRIGHT, W.D. (1958) *The Measurement of Color.* New York: The Macmillan Company, 263 pp.

WYLLIE, P.J. (1959) Discrepancies between optic axial angles of olivines measured over different bisectrices. *American Mineralogist 44:*49-64.

INDEX

Abbé refractometer, 40
Abnormal (anomalous) dispersion, 15
Abnormal interference colors,
    for biaxial crystals, 167
    for metatorbernite, 124
    for uniaxial crystals, 123
Absorption, Lambert's Law for, 14
    of light, 13-15
        allochromatic, 14
        in biaxial crystals, 182
        effect on dispersion, 15
        idiochromatic, 14
        in tourmaline, 122
        in uniaxial crystals, 122
Absorption coefficient, 14
Absorption formula, biaxial crystals, 183
Accessories,
    optical, 109
    addition with, 110
    Berek compensator, 119
    Brace-Köhler compensator, 119
    first-order red plate, 109
    gypsum plate, 109
    mica plate, 109
    quarter-wave mica plate, 109
    quartz wedge, 109
    Sénarmont compensator, 119
    slot for, 13
    subtraction with, 110
Actinolite, 204, 205, 211
Acute bisectrix, 138
    dispersion of, 164
Acute bisectrix interference figure, 150
    effect of 2E on appearance, 152
    effect of thickness on appearance, 152
    isochromatic curves of, 151
    isogyres in, 152
    use in sign determination, 171
Addition, 110
Adjustments of the microscope, 33-35, 37
    centering objectives, 34
    cross hairs, 34
    for Köhler illumination, 35
    polarizer, 33
Air, refractive index of, 5
Alpha (α), 136
    determining value of, 174
Alpha prime (α'), 137
Amosite, 204, 205, 209
Amphibole, extinction angle, convention, 178
Amplitude of wave, 4

resolution by vectors, 67, 85
Analyzer, 25, 31
    light transmission by, 90
Angle, critical, 9
    of extinction, 120, 178
    of incidence, 8
    optic, see Optic axial angle
    of reflection, 8
    of refraction, 8
    of total reflection, 5
Angular aperture, 29
    effect on interference figure, 153
Anisotropism, tests for, 61
Anomalous interference colors, see Abnormal
    interference colors
Antidrome end of isogyre, 102
Aperture,
    angular, 29
    numerical, 29
Apparent depth, 41
Apparent optic axial angle (2E), 142
Apparent thickness, 41
Armbruster, T., 199
Asbestiform minerals, 203ff.
Asbestos identification, 203ff.
Auxiliary condensing lens, 28
Axial angles, see Optic axial angle
Axis,
    of isotropy, 77
    of lens, 21
    of microscope, 22

Bartelmehs, K.L., 2, 190
Becke lines, 42ff.
    colored, 47
    significance of colors, 48
Berek compensator, 119
Bertin's surfaces, see Surfaces of equal
    retardation
Bermanec, V., 199
Besançon, J., 195, 198
Bertrand lens, 31
Beta (β), 136
    determination of, 173
Biaxial crystals, 135ff., 169ff.
    abnormal interference colors, 167
    absorption by, 183
    acute bisectrix, 138, 150
    apparent optic axial angle (2E), 142
    determination of optic orientation, 173
        Kamb's method, 158

dispersion in, 161*ff.*
indicatrix for, 137
  circular sections of, 138
  equations, 139, 140
  nomenclature, 138, 145
indices, alternative nomenclatures, 136
interference figures, *see* Biaxial interference
  figures
internal conical refraction in, 148
nomenclature for planes of, 146
normal incidence upon, 145
  circular section, 148
  principal plane, 148
  random plane, 145
  semirandom plane, 147
obtuse bisectrix, 138
optic axes of, 138
optic axial angle, 138
optic normal, 138
optic sign, 139
optical examination, 169*ff.*
  form for recording data, 227
orientation and dispersion of *X, Y,* and *Z* ,
  161*ff.*
pleochroism in, 183
principal indices of, 136
principal plane, definition, 145
random plane, definition, 145
refractive index measurement, 173*ff.*
semirandom plane, definition, 147
symbols for planes, 146
vibration directions in, 145
Biaxial indicatrix, 137
Biaxial interference figures, 149*ff.*
  acute bisectrix, 150, 154
  determination of sign from, 171*ff.*
    (*see* back cover)
  dispersion in, *see* Dispersion effects
  distinguishing between, 158
  distinguishing from uniaxial, 160
  explanation of, 149*ff.*
  isochromes in, 151
  isogyres in, 152, 176
  obtuse bisectrix, 154
  optic-axis centered, 152, 176
  optic normal (flash), 154
  random orientation, 157
  recognition of extinction position in, 160
  relation to orthoscopic view, 160
  straight isogyres in, significance of, 153
  trace of principal plane in, 153
  vibration directions in, 152
Biaxiality, verification of, 160, 170
Biaxial sign, 139
Biot-Fresnel rule, 144
  two-dimensional analog, 152
Birefringence, 70

devices for measuring, 144
estimation from interference colors, 117
Birefringence chart, *after* 118
Bisectrix,
  acute, 138
  dispersion of, 164, 165
  obtuse, 138
Brace-Köhler compensator, 119
Brewster's Law, 9
Brookite, dispersion in, 163

Calcite, 69
  birefringence of, 70
  double refraction, 69
  E and *O* rays in, 68
Calcite experiment, 70
Cartesian coordinates for microscope, 127
Cauchy's equation, 10, 11
Centering objectives, 33
Charts, determinative
  index difference from Becke line color, 49
  interference colors and birefringence, *after*
    118
  V from centered biaxial figures, melatopes
    in field (Tobi chart), 177
  melatopes outside field (Kamb chart), 158
  2*V* from α, β, γ values (Mertie chart), 142
Circular sections,
  biaxial, 138
    normal incidence on, 148
  optical significance of, 67
  uniaxial, 73
    normal incidence on, 77
Circularly polarized light, 90
Cleavage fragments of isotropic grains, 62
Coefficient of dispersion, 13
Coherent light, 149
Color, 2
  interference, *see* Interference colors
  transmission in biaxial crystals, 182
  transmission in isotropic media, 13
  transmission in uniaxial crystals, 122
  wavelength limits in spectrum, 2
Color spectrum, 2
Colored Becke lines, 47
  use in index determination, 49
Colored oblique shadows, 50
Compensation, 109*ff.*
  addition, 110
  general rules for, 111
  subtraction, 110
Compensators, 109, 119
Composition and resolution of light wave, 79,
  88, 89
Compound microscope, 21
  magnifying power of, 22
Condensing lens, 28

Cones of equal retardation, 97
Conical refraction, internal, 148
Conjugate distances, 19
Conjugate foci, 19
Conjugate radii of an ellipse, 225
Conoscope, 95
Conoscopic observations (interference figures), 98*ff.*
   relation to orthoscopic, 160
Constructive interference, 86
Critical angle, 9
Crocidolite, 204, 205, 208
Crossed axial plane dispersion, 163
Crossed dispersion, 166
Crossed polarizers, 25
CSDS (see Dispersion staining)

Daylight, energy distribution in, 3
de Chaulnes' method of index measurement, 41
Delta (Δ), 896
Delta (δ), 158
Depth of focus, 30
Destructive interference, 86
Determination of refractive indices, *see* Index of refraction
Determinative charts, *see* Charts
Diaphragms, 27
Differentiation of interference figures, 158*ff.*
Dispersion, 10, 116
   anomalous, 15
   coefficient of, 13
   formulas for, 11, 15
   normal, 15
   of optic axes, 161
   of X, Y, and Z axes, 164*ff.*
Dispersion colors, 45
Dispersion curves, 15, 46
   for barite, 162
   for brookite, 163
   plotted on Hartmann paper, 46
   for metatorbernite, 117
Dispersion effects in interference figures, 185*ff.*
   brookite, 163
   comparison of crystal systems, 167
   crossed, 166
   crossed axial plane, 163
   inclined, 164
   normal orthorhombic, 162
   parallel (horizontal), 165
   triclinic, 167
Dispersion staining, 51*ff.*
   central-stop (CSDS), 203, 213-215
Dispersive power, 13
Distance of distinct vision, 22
Double refraction, 69

E
2E, 142
   determination by Mallard's method, 176
   determination by Tobi's method, 177
E rays, 68
Electromagnetic spectrum, 2
Ellipses, Appendix II
   conjugate radii of, 225
   locating foci in, 225
   properties and nomenclature, 225
   semiaxes of, 72
Ellipsoid, triaxial, 138
Elliptically polarized light, 90
Elongation, sign of, 121, 181
Epsilon (ε), defined, 71
   measurements of, 116
Equations (selected)
   biaxial indicatrix, 139
   Brewster's, 9
   Cauchy's, 10-11
   de Chaulnes', 41
   dispersive power, 13
   Hartmann's, 46
   Lambert's, 14
   magnification by microscope, 22
   Mallard's, 176
   numerical aperture, 29
   relationships,
      (α, β, γ, ϕ, ρ), 139
      (α, β, γ, V_Z), 140
      (α, β, γ, 2V), 141
      (Δ, t, N, n), 86
      (ε, ε', ω, θ), 71
   Sellmeier, 15
   Snell's, 8, 69
   temperature correction of oil, 61
   thin lens, 19
   transmission by analyzer, 92
Extinction angles, 120, 178
Extinction position, 95
Extraordinary ray, *see E* rays
Eyepiece (ocular), 31-33
Exit pupil, 31

Fast direction, 87
Fast wave, 86
Feldspar, extinction angle convention, 178
Field diaphragm, 27, 37
First-order red, spectral composition of, 92
First-order red plate, 109
   use in sign determination, 111, 171
First-order white, 93
Flash figure, origin, 102
Fletcher, L., 67
Focal length, 18
Focal screening, 52
Foci of ellipse, locating, 225

Focus, depth of, 30
Fraunhofer lines, 12
Free working distance, 30
Frequency of waves, 5
Fresnel, *see* Biot-Fresnel rule

Gamma (γ), 136
    determination of, 174
Gamma prime (γ'), 137
Gunter, M.E., 201
Gypsum plate, 109
    use in sign determination, 112, 198

Hartmann dispersion paper, 46
High-order white, 93
Homodrome end of isogyre, 102
Horizontal dispersion, 165
Huygenian ocular, 32

Identification of minerals, *see* Mineral
    identification
Illumination, oblique, 43
Immersion methods, 42
Incidence, angle of, 8
    plane of, 8
Inclined dispersion, 164
Inclined extinction, 178
Index of refraction,
    of air, 5
    change with temperature, 51, 61
    definition, 5
    determination of, Becke method, 42, 55
        for biaxial crystals, 173*ff.*
        de Chaulnes' method, 41
        for isotropic solids, 41*ff.*
        in liquids, 40
        by oblique illumination, 43
        Su's methods, 55-59, 203*ff.*
        temperature correction, 61
        for uniaxial crystals, 114*ff.*
        use of interference figures, 115*ff.*, 201
    relation to density and composition, 5
    relation to wavelength, 5
    symbols for, biaxial crystals, 136
        uniaxial crystals, 71
Indicatrix, optical, *see* Optical indicatrix
Intensity, relation to amplitude, 78
Interference of light waves, 86, 97*ff.*
Interference colors, 91
    abnormal, 123, 124, 167
    chart for, *after* 118
    effect of rotating crystal, 93
    nomenclature for, 92
    orders of, 92
    origin, 91
    symbolism for, 92
Interference figures, 96

biaxial, *see* Biaxial interference figures
differentiation of, 158
uniaxial, *see* Uniaxial crystals
Internal conical refraction, 148
Iris diaphragm, 27
Isochromes, viewed conoscopically, 97, 151
    viewed orthoscopically, 96
Isogyres, 97 (*see* back cover)
    (*The Isogyre*, a poem, 217)
    biaxial, 152
    uniaxial, 109, 223
Isotropic indicatrix, 65*ff.*
Isotropic materials, definition, 5
    indicatrix for, 65
    test for, 61, 66

Johannsen, A., 90

Kamb, W.B., 158
Köhler illumination, 35, 213

Lambert's law, 14
Leica microscope, 36
Length-fast crystal, 121
Length-slow crystal, 121
Lens,
    axis of, 17
    basic shapes, 18
    care of, 35
    equation, 19
    focal length, 18
    principal focus, 18
    real focus or point source, 18
    resolving power, 30
    thin, 17
    thin-edged, 18
    virtual focus or point source, 18
Light,
    circularly polarized, 90
    coherent, 149
    and color, 1
    elliptically polarized, 90
    monochromatic, 3
    plane-polarized, 4, 88
    polychromatic, 3
    sodium, 3
    sources, 3
    spectrum, 1, 2
    speed, 4
    tungsten, 3
Light waves, 3
    amplitude, 4
    coherent, 149
    composition, 85
    equation, 4
    frequency, 4
    resolution, 92

vector analysis, 67, 93
wavelength, 4
Line of collimation, 22
Lommel's Rule, 103
Lower condensing lens, 28

M-axis, 127
Magnification, 20, 22
Mallard method, 176
McCrone, W.C., 35, 201, 205, 215, 216
Melatope, 97
Mendenbach, O., 191, 199
Mertie, J.B., 142
Metatorbernite, 117, 124
Mica compensator, 109
Michel-Levy color chart, *after* 118
Micrometer ocular, 32
Microscope,
    accessories, 109, 119
    adjustments, 33-37
    axis of, 22
    Cartesian coordinates, 127
    compound, 21
    as conoscope, 96
    Leica, 35
    magnification, 22
    as orthoscope, 96
    polarizing, 25, 35
MinIdent, 195
Mirwald, 191
Monochromatic light, 3
Monoclinic crystals, dispersion in, 164*ff.*
Morse, S.A., 50, 60, 62, 208

Negative biaxial crystals, 139
Negative elongation, 121
Negative uniaxial crystals, 72
Newton's colors, 2
Normal incidence,
    vibration directions for, 75, 145
North sky light, 3
Nu (ν) 101
Numerical aperture, 29
    effect on interference figure, 153

O
O rays, 68
Objectives, 28, 30
    angular aperture of, 28
    centering, 33
    depth of focus, 30
    free working distance, 29
    numerical aperture of, 29
Oblique illumination method, 43
Obtuse bisectrix, 138
    interference figure, 154
Oculars, 31-33

micrometer, 32
Off-centered figures,
    random, 157
    uniaxial, 160
Omega (ω), 71
    measurement of, 115
Optic axial angle (2V), 138
    determination by Mallard method, 176
    determination by Tobi method, 177
    estimated from curvature of isogyres, 176
    formula for calculating, 140
    nomogram for determining, 142
    variation with wavelength, 161
Optic axis, 72, 138
Optic axis figure (*see* back cover)
    biaxial, 157
        curvature of isogyres in, 176
    uniaxial, 101
        off-centered, 102
Optic normal (Y), 138
Optic normal (flash) figure, 154
Optic plane, 138
Optic sign, biaxial, definition, 139
    determination of, 111, 116, 128, 171
    uniaxial, definition, 72
Optical examination of crystals, biaxial, 169*ff.*
    isotropic, 39*ff.*
    uniaxial, 107*ff.*
Order of interference colors, 92
Ordinary ray, 68
Orthorhombic crystals, dispersion and optic
    orientation, 162*ff.*
Orthoscope, 95

Parallel polarizers, 25
Path difference (Δ), 85
    calculation of, 86
    effect on emerging rays, 88*ff.*
    see also Retardation
Period of a wave, 88
Phase, 4, 65, 85
Plane of incidence, 8
Plane light, 25
Plane of vibration, 4
    from Biot-Fresnel rule, 144
Plane-polarized light, 4, 88
    composition and resolution of, 79
    by reflection and refraction, 8-9
Pleochroism,
    in biaxial crystals, 183
    in uniaxial crystals, 122
Polarization, by reflection and refraction, 8-9
Polarized light, 3, 4
    convergent, 95, 96
Polarizer, 4, 25
Polarizing microscope, 25*ff.*
Polychromatic light, 3

Positive biaxial crystals, 139
Positive uniaxial crystals, 72
Principal focus, 18
Principal indices,
    biaxial, 135-136
    uniaxial, 72
Principal plane,
    of biaxial crystal, 145
        normal incidence on, 148
    of uniaxial crystal, 72
        normal incidence on, 77
Principal ellipse, *see* Principal plane
Principal section, *see* Principal plane
Principal vibration axes, 137
    relation to crystallographic axes, 161, 164,
        167
Privileged direction, 4
    for normal incidence, 76, 145
Procedures in index determination, microscopic
        observations,
    on biaxial crystals, 169*ff.*
    on isotropic materials, 39*ff.*
    on uniaxial crystals, 107*ff.*
    mount preparation, 60, 108
    spindle stage methods, 125*ff.*, 185*ff.*
Pyroxenes, extinction angles, 178

Quarter-wave mica plate, 109
    sign determination with, 112
Quartz, indices of, 109
Quartz wedge, 109
    sign determination with, 113

R
r, 161
Random section, of biaxial crystal, 145
        normal incidence on, 145
    of uniaxial crystal, 75
        normal incidence on, 79
Ray, 64
    extraordinary (*E*), 68
    ordinary (*O*), 68
    wave-normal relationships,
        in biaxial crystals, 143*ff.*
        in uniaxial crystals, 73
Real image, 20
Real point source, 18
Reference azimuth, 129
Reflection of light,
    law of, 8
    polarization by, 8
Refraction of light, 8-11
    double, 69
    polarization by, 8
Refractive index, *see* Index of refraction
Refractive index liquids, 213*ff.*, 219-223
Relief, 42

Resolution of light by crystals, 78
Retardation (*Δ*), 85
    calculation of, 96
    effect on transmission by analyzer, 90
    precise measurement, 119
    relation to interference color produced, *after*
        118
    see also Path difference
Riebeckite, 204, 205, 208
Rosenfeld, J.L., 125

S
s-axis, 127
Schroeder van der Kolk method, 43
Sellmeier's formula, 15
Semiaxes of an ellipse, 72
Semirandom plane, 147
    interference figures from, 155
    normal incidence on, 147
Sénarmont compensator, 119
Sensitive violet, 93
Sign, of elongation, 121, 181
    optic, *see* Optic sign
Slow direction, 87
Slow wave, 86
Smith, D.G.W., 195
Snell's law, 8
    limitations, 69
Sodium vapor lamp, 3
Sources of light, 3
Spectrum, electromagnetic, 2, 3
Speed of light, 1
Spindle stage, 125*ff.*, 185*ff.*
    automated, 195
    axes, 127
    conoscopic method, 186
    dispersion analysis with, 194
    E-angle defined, 187
    EXCALIBR, 188
    history of, 125
    Mendenbach's, 191
    orthoscopic method, 188
    photometric, 194, 195
    poster-board type, 133
    reference azimuth, 128, 193
    skip signal, 192
    uniaxial methods, 125
    web site, 132
Stage micrometer, 32
Stage of microscope, 28
Strategic settings, 186
Stoiber, R.E., 50, 60, 62, 208
Su, S.C., 55, 59, 62, 201, 203*ff.* (Ch. 13)
Substage assembly, 27
Substage condensing lenses, 30
Substage mirror, 28
Subtraction, 110

Surfaces of equal retardation,
  biaxial, 151
  uniaxial, 98
Symmetrical extinction, 178

Tau (τ), 78
Tobi method, 177
Total reflection, 9
Tourmaline, absorption of, 122
Transverse wave motion, 3, 84
Tremolite, 204, 205, 210
Triclinic crystals, dispersion in, 167
Tungsten lamp, 3

U
u (one-half angular aperture), 28
Uniaxial crystals,
  abnormal interference colors, 123
  absorption by, 122
  circular section, 73
  dispersion of indices in, 117
  double refraction in, 117
  double refraction in, 70
  indicatrix for, 71
    equation, 71
    nomenclature, 72
  interference figures, 96*ff.*
    centered, 101, back cover
    flash, 102
    isogyres in, 97, 99
    isochromes in, 99, 104
    off-centered, 101
    sign determination from, 111
      (*see* back cover)
    trace of principal plane in, 97
    vibration directions in, 97
  normal incidence upon, 75
    circular section, 76
    principal section, 77
    random section, 79
  optic axis of, 72
  optical examination, 108*ff.*
  optic sign, 72 (*see* back cover)
  pleochroism in, 122
  principal indices of, 72
  principal plane, definition, 72
  random plane, definition, 73
  refractive indices, measurement of, 114*ff.*
  retardation produced by, 86
  wave normals and ray paths in, 73
Uniaxial indicatrix, 71
Uniaxial interference figures, 100*ff.*, 108
  (*see* back cover)

V
v, 161
2V, 138
2V_x, 2V_z, 139
Vector resolution of light,
  at analyzer, 67
  by crystal, 78
Velocity,
  of electromagnetic waves, 1
  of light waves, 1
Vibration, plane of, 4
Vibration directions
  in biaxial interference figures, 152
  in uniaxial interference figures, 99, 111
  for normal incidence, 75, 145
  relation to ray paths, 73, 80
Virtual image, 20
Virtual point source, 18
Visible spectrum, 1, 2
  reference wavelengths, 12

Wave front, 65
Wavelength, 4-5
  of Fraunhofer lines, 12
  of light, 1*ff.*
  and refractive index, 5
  and velocity, 5
Wave motion, 4, 5
  period of, 88
Wave normal, 64
  associated ray paths, 73, 143
Wave period, 88
White of high order, 93
White light, 3
Wilcox, R.E., 2, 62, 188

X
X, 137
X', 145

Y
Y, 137
YC section, 145

Z
Z, 137
Z', 145
Zones in crystals, 179
  effect on extinction, 180